SYNTHESIS
OF PROSTAGLANDINS

by

Cs. SZÁNTAY

and

L. NOVÁK

AKADÉMIAI KIADÓ

PUBLISHING HOUSE OF THE HUNGARIAN ACADEMY OF SCIENCES

BUDAPEST 1978

CHEMISTRY

Series ISBN 963 05 0702 1
Vol. 8 ISBN 963 05 1303 X

PRINTED IN HUNGARY

CONTENTS

PREFACE

Many share the opinion nowadays that the discovery of prostaglandins opened up a new chapter in human and veterinary medicine. Whether this optimism will be justified can only be revealed by the future since extensive clinical trials have only recently been started. It is promising that in some countries the use of prostaglandin $F_{2\alpha}$ in clinics has already been licensed for the termination of pregnancy during the second trimester. In 1974, I.C.I. started marketing its first prostanoid preparation "Equimate" for use in regulating the mating of horses.

In Hungary, Chemical and Pharmaceutical Works Chinoin had prostaglandin $F_{2\alpha}$ registered in 1975 under the proprietary name "Enzaprost" for the following main indications: (a) menstrual regulation, (b) termination of pregnancy, (c) dilatation of the human cervix prior to labour, or to induce abortion. Compared with mechanical dilatation the use of prostaglandin is a simple and safe clinical procedure.

This group of compounds belongs to the family of natural fatty acids and the members of the group are widely distributed in mammalian tissues. The concentration of prostaglandins is, however, extremely low, generally of the order of 1 $\mu g/g$ and never exceeding the limit of 300 $\mu g/g$ of undried tissue.

According to present-day concepts, prostaglandins control many a function of the human body, among others lipid metabolism, the activity of smooth muscles, the reproductive system, and they also affect the central nervous system. Prostaglandins are almost unrivalled in their activity judged on a weight basis: human smooth muscles respond to concentrations as low as 10^{-11} g/kg. Prostaglandins may well become useful in menstrual regulation, fertility control, contraception, and induction of labour; they may find application as hypotensives, antithrombotics, antiasthmatics, etc., and for the prolonged alleviation of obstruction of the nose in rhinitis. It has been reported that one of the prostaglandins has been used to regulate gastric acid secretion in dogs and rats and that it acts as a preventive against the inducement of experimental ulcer in the rat.

Prostaglandin research has a history of more than forty years and dates back to 1930 when two New York gynaecologists, R. Kurzrok and C. C. Lieb, reported the observations on human semen inducing contraction and relaxation of the human uterus. A few years later M. W. Goldblatt in England and U. S. von Euler in Sweden started their respective investigations on the lipid fractions isolated from human semen and on the vesicular gland of sheep. Von Euler coined the name prostaglandin for the active component. After the interruption caused by the war progress still remained rather slow because of lack of material to be investigated and the absence of suitable techniques for the separation and identification of the minute amounts that were available of these very sensitive substances.

Reinvestigation of the problem by S. Bergström at the Karolinska Institute in Stockholm from 1956 on with a team of experts in chromatography, ultramicroanalysis and mass spectroscopy, supported by the Upjohn Company, brought — after one year of intensive work the long due breakthrough with the prize of the isolation of the first crystalline prostaglandin.

The structural elucidation in 1962 of the first two members of the prostaglandin family was also accomplished at the Karolinska Institute, about three decades after the discovery of the biological activity.

Prostaglandin research gained momentum in 1964 when an *in vitro* method for the preparation of reasonable amounts of prostaglandins was developed concurrently in the United States, Sweden and the Netherlands, based on incubation of fatty acid precursors with an extract of sheep vesicular glands.

The first total syntheses of prostaglandins were achieved in 1968 by a team at the Upjohn Laboratories and a group led by E. J. Corey at Harvard University.

The availability of prostaglandins through biochemical and through total chemical synthesis stimulated extensive biological studies, including aspects related to human medicine. Scientific publications on prostaglandins began to appear from that time on at an ever increasing rate amounting now to about seven papers per day. A special journal devoted to the topic and entitled "Prostaglandins" was founded in 1972.

The competition in research on the synthesis, physiology and therapeutic applications of prostaglandins is exceptionally keen and overshadows even that on steroids in the postwar period. The most abundant, though still extremely meagre source of prostaglandins is the seminal fluid of man and sheep. Minimal quantities are detectable in the uterus, lung, brain, eye, pancreas and kidney. It is generally believed that sooner or later it will be possible to trace prostaglandins in almost every tissue of mammals. Exceptionally, prostaglandins can be isolated from some lower organisms, e.g., as demonstrated by A. J. Weinheimer and R. L. Sproggins of Oklahoma University, from the Gorgonian *(Plexaura homomalla)*, a coral indigenous to the Caribbean.

Different kinds of prostaglandins exert different physiological effects both in the qualitative and in the quantitative sense. The number of natural prostaglandins known now exceeds twenty (for structure and nomenclature see Chapter 1). In the living organism they are formed by oxidation and successive cyclization of polyunsaturated fatty acids, called essential fatty acids. These have long been recognized as indispensable nutritional factors, their deficiency causing a special syndrome (including dermatosis, retarded growth, decreased fertility, increased loss of water through the skin) that can be eliminated by the administration of small amounts of polyunsaturated fatty acids. This phenomenon can now be partly explained by the role of the essential fatty acids as prostaglandin precursors.

This hypothesis has found support in the fact that it is possible to convert di-homo-γ-linoleic acid and arachidonic acid to prostaglandins by an enzyme preparation obtained from the vesicular gland of sheep.

Prostaglandins research threw new light on the mechanism of the action of certain long established drugs. For example, the anti-inflammatory effect of acetylsalicylic acid and its congeners has been interpreted by their action as prostaglandin antagonists.

Though it would be premature to draw final conclusions, many share the opinion that prostaglandins may achieve in therapy a place similar in importance to that held earlier by steroid hormones.

The potentials of prostaglandins stimulated Hungarian researchers at a quite early stage to join the world-wide race for their utilization. Two years after the accomplishment of the first total synthesis in 1968, research teams at the Institute of Organic Chemistry of the Technical University of Budapest and at Chemical and Pharmaceutical Works Chinoin undertook, as a joint venture, the development of an industrially viable process of synthesizing prostaglandins. The first few milligrams of the end product saw the light of day in 1972; pilot plant production started in 1974. Thus, preceded only by Upjohn in America and the Ono Company in Japan, Chinoin was the third to put prostaglandins on the market.

The extremely high physiological potency of natural prostaglandins is, however, associated with a very fast turnover of these substances. Prostaglandin E_2, which would be useful owing to its smooth muscle contracting effect for labour induction or for the termination of pregnancy, becomes up to 96% inactivated within 90 seconds of intravenous administration. Lack of organ- and tissue specificity presents further problems since, for example, prostaglandin E_2 induces the contraction not only of the smooth muscle of the uterus, but also those of the gastrointestinal tract thereby causing spasms and diarrhoea. The same compound is beneficial when inhaled as it dilates the bronchi and alleviates asthmatic fits, but as a side effect it leads to sore throat and coughing.

All this gives impetus for chemical research directed towards the synthesis of modified prostaglandins which, ideally, should combine high specificity with sufficiently slow degradation in the organism so as to permit their application as pharmaceuticals. The achievement of this end will require concentrated and tenacious efforts from organic chemists for many years to come. The very aim of this book is to further this work by reviewing the most important synthetic achievements in the prostaglandin field published up to the end of 1976, affording thus a guideline for the planning of strategy and tactics of further synthesis.

The authors gratefully acknowledge the help of Jenő Marosfalvi in his artful treatment of the figures and Béla Majoros in supplying the draft which aided in the writing of Section 3.7.

1. THE PROSTAGLANDINS

1.1 STRUCTURE AND NOMENCLATURE

Prostaglandins as defined by Bergström and co-workers in the early sixties can be derived from prostane, a hydrocarbon of twenty carbon atoms. Prostane (**1.1**) contains a cyclopentane ring in which the hydrogen atoms at the junction of the side chains are in *trans* relationship to each other [1–12].

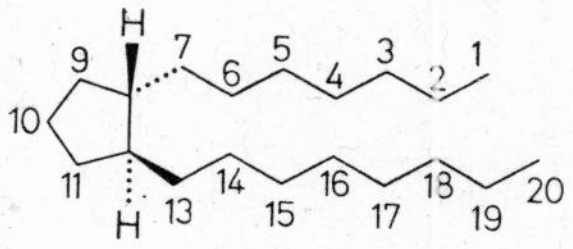

1.1

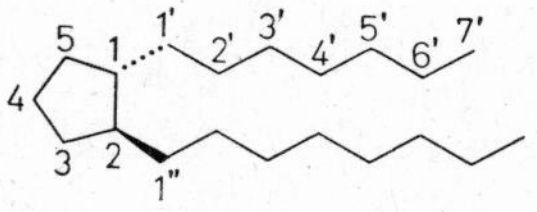

1.2

Because of the cumbersome nature of the nomenclature recommended by the IUPAC, that of Chemical Abstracts (C.A.) will be used [13]. Prostaglandins will be considered as derivatives of prostane or of the acid — prostanoic acid (**1.3**) — derived from it, and the numbering shown in formula **1.1** will be used. It should, however, be noted that certain authors apply another numbering system and denote prostaglandins as substituted cyclopentanes (**1.2**).

Prostanoic acid (**1.3**) contains two chiral carbon atoms (C_8 and C_{12}) of different constitution, thus the molecule can have four optical isomers of which two pairs are mirror images: prostanoic acid (**1.3**) and its mirror image, *ent*-prostanoic acid (**1.4**) are *threo* stereoismers, while isoprostanoic acid (**1.5**) and *ent*-isoprostanoic acid (**1.6**) represent the *erythro* forms.

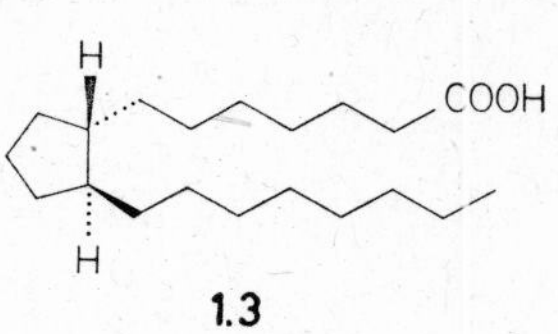

1.3

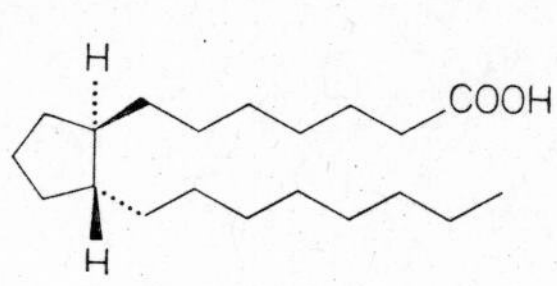

1.4

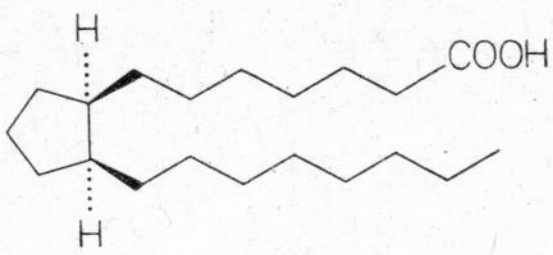

1.5 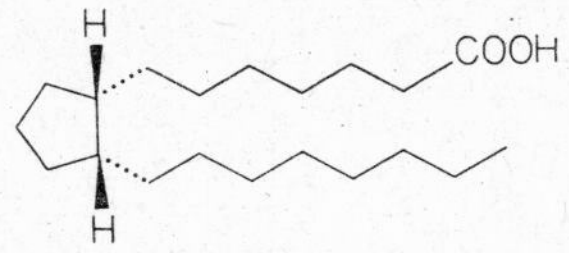   1.6

For the characterization of individual centres the descriptors α and β are used. The substituents of cyclopentane (as depicted in formulae **1.3–1.6**) may be below the plane of the ring, i.e. in the α configuration, or above this plane, i.e. in the β configuration.

Consequently, the basic skeleton of prostaglandins (**1.3**) may be given the following names:

(a) prostanoic acid (according to C.A.); this is the name which will be used in this book;

(b) 1α-(6-carboxyhexyl)-2β-octylcyclopentane (conforming to the numbering of **1.2**);

(c) 7-[(2β-octyl)cyclopentyl-1α]-heptanoic acid (according to IUPAC).

Depending on the substitution of the cyclopentane ring, there are six main types of prostaglandings (**1.7** to **1.12**). Type E (**1.7**) is characterized by the presence of a keto group in position 9 and an α-hydroxyl at C_{11}. In the F series (**1.8**) there are hydroxyl groups in both (9 and 11) positions.

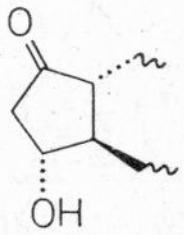

PGE   PGF   PGA

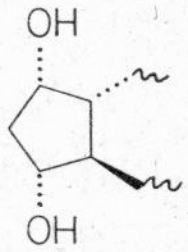

1.7   1.8   1.9

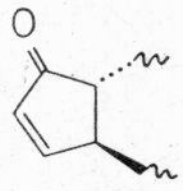

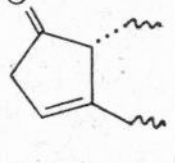

PGC   PGB   PGD

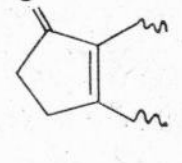

1.10   1.11   1.12

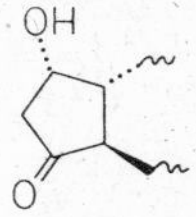

Types A (**1.9**), B (**1.11**) and C (**1.10**) contain a keto group in the 9-position and an endocyclic double bond. Compounds of the E and F series are also called primary prostaglandins. The designation A indicates that the compound can be prepared from type E by acid-catalyzed dehydration. In a similar way, B points to the elimination of water from type E by a base-catalyzed reaction. Representatives of type A can be converted by base catalysis *via* C into the more stable B-type compounds.

Later on, a natural D-type prostaglandin (**1.12**) was also isolated [14–16]. Members of this group of compounds contain a hydroxyl group at C_9 and a keto group in the 11-position.

Recently the range of natural prostaglandins has been extended by the isolation of endoperoxides (prostaglandins G and H), which are characterized by a peroxy function between C_9 and C_{11} (**1.13**). (*cf.* also Chapter 6.).

1.13

The number of double bonds in the side chains of prostaglandins varies from one to three and is indicated by a subscript numeral. All prostaglandins contain a double bond of a *trans-* or (*E*)-geometry in the hydroxyoctyl chain between C_{13} and C_{14} (e.g. **1.14**). Compounds with the subscript 2 possess an additional double bond of *cis-* or (*Z*)-geometry between C_5 and C_6. There is a third double bond also of (*Z*)-geometry between C_{17} and C_{18} in compounds with the subscript 3.

1.14

PGE$_1$: no double bond between C_5 and C_6, and C_{17} and C_{18}.
PGE$_2$: a double bond of (*Z*)-geometry between C_5 and C_6, no double bond between C_{17} and C_{18}.
PGE$_3$: double bonds of (*Z*)-geometry between C_5 and C_6, and C_{17} and C_{18}.

In 1968 IUPAC suggested the use of the letters *Z* (German, zusammen = together = *cis*) and *E* (German, entgegen = opposite = *trans*) [17, 18] for the description of the geometrical isomers instead of the earlier prefixes *cis* and *trans*. When classifying a compound, the sequence of substituents on the double bond is determined according to the sequence rule of Cahn, Ingold and Prelog, and when the two vicinal substituents of highest priority are on the same side (*cis*) the symbol *Z*, when they are on opposite sides (*trans*) the prefix *E* is used.

In F prostaglandins the letter α or β after the subscript numeral (or the term *"epi"*) refers to the steric orientation of the C_9 hydroxyl group. A substituent is α-oriented if it is on the same side of the cyclopentane ring as the carboxyhexyl (C_1–C_8) side chain, and β-oriented (*epi*-compounds) if it is opposite to this, i.e. *cis* to the hydroxyoctyl (C_{13}–C_{20}) side chain. In the other series of prostaglandins, the prefix *"epi"* designates configurational changes at C_{11} and C_{15}; the place is indicated in the name of the compound.

The absolute configuration of prostaglandins was determined by Nugteren and co-workers [19] in 1966. The hydroxyoctyl chain of prostaglandin E_1 was removed by oxidative ozonolysis, and the product was identified with the known (S)-2-hydroxyheptanoic acid. Since the relative configuration of natural prostaglandin $F_{1\alpha}$ was already known from Abrahamsson's earlier X-ray work [20], the absolute configuration of all of the centres of natural prostaglandins followed from the above configurational correlation.

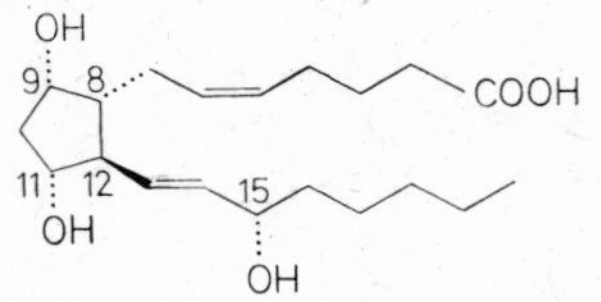

1.15

The absolute configuration of prostaglandin $F_{2\alpha}$ (**1.15**) is 8*R*, 9*S*, 11*R*, 12*R*, 15*S*. It should be noted that $2^5 = 32$ stereoisomers are possible due to the five chiral centres and 128 if allowing for the geometrical isomerism of the two double bonds.

Table 1.1

Structure and Nomenclature of Prostaglandins

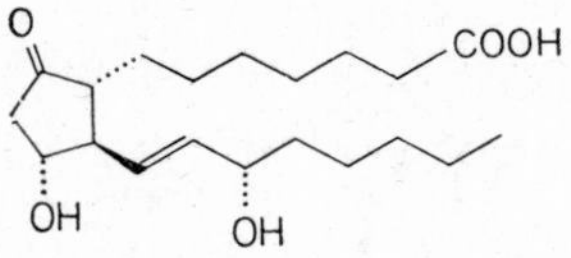

PGE₁

1.16

11α,(15S)-dihydroxy-9-oxo-(13E)-prostenoic acid;
7-[3α-hydroxy-2β-(3α-hydroxy-(1E)-octenyl-5-oxo-cyclopentyl-1α]-
heptanoic acid

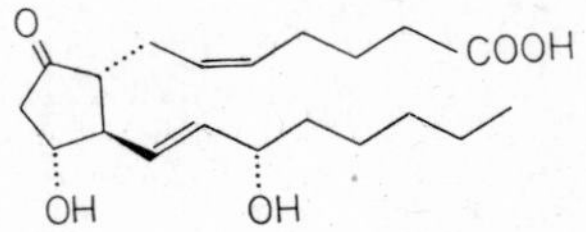

PGE₂

1.17

11α,(15S)-dihydroxy-9-oxo-(5Z,13E)-prostadienoic acid;
7-[3α-hydroxy-2β-(3α-hydroxy-(1E)-octenyl)-5-oxocyclopentyl-1α]-
(5Z)-heptenoic acid

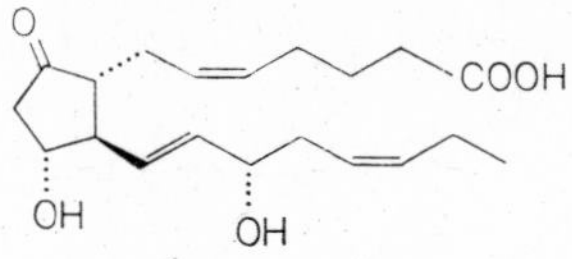

PGE$_3$

1.18

**11α,(15*S*)-dihydroxy-9-oxo-(5*Z*,13*E*,17*Z*)-prostatrienoic acid;
7-[3α-hydroxy-2β-hydroxy-(1*E*,5*Z*)-octadienyl)-5-oxocyclopentyl-1α]-(5*Z*)-heptenoic acid**

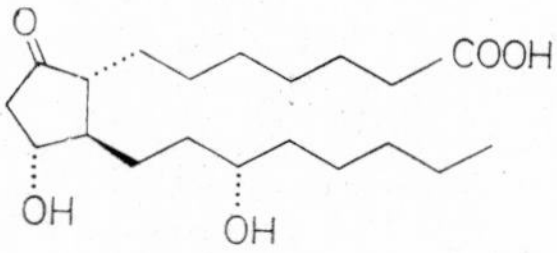

dihydro-PGE$_1$

1.19

**11α,(15*S*)-dihydroxy-9-oxoprostanoic acid;
7-[3α-hydroxy-2β-(3α-hydroxyoctyl)-5-oxocyclopentyl-1α]-heptanoic acid**

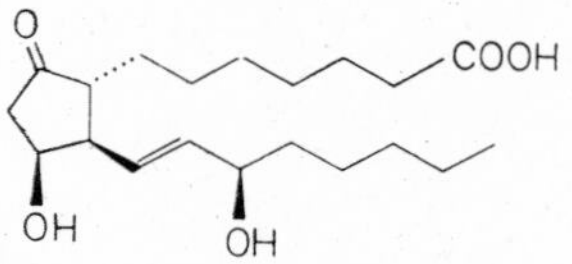

11,15-*epi*-PGE$_1$

1.20

**11β,(15*R*)-dihydroxy-9-oxo-(13*E*)-prostenoic acid;
7-[3β-hydroxy-2β-(3β-hydroxy-(1*E*)-octenyl)-5-oxocyclopentyl-1α]-heptanoic acid**

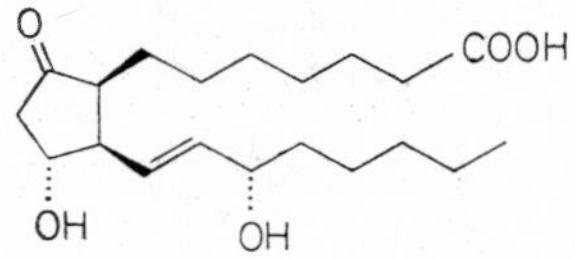

8-iso-PGE$_1$

1.21

**11α,(15*S*)-dihydroxy-9-oxo-(13*E*)-isoprostenoic acid;
7-[3α-hydroxy-2β-(3α-hydroxy-(1*E*)-octenyl)-5-oxocyclopentyl-1α]-heptanoic acid**

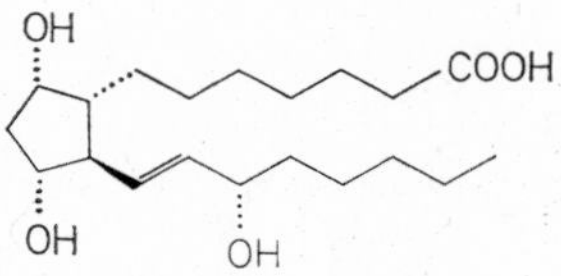

PGF$_{1α}$ (PGF)

1.22

**9α,11α,(15*S*)-trihydroxy-(13*E*)-prostenoic acid;
7-[3α,5α-dihydroxy-2β-(3α-hydroxy-(1*E*)-octenyl)-cyclopentyl-1α]-heptanoic acid**

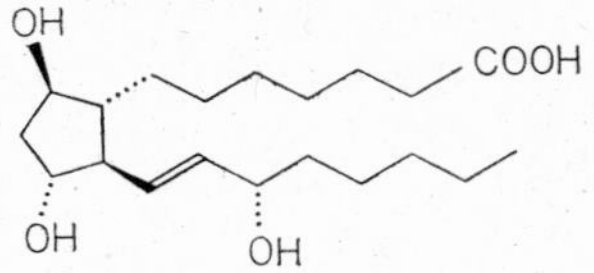

PGF$_{1\beta}$ (*epi*-PGF)

1.23

9β,11α,(15S)-trihydroxy-(13E)-prostenoic acid;
7-[3α,5β-dihydroxy-2β-(3α-hydroxy-(1E)-octenyl)-cyclopentyl 1α
heptanoic acid

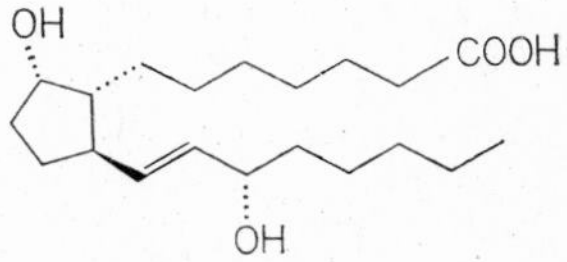

11-deoxy-PGF$_{1\alpha}$

1.24

9α,(15S)-dihydroxy-(13E)-prostenoic acid;
7-[5α-hydroxy-2β-(3α-hydroxy-(1E)-octenyl)-cyclopentyl-1α]-heptanoic acid

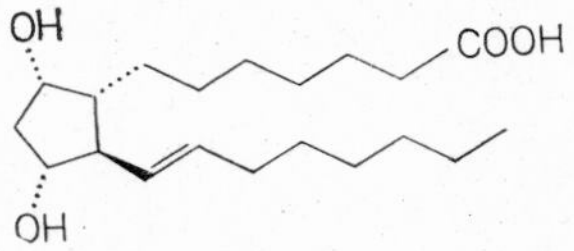

15-deoxy-PGF$_{1\alpha}$

1.25

9α,11α-dihydroxy-(13E)-prostenoic acid;
7-[3α,5α-dihydroxy-2β-(1E)-octenyl-cyclopentyl-1α]-heptanoic acid

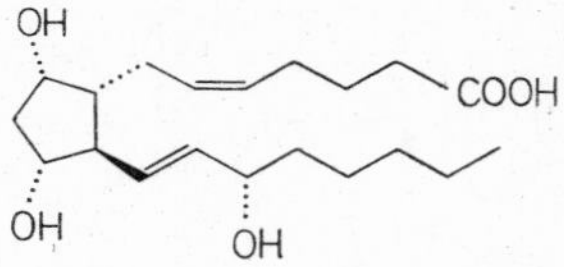

PGF$_{2\alpha}$(bisdehydro-PGF)

1.15

9α,11α,(15S)-trihydroxy-(5Z,13E)-prostadienoic acid;
7-[3α,5α-dihydroxy-2β-(3α-hydroxy-(1E)-octenyl)cyclopentyl-1α]-(5Z)-
heptenoic acid

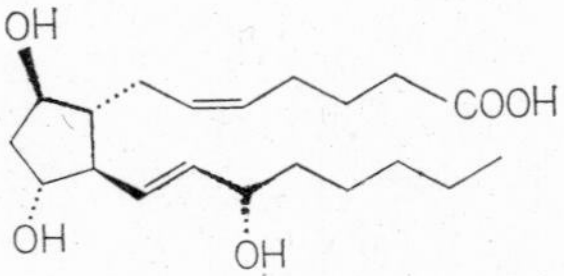

PGF$_{2\beta}$

1.26

9β,11α,(15S)-trihydroxy-(5Z,13E)-prostadienoic acid;
7-[3α,5β-dihydroxy-2β-(3α-hydroxy-(1E)-octenyl)-cyclopentyl-1α]-(5Z)-
heptenoic acid

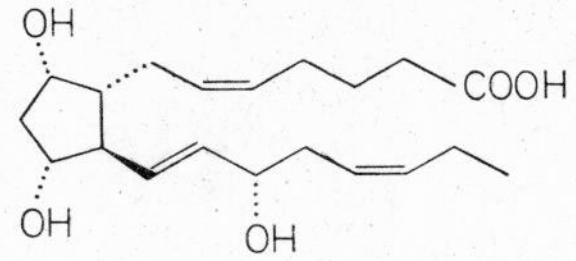

PGF$_{3\alpha}$

1.27

9α,11α,(15*S*)-trihydroxy-(5*Z*,13*E*,17*Z*)-prostatrienoic acid;
7-[3α,5α-dihydroxy-2β-(3α-hydroxy-(1*E*,5*Z*)-octadienyl)-cyclopentyl-1α]-(5*Z*)-heptenoic acid

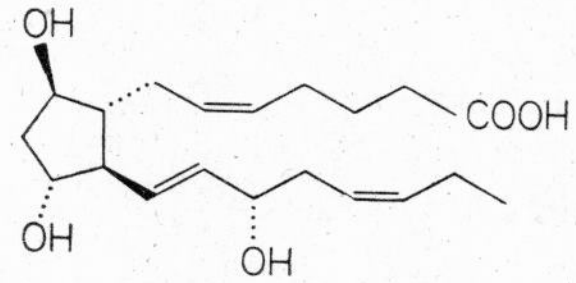

PGF$_{3\beta}$

1.28

9β,11α,(15*S*)-trihydroxy-(5*Z*,13*E*,17*Z*)-prostatrienoic acid;
7-[3α,5β-dihydroxy-2β-(3α-hydroxy-(1*E*,5*Z*)-octadienyl)-cyclopentyl-1α]-(5*Z*)-heptenoic acid

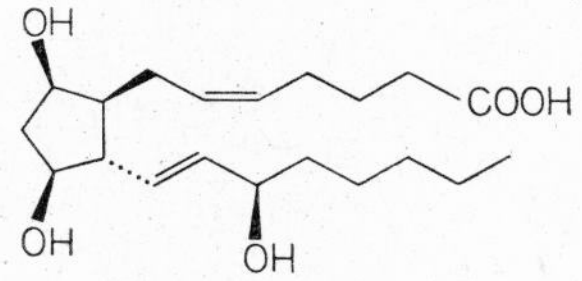

ent-PGF$_{2\alpha}$

1.29

9β,11β,(15*R*)-trihydroxy-(5*Z*,13*E*)-*ent*-prostadienoic acid; 7-[3β,5β-dihydroxy-2α-(3β-hydroxy-(1*E*)-octenyl)cyclopentyl-1β]-(5*Z*)-heptenoic acid

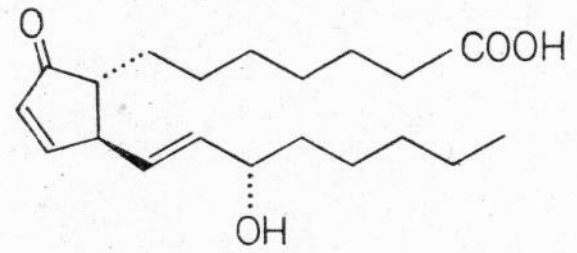

PGA$_1$

1.30

(15*S*)-hydroxy-9-oxo-(10,13*E*)-prostadienoic acid;
7-[2β-(3α-hydroxy-(1*E*)-octenyl)-5-oxo-3-cyclopentyl-1α]-heptanoic acid

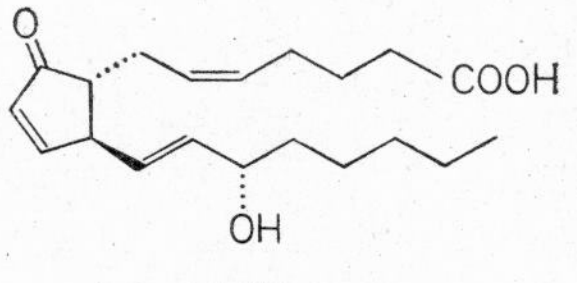

PGA$_2$

1.31

(15*S*)-hydroxy-9-oxo-(5*Z*,10,13*E*)-prostatrienoic acid;
7-[2β-(3α-hydroxy-(1*E*)-octenyl)-5-oxo-3-cyclopentyl-1α]-(5*Z*)-heptenoic acid

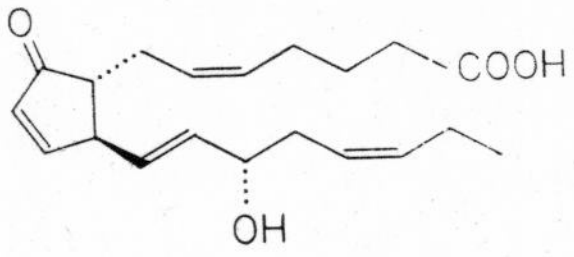

PGA$_3$

1.32

(15*S*)-hydroxy-9-oxo-(5*Z*,10,13*E*,17*Z*)-prostatetraenoic acid;
7-[2β-(3α-hydroxy-(1*E*,5*Z*)-octadienyl)-5-oxo-3-cyclopentyl-1α]-(5*Z*)-heptenoic acid

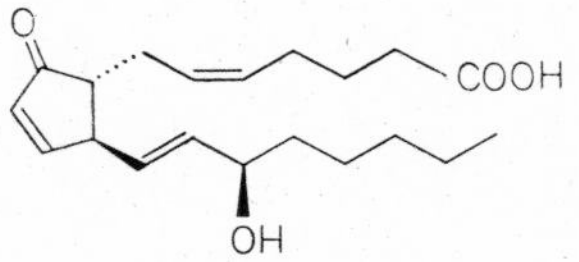

15 (R) – PGA$_2$
(15-*epi*-PGA$_2$)

1.33

(15*R*)-hydroxy-9-oxo-(5*Z*,10,13*E*)-prostatrienoic acid;
7-[2β-(3β-hydroxy-(1*E*,5*Z*)-octadienyl)-5-oxo-3-cyclopentyl-1α]-
(5*Z*)-heptenoic acid

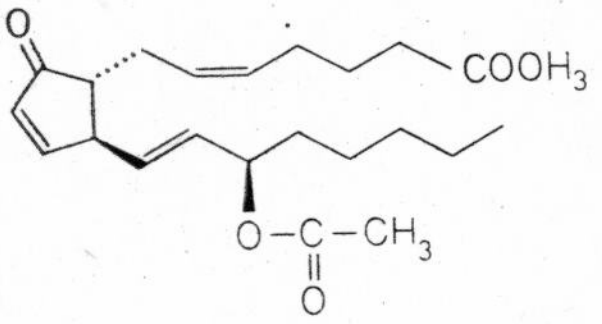

15(R)-PGA$_2$-acetate,
methyl ester

1.34

(15*R*)-acetoxy-9-oxo-(5*Z*,10,13*E*)-prostatrienoic acid, methyl ester;
7-[2β-(3β-acetoxy-(1*E*,5*Z*)-octadienyl)-5-oxo-3-cyclopentyl-1α]-(5*Z*)-
heptenoic acid, methyl ester

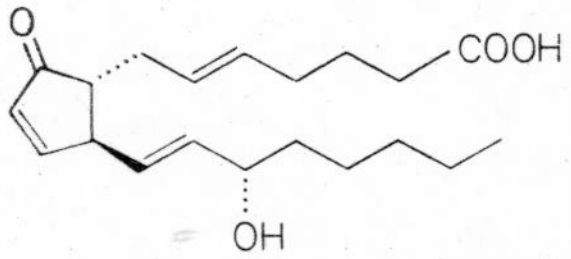

5(E) – PGA$_2$
(5-*trans* – PGA$_2$)

1.35

(15*S*)-hydroxy-9-oxo-(5*E*,10,13*E*)-prostatrienoic acid;
7-[2β-(3α-hydroxy-(1*E*)-octenyl)-5-oxo-3-cyclopentyl-1α]-(5*E*)-heptenoic acid

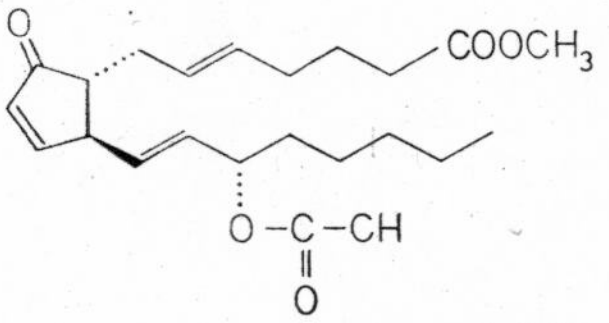

5(E)-PGA$_2$-acetate,
methyl ester

1.36

(15*S*)-acetoxy-9-oxo-(5*E*,10,13*E*)-prostatrienoic acid, methyl ester;
7-[2β-(3α-acetoxy-(1*E*)-octenyl)-5-oxo-3-cyclopentyl-1α]-(5*E*)-heptenoic
acid, methyl ester

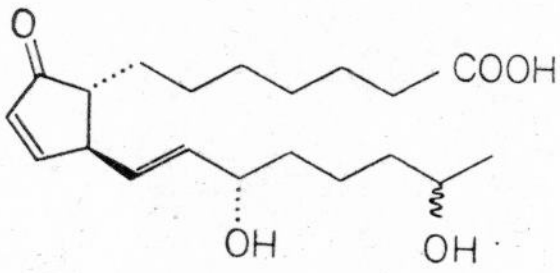

19-hydroxy-PGA₁

1.37

(15S),19-dihydroxy-9-oxo-(10,13E)-prostadienoic acid;
7-[2β-(3α,7-dihydroxy-(1E)-octenyl)5-oxo-3-cyclopentyl-1α]-heptanoic acid

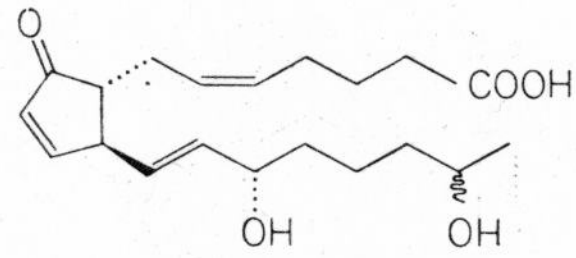

19-hydroxy-PGA₂

1.38

(15S),19-dihydroxy-9-oxo-(5Z,10,13E)-prostatrienoic acid;
7-[2β-(3α,7-dihydroxy-(1E)-octenyl)-5-oxo-3-cyclopentyl-1α]-(5Z)-heptenoic acid

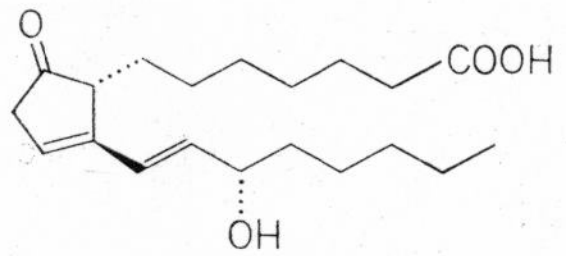

PGC₁

1.39

(15S)-hydroxy-9-oxo-(11,13E)-prostadienoic acid;
7-[2-(3α-hydroxy-(1E)-octenyl)-5-oxo-2-cyclopentyl-1α]-heptanoic acid

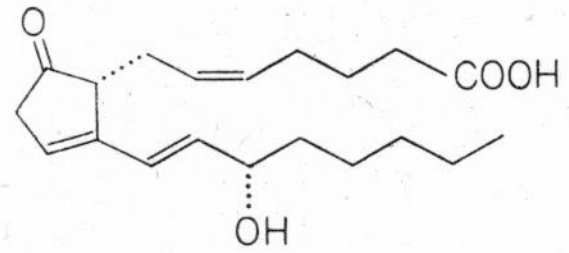

PGC₂

1.40

(15S)-hydroxy-9-oxo-(5Z,11,13E)-prostatrienoic acid;
7-[2-(3α-hydroxy-(1E)-octenyl)-5-oxo-2-cyclopentyl-1α]-(5Z)-heptenoic acid

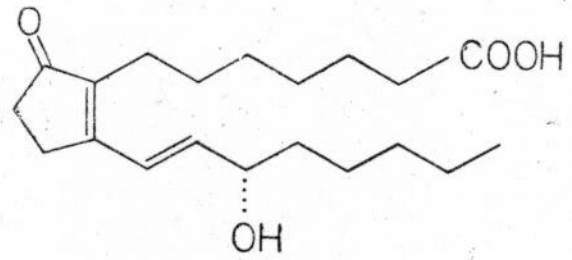

PGB₁

1.41

(15S)-hydroxy-9-oxo-8(12),(13E)-prostadienoic acid;
7-[2-(3α-hydroxy(1E)-octenyl)-5-oxo-1-cyclopentyl]-heptanoic acid

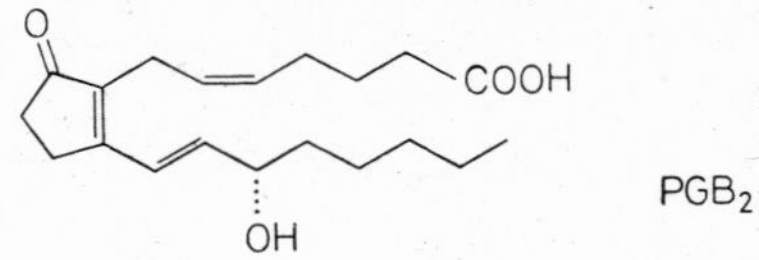

PGB₂

1.42

(15S)-hydroxy-9-oxo-(5Z),8(12),(13E)-prostatrienoic acid;
7-[2-(3α-hydroxy-(1E)-octenyl)-5-oxo-1-cyclopentyl]-(5Z)-heptenoic acid

PGB₃

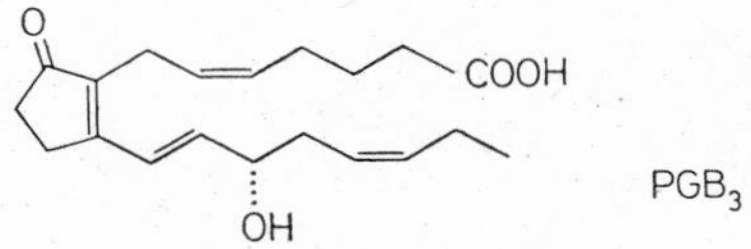

1.43

(15S)-hydroxy-9-oxo-(5Z),8(12),(13E,17Z)-prostatetraenoic acid;
7-[2-(3α-hydroxy-(1E,5Z)-octadienyl)-5-oxo-1-cyclopentyl]-(5Z)-
heptenoic acid

19–hydroxy–PGB₁

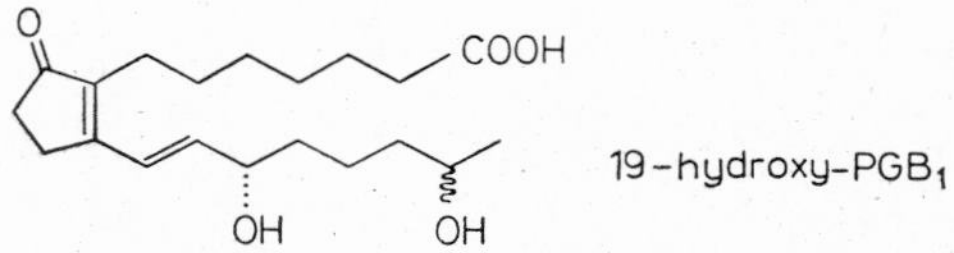

1.44

(15S),17-dihydroxy-9-oxo-8(12),(13E)-prostadienoic acid;
7-[2-(3α,7-dihydroxy-(1E)-octenyl)-5-oxo-1-cyclopentyl]-heptanoic acid

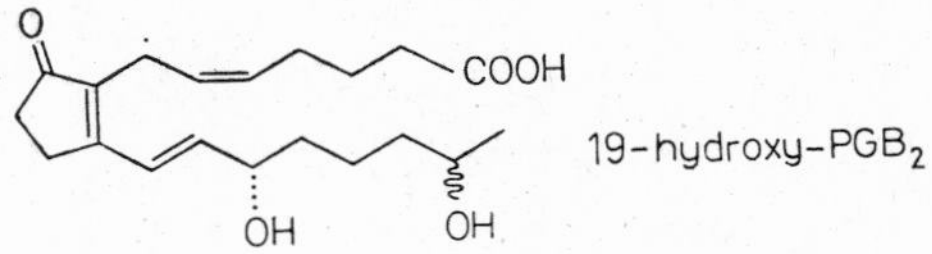

19–hydroxy–PGB₂

1.45

(15S),17-dihydroxy-9-oxo-(5Z),8(12),(13E)-prostatrienoic acid;
7-[2-(3α,7-dihydroxy-(1E)-octenyl)-5-oxo-1-cyclopentyl]-(5Z)-heptenoic acid

PGD₁

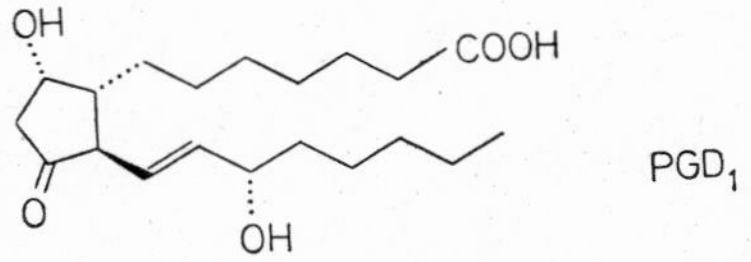

1.46

9α,(15S)-dihydroxy-11-oxo-(13E)-prostenoic acid;
7-[5α-hydroxy-2β-(3α-hydroxy-(1E)-octenyl)-3-oxo-cyclopentyl-1α]-
heptanoic acid

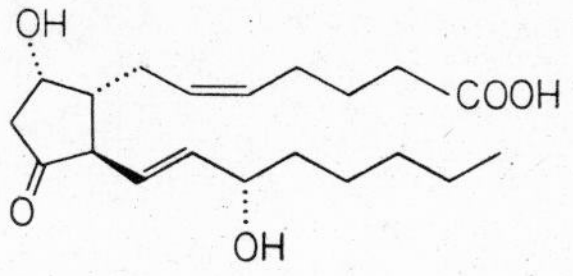

PGD₂

1.47

9α,(15S)-dihydroxy-11-oxo-(5Z,13E)-prostadienoic acid;
7-[5α-hydroxy-2β-(3α-hydroxy-(1E)-octenyl)-3-oxo-cyclopentyl-1α]-
(5Z)-heptenoic acid

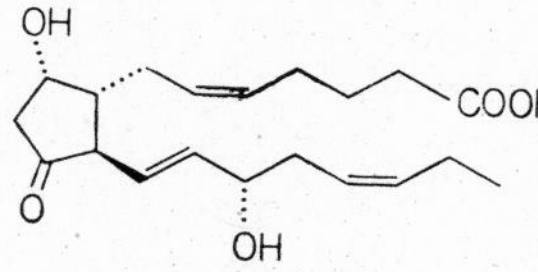

PGD₃

1.48

9α,(15S)-dihydroxy-11-oxo-(5Z,13E,17Z)-prostatrienoic acid;
7-[5α-hydroxy-2β-(3α-hydroxy-(1E,5Z)-octadienyl)-3-oxo-cyclopentyl-1α]-
(5Z)-heptenoic acid

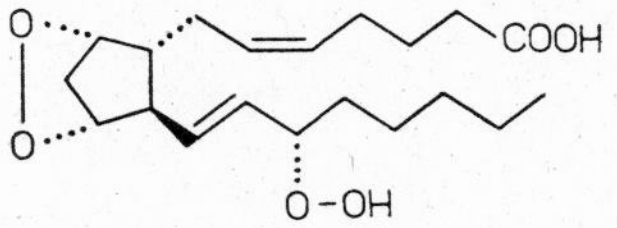

PCG₂

1.49

9α,11α-peroxy-(15S)-hydroperoxy-(5Z,13E)-prostadienoic acid

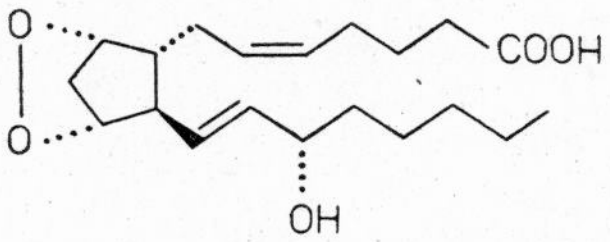

PGH₂

1.50

9α,11α-peroxy-(15S)-hydroxy-(5Z,13E)-prostadienoic acid

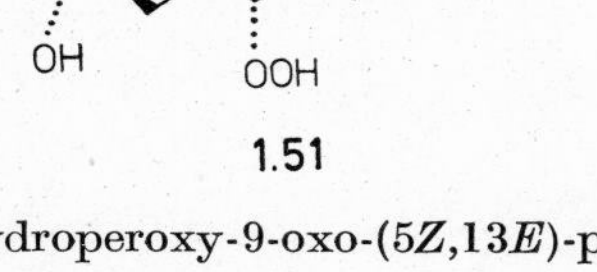

1.51

11α-hydroxy-(15S)-hydroperoxy-9-oxo-(5Z,13E)-prostadienoic acid

1.52

thromboxane B_2
(PHD)

(9,12S)-8-[(1R)-1-hydroxy-3-oxopropyl]-9,12-dihydroxy-(5Z,10E)-
heptadecadienoic acid (hemiacetal form)

The conformation of prostaglandins was studied by means of X-ray diffraction and ^{13}C nuclear magnetic resonance. For X-ray diffraction the tribromobenzoate derivatives of PGF-type compounds were used by Abrahamsson [20]; Duax and Edmonds worked with prostaglandins A_1 and $F_{1\beta}$ [21, 22]. ^{13}C-NMR studies have been reported by Cooper and Fried [23] and those based on the ^{13}C relaxation time by Lukacs *et al.* [24, 25].

The cyclopentane ring can exist in two non-planar conformations [26]. In the half-chair conformation (**1.53**) one carbon atom is below, and one above the plane which is formed by the other three neighbouring carbon atoms. The substituents of four carbon atoms occupy alternately so-called *pseudoaxial* and *pseudoequatorial* positions, but those on the fifth carbon atom are equivalent. In the envelope conformer (**1.54**) four carbon atoms are in a common plane from which the fifth stands out.

1.53

1.54

The predominant conformer of the cyclopentane ring in the prostaglandins $F_{1\alpha}$ and $F_{2\alpha}$ is the half-chair form (**1.53**); of the four substituents of the ring those on C_8, C_{11} and C_{12} are *pseudoequatorial*; the C_9 hydroxyl group is *pseudoaxial*. In this conformer the hydroxyl group at C_9 is considerably more shielded than those on C_{11} and C_{15}. This is indicated by the fact that it is possible to silylize selectively the C_{11} and C_{15} hydroxyls of prostaglandin $F_{2\alpha}$ with N-trimethylsilyldiethylamine [27]. In prostaglandins $F_{1\beta}$ and $F_{2\beta}$ the half-chair conformation is even more favoured, since in the β-series all ring substituents occupy *pseudoequatorial* positions.

The foregoing interpretation concerning the conformation of the cyclo-pentane ring in prostaglandin F type compounds is grossly simplified. In fact, for a tetrasubstituted cyclopentane ten different "twist" and ten "envelope" conformers have to be considered. With simpler cyclopentanes showing the substitution pattern (all-*trans*) as prostaglandin $F_{1\beta}$, it is the $^8_{12}T$ form which is of smallest energy, but two envelope forms, ^8E and $_{12}E$ have nearly the same energy (Fig. 1.1).

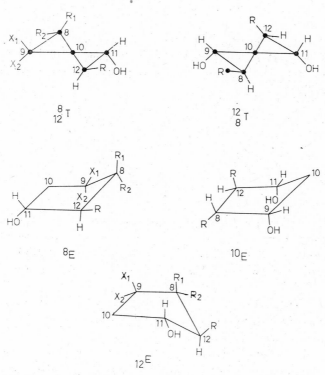

Fig. 1.1. Conformations for 1,4-dihydroxy-2,3-dialkyl-cyclopentanes with configuration
$(R_1 = X_2 = H; \ X_1 = OH)$ (PGF$_{1\beta}$ type)
$(R_2 = X_1 = H; \ X_2 = OH)$ (8-*epi*-PGF$_{1\alpha}$ type)
$(R_1 = X_1 = H; \ X_2 = OH)$ (PGF$_{1\alpha}$ type)
With designations T and E superscripts refer to carbon atoms above the plane, whereas subscripts to atoms below the plane formed by the rest of the carbon atoms.

With 8-*epi*-prostaglandins $F_{1\alpha}$ two twist conformers, $^8_{12}T$ and $^{12}_8T$, are favoured, whereas with the prostaglandin $F_{1\alpha}$ type it is the $^8_{12}T$ form.

However, the conformations of prostaglandins may be strongly influenced by other factors as well, such as hydrogen bonding between the hydroxyl groups (C_9 and C_{11}), eventual interaction between the C_{11} hydroxyl and the double bond of the side chain, as well as dispersion interactions between the two side chains. NMR studies by Vandewalle *et al.* [90] suggested one of the envelope conformers (^8E or $_{12}E$) for prostaglandin $F_{1\beta}$; $_{12}E$ and $_{12}^8T$ for 8-*epi*-prostaglandin $F_{1\alpha}$; and $_{12}^8T$, $_{12}E$ and ^8E for prostaglandin $F_{1\alpha}$.

The conformation of the cyclopentane ring in the E series of prostaglandins is essentially the same as in type F. There is, however, a substantial difference in this respect in the A and B series, in which the cyclopentenone ring is nearly planar.

The saturated parts of the side chains of prostaglandins (C_{1-7} or C_{1-4} and C_{15-20}) possess an *anti*-conformation with respect to the individual carbon-carbon bonds and the two side chains approach each other as closely as possible (**1.55**).

1.55

Hoyland and Kier [28] applied quantum chemical calculations using the extended Hückel method to determine the conformation of prostaglandin E_1. Of the 400 possibilities investigated the conformer **1.55** was of lowest energy; in this the two side chains are kept parallel by dispersion interactions.

The same authors have pointed out an interesting geometrical feature of the favoured conformer (**1.55**), namely, that the distance between the ring and the C_{15} hydroxyl was 5.1 Å, the same as the oxygen–oxygen distance in β-adrenergic antagonists. Similarly, the distance between the carboxyl group and the oxo group in the ring (10.5 Å) agrees with that between the two carbonyl groups in biologically active 3,20-ketosteroids.

These parameters might serve as valuable guidelines when planning more potent prostaglandin analogues, or such with a narrower biological activity spectrum. Presumably, no modification of the molecule counteracting the dispersional interaction between the side chains is worth trying.

Browster *et al.* [29] drew attention to the interesting structural relationship between prostaglandins and steroids. If a propyl group is introduced in position 4 of the steroid (**1.56**), the C_3-C_4 bond is cleaved and the rings A/B and B/C are opened by means of a retro-Diels–Alder reaction on ring B followed by the introduction of a hydroxyl group into the cyclopentane ring, a prostaglandin-like compound (**1.57**) is obtained. This structural resemblance, however, is, in appearance only, since the configuration of the compound obtained by these transformations does not, in fact, agree with that of natural prostaglandins — the compound being a derivative of *ent*-prostanoic acid [30].

1.56   **1.57**

1.2 PHYSICAL AND SPECTRAL PROPERTIES

Some prostaglandins are crystalline substances with low melting points, others are viscous oils. The compounds are soluble in water and in polar solvents and usually crystallize from ethyl acetate–hexane mixtures. They cannot be purified by distillation because even in vacuum they undergo substantial decomposition below their boiling points. The more important physical parameters of the prostaglandins are summarized in Table 1.2.

In the UV spectra of the E-, D- and F series of prostaglandins the band system pertaining to the excitation of the double bond ($\pi \rightarrow \pi^*$) appears in the range below 200 nm thus it is difficult to measure and not very suitable for identification purposes. The absorption of the enone system of type A prostaglandins ($\pi \rightarrow \pi^*$; 217 nm, $\varepsilon = 10\,800$) and that of the conjugated diene chromophore in the C series ($\pi \rightarrow \pi^*$; 234 nm, $\varepsilon = 16\,000$) may be used for the characterization of these compounds. Because of extensive conjugation, representatives of type B prostaglandins absorb at even greater wavelengths ($\pi \rightarrow \pi^*$ and $n \rightarrow \pi^*$; 278 nm, $\varepsilon = 28\,600$). (The observed wavelength is in good agreement with that calculated using the law of additivity of enone absorption [52]: cyclopentanone (202 nm) + γ,δ-double bond (30 nm) + α-substituent (10 nm) + β-substituent (12 nm) + δ-substituent (18 nm); total 272 nm.)

The rotational dispersion curves of type E prostaglandins (Fig. 1.2) are in agreement with the conformation of these compounds [53–55]. The significant negative Cotton effect of prostaglandins E_1 and E_2 ($a \sim -150$) supports the assumption of a half-chair conformation for the cyclopentane ring in these compounds.

Table 1.2

Some Physical Properties of Prostaglandins

Compound	M.p., °C	α_D	t, °C	Conc.	Solvent	Mol. wt.	Empirical formula	References
PGE₁	115–115.5	−61.7	25	0.47	THF	354.49	$C_{20}H_{34}O_5$	[31, 32]
PGE₂	65–66	−61	26	1	THF	352.48	$C_{20}H_{32}O_5$	[33, 34]
PGE₃	–	−48.9	24	1.2	THF	350.46	$C_{20}H_{30}O_5$	[34, 35]
PGF₁α	100–101.5	+25	20	1.1	THF	356.51	$C_{20}H_{36}O_5$	[31, 32]
PGF₁β	127–130	−20	25		EtOH	356.51	$C_{20}H_{36}O_5$	[36]
PGF₂α	30–35	+23.5	25	1	THF	354.49	$C_{20}H_{34}O_5$	[33, 37]
PGF₂β	96.5–97					354.49	$C_{20}H_{34}O_5$	[36]
PGF₃α	–	+29	25	1	THF	352.48	$C_{20}H_{32}O_5$	[34, 38]
PGA₁	42–44	+140	20			336.48	$C_{20}H_{32}O_4$	[39, 40]
PGA₂	–			1.15	CHCl₃	334.46	$C_{20}H_{30}O_4$	[39, 40]
PGB₁	70–71					336.48	$C_{20}H_{32}O_4$	[8]
PGB₂	–					334.46	$C_{20}H_{30}O_4$	[8]
PGD₁	62–65					354.49	$C_{20}H_{34}O_5$	[41]
PGD₂	68					352.48	$C_{20}H_{32}O_5$	[16]
ent-PGE₁	112–113	+58			THF	354.49	$C_{20}H_{34}O_5$	[42]
8-iso-PGE₁	87–88					354.49	$C_{20}H_{34}O_5$	[53]
11-epi-PGE₁	92.5–93					354.49	$C_{20}H_{34}O_5$	[31]
(13Z)-PGE₁	84–85	−81		0.41	MeOH	354.49	$C_{20}H_{34}O_5$	[43]
ent-(13Z)-PGE₁	84.4–85.5	+90		0.48	MeOH	354.49	$C_{20}H_{34}O_5$	[43]
11-deoxy-PGE₁	95–97	−51.8			CHCl₃	338.49	$C_{20}H_{34}O_4$	[44]
(15R)-11-deoxy-PGE₁		−52.9			CHCl₃	338.49	$C_{20}H_{34}O_4$	[44]
(5E)-PGE₂	76–77	−66		0.98	EtOH	352.48	$C_{20}H_{32}O_5$	[45, 46]
8,12-diiso-PGE₂		+33.2		1	EtOH	352.48	$C_{20}H_{32}O_5$	[47]
(15R)-8,12-diiso-PGE₂		+22		0.3	EtOH	352.48	$C_{20}H_{32}O_5$	[47]

Table 1.2 (cont.)

Compound	M.p., °C	α_D	t, °C	Conc.	Solvent	Mol. wt.	Empirical formula	References
11-iso-(15R)-PGE$_2$		−26.7	25	0.49	THF	352.48	C$_{20}$H$_{32}$O$_5$	[48]
(15R)-PGF$_{1\alpha}$	67.5–69	+9	—	—	EtOH	356.51	C$_{20}$H$_{36}$O$_5$	[49]
(5E)-PGF$_{2\alpha}$	94.8–95.8	−8	—	—	EtOH	354.49	C$_{20}$H$_{34}$O$_5$	[46]
(5E)-PGF$_{2\beta}$	68–69	+34	—	0.66	EtOH	351.41	C$_{20}$H$_{34}$O$_5$	[46]
13-dehydro-PGE$_{2\alpha}$		+128	—	—	CHCl$_3$	352.39	C$_{20}$H$_{32}$O$_5$	[50]
(5E)-PGA$_2$		+108	—	—	MeOH	334.46	C$_{20}$H$_{30}$O$_4$	[46]
PGA$_2$, methyl ester		+104	—	—	CHCl	348.48	C$_{21}$H$_{32}$O$_4$	[51]
15-Ac-PGA$_2$, methyl ester						390.52	C$_{23}$H$_{34}$O$_5$	[51]

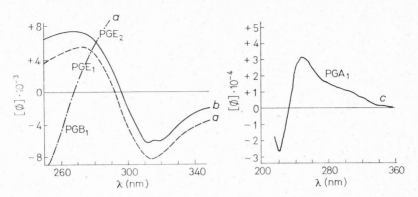

Fig. 1.2. Rotational dispersion curves of (a) PGE_1, (b) PGE_2, (c) PGA_1, and (d) PGB_1

It can be expected that ($n \rightarrow \pi^*$ and $\pi \rightarrow \pi^*$) electron excitations of the enone system in the A and B series will be associated with Cotton effects of opposite sign. The rotational dispersion curve of prostaglandin A_1 (Fig. 1.2: negative $n \rightarrow \pi^*$ Cotton effect at 320 nm, and positive $\pi \rightarrow \pi^*$ Cotton effect at 320 nm) is the resultant of the two opposing effects. In the case of type B prostaglandins a further complication is introduced by the fact that the dienone system exists in two conformations of almost identical energy content (i.e. a *cisoid* and a *transoid*) for which the $\pi \rightarrow \pi^*$ transitions produce different Cotton effects. The rotational dispersion curve obtained (Fig. 1.2) is the superposition of the curves of the two conformers.

The infrared spectra of prostaglandins show, besides the bond-stretching vibrations characteristic of the functional groups (OH, COOH, C=O and C=C), a C—H out-of-plane deformation band at 970 cm^{-1} perpendicular to the plane and indicating the (*E*)-geometry of the C=C double bond.

The infrared spectra of some compounds in this group are shown in Fig. 1.3.

The ^{1}H-NMR spectra of prostaglandins E_1, E_2 and E_3 (**1.16**, **1.17** and **1.18**) methyl esters are rather similar in the region of δ 3.4–4.4 ppm indicating the identical configuration of these compounds at both C_{11} and C_{15}. Of the six olefinic proton signals of prostaglandin E_3 methyl ester, the position of two (δ 5.5–5.75 ppm) coincide with those of prostaglandin E_1 methyl ester. The position of the other four in turn corresponds to that of the C_4-C_5 olefinic protons of prostaglandin E_2 methyl ester. A significant downfield shift of the terminal (C_{20}) methyl signal is characteristic of prostaglandin E_3 methyl ester and can be explained by the proximity of the third (C_{17}-C_{18}) double bond [56, 57].

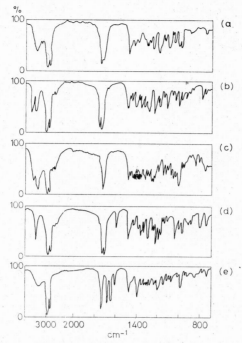

Fig. 1.3. Infrared spectra of (a) PGE$_1$, (b) PGE$_2$, (c) PGF$_{1\alpha}$, (d) PGA$_1$ and (e) PGB$_1$

In the nuclear magnetic resonance spectrum (Fig. 1.4) of prostaglandin F$_{2\alpha}$ (**1.15**) one can identify the multiplet (δ 5.48) originating from the four protons of the olefin chain, the absorption of the protons of the hydroxyl and carboxyl groups (δ 5.12, s), the multiplet (δ 4.05, 3H) of the so-called carbinol protons and the triplet (δ 0.9) of the terminal methyl group. Because of the presence of several protons with almost identical chemical shifts, it is not possible to assign the rest of the spectrum. Moreover, the determination of the spin–spin coupling constants, and thereby, the geometry of the double bonds is not feasible. Similar difficulties are encountered when evaluating the NMR spectra of other prostaglandins. More informative NMR spectra can be obtained by using spin decoupling or shift reagents.

The lanthanide shift reagents (e.g. tris(dipivaloylmethanato)europium(III)) are rare earth complexes of 1,3-diones.

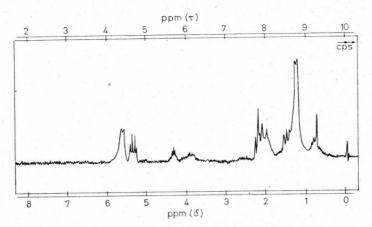

Fig. 1.4. NMR spectrum of prostaglandin $F_{2\alpha}$ (60 MHz)

The coordination number of the metal is six in the complex; this number can be raised to 7 or 8 which means that the lanthanide complex behaves like a Lewis acid. When the complex is added to an organic compound displaying Lewis basicity (alcohols, amines, carboxylic acids and their esters) a loose dipole–dipole complex is formed in whose NMR spectrum the metal alters the chemical shift of protons. The effect is dependent on the direction and decreases with the cube of the distance between the metal ion and the proton:

$$\delta \varDelta = \frac{k(3 \cos^2\theta - 1)}{r^3}$$

where $\delta\varDelta$ is the difference between the chemical shifts of a particular proton in the non-complexed and complexed substrate, r is the distance between the metal ion and the proton and θ is the angle enclosed by the symmetry axis of the lanthanide complex and the vector r.

The substantial increase of chemical shifts in the presence of lanthanide shift reagents may largely simplify NMR spectra by eliminating partly or completely both the overlap of individual bands and the second order spin–spin interactions. The use of lanthanide complexes containing chiral ligands — so-called 'optishift' regents — may enable the determination of the optical purity of chiral substances [58, 59].

Crabbé *et al.* studied the NMR spectrum of the methyl ester of prostaglandin A_2 (**1.58**) with the help of the shift reagent tris(dipivaloylmethanato)europium(III) (Table 1.3) [60, 61].

1.58

The shift reagent is complexed by that part of the molecule which has the highest basicity, i.e. by the hydroxyl group in the allylic position. Since the effect of the reagent decreases with the cube of the distance, the greatest change of shifts is experienced for the protons of the allyl alcohol (C_{13}-C_{15}) moiety ($\delta\Delta = 5.24$; 3.15; 2.65). Essentially, all protons absorb at different fields and it is possible to determine the spin-spin coupling constants too. The small coupling constant of protons of the double bond in the upper chain ($J_{5,6} = 11$ Hz) suggests a (Z)-geometry, while that for the double bond in the lower chain ($J_{13,14} = 15$ Hz) points to an (E)-geometry.

Jenny et al. studied prostaglandin D_2 (**1.47**) by means of spin decoupling [62]. This method involves the irradiation of the sample at the resonance frequency of the proton in spin coupling interaction with the proton under investigation. No signal will appear at the frequency of irradiation and the spin–spin coupling between the two protons will disappear.

Table 1.3

NMR Spectral Data of Prostaglandin A_2 Methyl Ester (**1.58**) (*a:* in $CDCl_3$ solution; *b:* in the presence of equimolecular shift reagent [tris(dipivaloylmethanato) europium(III)]

	a (δ, multiplicity)		b (δ, multiplicity, J Hz)			
1-$COCH_3$	3.61	s	4.06	s	$J_{2,3}$	7
2-H	2.26	t	2.94	t	$J_{3,4}$	7
3-H			2.30	qt	$J_{3,4}$	7
4-H	2.06	m	2.70	q	$J_{4,5}$	7
5-H	5.34	m	5.84	m	$J_{5,6}$	11
6-H	5.34	m	6.20	m	$J_{6,7}$	7
7-H	2.08	m	3.50	m		
10-H	6.08	dd	7.0	dd	$J_{10,11}$	6
11-H	7.39	dd	8.02	dd	$J_{11,12}$	2.6
12-H	2.18	m	4.50	m	$J_{10,12}$	2
13-H	5.53	m	8.18	dd	$J_{12,13}$	8
14-H	5.53	m	8.68	dd	$J_{13,14}$	15
15-H	3.98	m	9.22	m	$J_{14,15}$	6
18-H			1.98	qt	$J_{17,18}$	7
19-H			1.64	sx	$J_{18,19}$	7
20-H	0.9	t	1.04	t	$J_{19,20}$	7

The proton in the allylic position (15-H) in prostaglandin D_2 absorbs at δ 4.09. When the sample is irradiated at δ 4.09 the spin–spin coupling to the olefinic proton will be eliminated (δ 5.63, q, $J = 7$ and 16 Hz) and the 14-H signal collapses to a doublet ($J = 16$ Hz). The anellation proton (12-H)

3 R.D.C.

absorbs at δ 2.87. Irradiating the sample at δ 2.87 the signal of the C_{13} olefinic proton (δ 5.43, q, $J = 16$ and 8.5 Hz) is reduced to a doublet. The coupling constant between the two olefinic protons determined in this way ($J = 16$ Hz) confirms the assumed (E)-geometry. The coupling constant (8.5 Hz) determined in a similar manner for the two anellation protons (8-H and 12-H) suggests their *trans* arrangement.

Recently M. Vandewalle *et al.* have reported a detailed NMR analysis of prostaglandin $F_{1\alpha}$, $F_{1\beta}$ and 8-*epi*-prostaglandin $F_{1\alpha}$ (Tables 1.4–1.6, pp. 36–41) [90].

As already mentioned, the ^{13}C nuclear magnetic resonance spectra of prostaglandins have been studied by several research teams [23, 24]. The broad-band proton decoupled CMR spectrum of the methyl ester of prostaglandin $F_{2\alpha}$ is shown in Fig. 1.5.

Cooper and Fried carried out assignments of ^{13}C NMR spectra for several natural prostaglandins; a correlation diagram of the shifts is also given in Fig. 1.5.

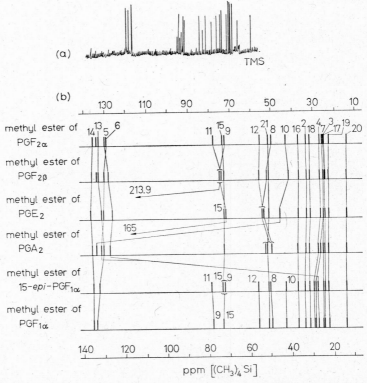

Fig. 1.5 CMR spectrum of the methyl ester of prostaglandin F_α, (a) with broad band proton decoupling and (b) correlation diagram for the CMR spectrum of prostaglandins

In the mass spectra of primary prostaglandins recorded under the conditions of electron bombardment, the molecular ions cannot be detected owing to rapid dehydration and subsequent decomposition of the formed ion $(M-18)$ leading to fragments of lower mass numbers (Fig. 1.6, p. 42).

Prostaglandins of the A and B series being more stable than the primary ones give, on electron impact, mass spectra showing molecular ions of considerable abundance. In the mass spectrum of prostaglandin A_1 (**1.30**) (Fig. 1.7, p. 42), besides the molecular ion of about 20% relative intensity, the peak of an ion derived from this by hydrogen migration and subsequent elimination of water is also intensive (Fig. 1.8, Process (a), p. 43). The ion radical formed by rearrangement can lose a pentyl radical by homolysis of the C_{15}-C_{16} bond, followed by the loss of water from the remaining cation giving the base peak of the spectrum at $m/e = 247$ [63].

The first rearrangement of the molecular ion may be succeeded by another one and by hydrogen transposition and cleavage to give a cation $(m/e = 237)$

Assignment of Compounds Listed in Tables 1.4—1.6

(a)   (b)   (c)

1.59; $R_1 = CH_3$, $R_2 = R_3 = R_4 = H$
1.60; $R_1 = CH_3$, $R_2 = COCH_3$, $R_3 = H$, $R_4 = OH$
1.61; $R_1 = CH_3$, $R_2 = COCH_3$, $R_3 = OH$, $R_4 = H$
1.62; $R_1 = R_2 = R_3 = H$, $R_4 = OH$
1.63; $R_1 = R_2 = R_4 = H$, $R_3 = OH$
1.64; $R_1 = CH_3$, $R_2 = R_4 = H$, $R_3 = OH$

(a)   (b)   (c)

1.65; $R_1 = COCH_3$, $R_2 = R_3 = CH_3$
1.66; $R_1 = H$, $R_2 = R_3 = CH_3$
1.67; $R_1 = COCH_3$, R_2 and R_3 are side chains attached to the cyclopentane through sp^3 C atoms
1.68; $R_1 = H$, R_2 and R_3 are side chains attached to the cyclopentane through sp^3 C atoms
1.69; $R_1 = COCH_3$, $R_2 = (CH_2)_6CH=C(CH_3)_2$, $R_3 = CH_2CH=C(CH_3)_2$
1.70; $R_1 = H$, $R_2 = (CH_2)_6CH=C(CH_3)_2$, $R_3 = CH_2CH=C(CH_3)_2$

3*

Table 1.4

¹H-NMR Spectral Parameters

Product Solvent	1.59a CCl₄	1.60a CDCl₃ (CCl₄)	1.61a CDCl₃ (CCl₄)	1.63a (PGF₁α CD₃OD	1.64a CDCl₃
H-10[b]	1.70	c	c	1.57	1.77
H-10′[b]	2.00	2.55	2.50	2.36	2.16
H-9	4.06	5.15	5.13	4.10	4.19
H-11	3.80	4.87	4.90	3.81	3.95
H-8	c	c	c	c	c
H-12	c	2.55	2.50	2.21	2.27
		d	d		
J 10,10′	−14.5	(−15.5)	(−15.5)	−14.5	−15.0
		d	d		
J 9,10	d	(d)	(d)	2.0	1.0
		d	d		
J 10,11	d	(d)	(d)	5.5	2.5
		5.5[f]	d		
J 9,10′	d	(6.0[g])	(5.5[f])	6.2	5
		8.5[f]	d		
J 10,11	d	(9.5[g])	(9.0[f])	8.75	7.5
		d	d		
J 8,9	d	(d)	(d)	6	d
		d	d		
J 11,12	d	(7.75)	(8.75)	7	d
		d	d		
J 8,12	d	(12.0)	(12.0)	11	d
		d	d		
J 10	5.0	(d)	(d)	5.0	3.5
		d	d		
J 10′	d	(15.5)	(14.5)	15.0	12.5
		11	11		
J 9	9.5	(11)	(10)	14.0	12
		d	20		
J 11	14.5	(22.5)	(22)	22.0	16
H-13	5.17	5 47	5.47	5.42	5.46
H-14	5.42	5.57	5.55	5.47	5.54
H-15	1.96	4.09	4.09	3.98	4.06
J 12,13	9.0	8.0	7.75	7.5	8.0
J 13,14	15.2	15.25	15.5	15.0	15.0
J 14,15	6.8	6.25	6.0	6.4	5.5

[a] obtained at 300 MHz at room temperature: chemical shifts are given in ppm relative to TMS as interna standard: coupling contants are given in Hz.
[b] H-10: *cis* with OH-9 or Ac-9; H-10′: *trans* with OH-9 or Ac-9
[c] could not be located
[d] could not be measured
[e] sum of vicinal coupling constants given in Hz
[f, g] values in any vertical column may be reversed

of PGF and Related Cyclopentane Derivatives I[a]

1.65a CCl$_4$	1.66a CCl$_4$	1.67a CDCl$_3$	1.68a CDCl$_3$	1.69a CCl$_4$	1.70a CDCl$_3$
1.53	1.66	c	—	c	c
2.51	2.02	2.35	2.00	c	c
5.03	3.92	5.15	3.90	5.01^f	4.18^f
			to		
4.57	3.67	4.92	4.30	4.75^f	3.93^f
1.52	1.29	c	c	c	c
1.79	1.59	c	c	c	c
−15.7	−14.8	—	—	d	d
1.8	1.3	—	—	d	d
5.0	2.7	—	—	d	d
6.2	4.7	—	—	d	d
8.8	7.4	—	—	d	d
4.9	3.8	—	—	d	d
7.8	4.7	—	—	d	d
11.8	10.4	—	—	d	d
6.8	4.0	4–7	4–6	d	d
15.0	12	14–16	11–16	d	d
12.9	10	10–13	8–11	d^f	8.5^f
21.6	16	17–23	12–15	24^f	11.5^f
—	—	—	—	—	—
—	—	—	—	—	—
—	—	—	—	—	—
—	—	—	—	—	—
—	—	—	—	—	—
	—	—	—	—	—

Table 1.5

¹H-NMR Spectral Parameters

Product Solvent	1.59b CCl₄	1.60b CDCl₃	1.62b CD₃OD	1.63b PGF.β CD₃OD
H-10[b]	c^f	2.00	1.85	1.90[f]
H-10′[b]	1.76[f]	2.00	1.85	1.80[f]
H-9	3.88[g]	4.97[f]	3.95[f]	3.95[g]
H-11	3.83[g]	4.89[f]	3.88[f]	3.87[g]
H-8	c	c	c	c
H-12	c	2.18	c	1.90
J 10,10′	—15.0	d	d	—15.0
J 9,10	7.5	d	d	d
J 11,10	d	d	d	7.0
J 9,10′	7.5	d	d	7.0
J 11,10′	7.5	d	d	7.0
J 8,9	7.5	d	d	d
J 11,12	d	d	d	7.2
J 8,12	d	d	d	d
J 10	d^f	d	d	14.0
J 10′	15.0[f]	d	d	14.0
J 9	22.0[g]	23.5[f]	23.0[f]	21.6[g]
J 11	17.0[g]	17.5[f]	7.0[f]	18.5[g]
H-13	5.26	5.55	5.57	5.52
H-14	5.42	5.53	5.51	5.45
H-15	2.00	4.08	4.01	3.98
J 12,13	8.5	d	7.5	8.0
J 13,14	15.2	d	15.0	15.0
J 14,15	6.5	d	5.5	6.0

[a] obtained at 300 MHz at room temperature; chemical shifts are given in ppm relative to TMS as internal standard; coupling constants are given in Hz.
[b] H-10: *cis* with OH-9 or Ac-9; H-10′: *trans* with OH-9 or Ac-9
[c] could not be located
[d] could not be measured
[e] sum of vicinal coupling constants given in Hz
[f,g] values in any vertical column may be reversed

of PGF and Related Cyclopentane Derivatives II[a]

1.64b CDCl₃	1.65b CCl₄	1.66b CDCl₃	1.67b CDCl₃	1.68b CCl₄	1.69b CDCl₃
1.99^f	1.97	1.95	1.85	1.93	1.85
		to	to		
1.95^f	1.97	2.00	1.98	1.93	1.85
4.07^g	4.67	4.75	3.98	4.81	4.01^g
		to	to		
3.98^g	4.67	4.95	4.13	4.81	3.99^g
c	1.49	1.60	1.40	c	c
		to	to 1.60		
1.95	1.49	1.70	c	c	c
−13.5	—	—	—	—	d
3.5	7.1	—	—	6.5	d
7.5	7.1	—	—	6.5	d
d	7.1	—	—	6.5	d
d	7.1	—	—	6.5	d
d	7.6	—	—	d	d
d	7.6	—	—	d	d
d	10.4	—	—	d	d
11	14.2	12	11	13.0	d
		to	to		
d	14.2	14	13	13.0	d
d^g	21.8	16	15	17.0	18.6^g
		to	to		
18^g	21.8	24	21	17.0	19.8^g
5.54	—	—	—	—	—
5.52	—	—	—	—	—
4.07	—	—	—	—	—
d	—	—	—	—	—
d	—	—	—	—	—
d	—	—	—	—	—

Table 1.6

¹H-NMR Spectral Parameters

Product Solvent	1.59c CCl_4	1.60c CCl_4	1.61c CCl_4	1.62c CD_3OD
H-10[b]	1.55	c	c	c
H-10'[b]	2.32	2.68	2.68	2.47
H-9	3.85[f]	4.81[f]	4.82[f]	3.92[f]
H-11	3.80[f]	4.78[f]	4.77[f]	3.84[f]
H-8	1.97	2.12	2.11	2.04
H-12	2.59	2.73	2.72	2.67
J 10,10'	—15.0	—15.5	—14.5	d
J 9,10	d	d	3.4	d
J 10,11	d	d	d	d
J 9,10'	d	7.75	7.4	d
J 10',11	d	7.75	7.1	d
J 8,9	d	d	3.4	d
J 11,12	d	d	d	d
J 8,12	d	d	d	d
J 10	8	d	d	d
J 10'	14	14.5	16	d
J 9	12[f]	d	14[f]	d
J 11	19[f]	d	19[f]	d
H-13	5.05	5.38	5.36	5.45
H-14	5.43	5.55	5.53	5.55
H-15	1.97	3.98	3.95	4.03
J 12,13	9.8	9.2	9.1	d
J 13,14	15.2	15.2	15.2	d
J 14,15	6.8	5.8	6.1	d

[a] obtained at 300 MHz at room temperature; chemical shifts are given in ppm relative to TMS as internal standard; coupling constants are given in Hz;
[b] H-10: *cis* with OH-9 or Ac-9; H-10': *trans* with OH-9 or Ac-9
[c] could not be located
[d] could not be measured
[e] sum of coupling constants given in Hz
[f] values in any vertical column may be reversed

of PGF and Related Cyclopentane Derivatives III[a]

1.63c CD₃OD	1.64c CDCl₃	1.65c CCl₄	1.67c CCl₄	1.68c CDCl₃	1.70c CDCl₃
c	c	1.50	1.48	1.57 to 1.64	c
2.46	2.41	2.66	2.64	2.37	2.37
3.90[f]	4.0[f]	4.68	4.70	3.88 to	3.97[f]
3.81[f]	3.9[f]	4.68	4.70	3.97	3.94[f]
c	c	2.17	2.10 to	2.00 to 2.15	c
2.62	2.73	2.17	2.30	c	c
−14.0	−14.5	−15.7	—	—	−15.0
d	d	4.0	—	—	d
d	d	4.0	—	—	d
7.25	7.0	7.7	—	—	7.0
7.25	7.0	7.7	—	—	7.0
d	d	4.5	—	—	d
d	d	4.5	—	—	d
d	d	6.7	—	—	—
d	d	8.0	5–8	6–10	d
15	14.5	15.4	15–16	14–15	14
14[f]	d	16.2	d	14–21	13[f]
21[f]	d	16.2	d	14–21	15.4[f]
5.39	5.36	—	—	—	—
5.47	5.56	—	—	—	—
3.97	4.0	—	—	—	—
9.8	9.25	—	—	—	—
15.25	15.0	—	—	—	—
6.25	6.75	—	—	—	—

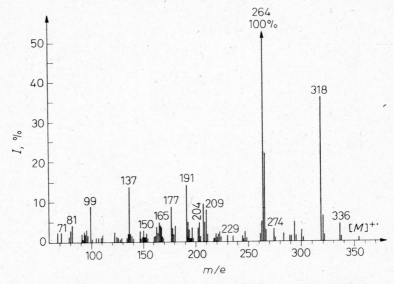

Fig. 1.6. Mass spectrum of prostaglandin $F_{2\alpha}$ at 12.5 eV [92]

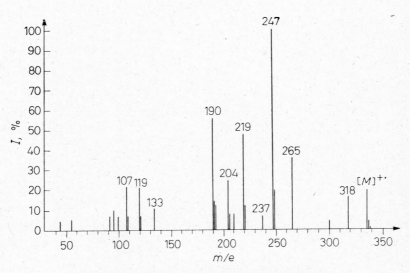

Fig. 1.7. Mass spectrum of prostaglandin A_1

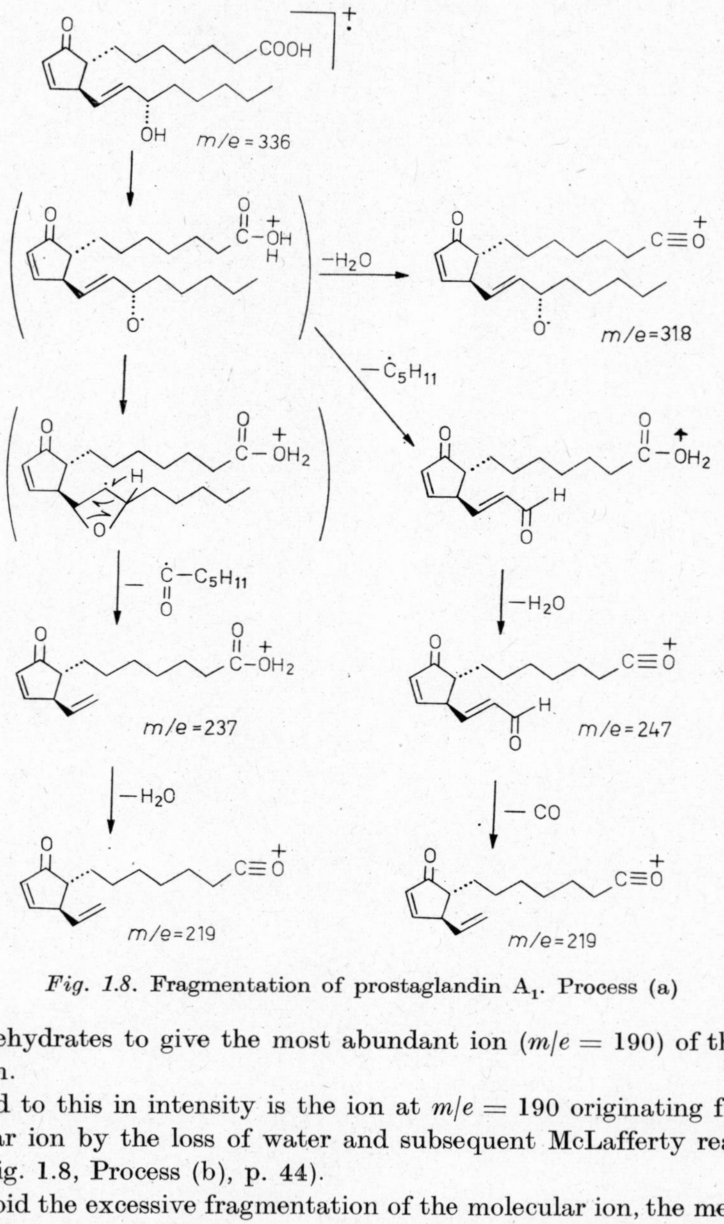

Fig. 1.8. Fragmentation of prostaglandin A_1. Process (a)

which dehydrates to give the most abundant ion ($m/e = 190$) of the mass spectrum.

Second to this in intensity is the ion at $m/e = 190$ originating from the molecular ion by the loss of water and subsequent McLafferty rearrangement (Fig. 1.8, Process (b), p. 44).

To avoid the excessive fragmentation of the molecular ion, the methyl esters of prostaglandins (Figs 1.9; 1.10, p. 45) or the easily prepared silyl ethers were used for mass spectrometry. In the mass spectrum (Fig. 1.11, p. 46) of the trimethyl silyl ether of prostaglandin E_1 (**1.71**) the molecular ion appears

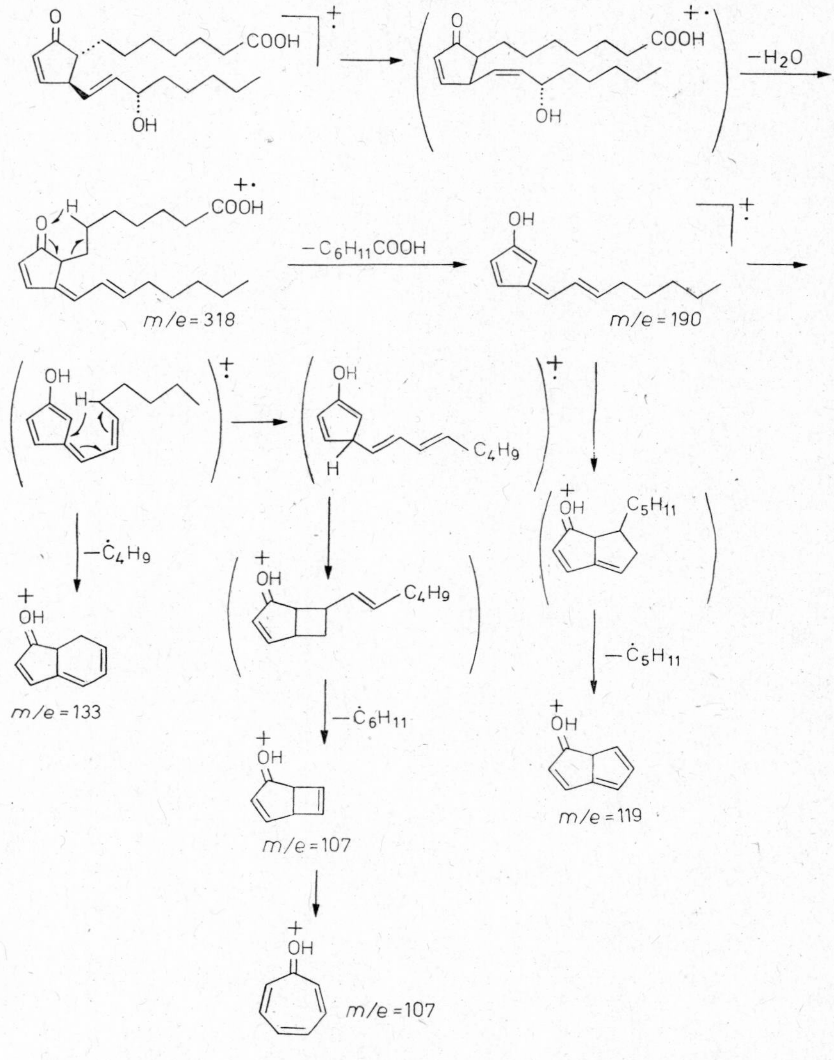

Fig. 1.8. Fragmentation of prostaglandin A_1. Process (b)

($m/e = 570$). Further fragmentations are decisively controlled by one of the trimethylsilyloxy groups (Fig. 1.12) [64–67].

If ionization takes place at the silyloxy group linked to C_{15}, there will be three preferred possibilities of fragmentation. The molecular ion may lose a pentyl radical by the homolysis of the C_{15}-C_{16} bond (Fig. 1.12, Process (a))

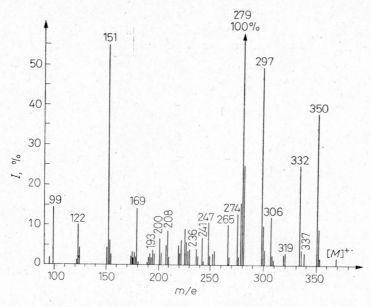

Fig. 1.9. Mass spectrum of prostaglandin E_1 methyl ester at 12.5 eV [91]

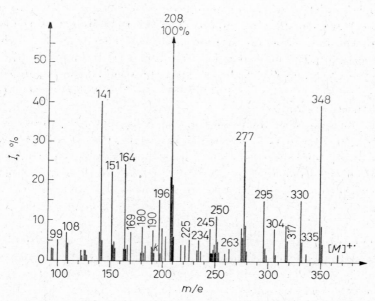

Fig. 1.10. Mass spectrum of prostaglandin E_2 methyl ester at 12.5 eV [91]

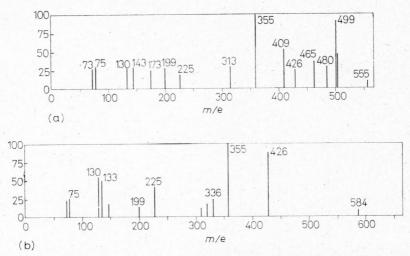

Fig. 1.11. Mass spectra of (a) silyl ether (**1.71**) and (b) of the 9-methyloximesilyl ether of PGE_1

and the ion formed ($m/e = 499$) will give an intensive peak. Alternatively, the molecular ion may suffer homolysis of the C_{12}-C_{13} bond (Fig. 1.12, Process (b)) followed by the elimination of a neutral particle (C_2H_2) from the cation formed. The two fragments of this process ($m/e = 199$ and 173, respectively) are of medium abundance. The third possibility for the fragmentation of the molecular ion is the cleavage of the cyclopentane ring (Fig. 1.12, Process (c)). The molecular ion loses a neutral fragment by the heterolysis of the C_8-C_9 and C_{11}-C_{12} bonds, and the residual ion is subject to the homolysis of the C_{15}-C_{16} bond. This ion ($m/e = 355$) represents the base peak of the spectrum.

If ionization takes place on the silyloxy group at C_{11}, the cleavage of the C_{11}-C_{12} bond will proceed readily (Fig. 1.12, Process (d)), because this bond is in α-position with regard to the silyloxy group, and in the β, i.e. in the allylic position relative to the C_{13}–C_{14} double bond. Fragmentation starts with the homolysis of the bond, and continues similarly to the complex decomposition of silyl ethers, with hydrogen migration and γ-cleavage, leading finally to an ion with a mass number of 143.

In the case of E prostaglandins, instead of the silyl ethers of the parent molecules those of their O-methylhydroximino derivatives are used. The compound shows a fragmentation similar to that of silyl ethers with the difference that the fragmentation is now controlled by the oxime group. Investigation of the methyloxime-silyl ether derivative of prostaglandin E_1

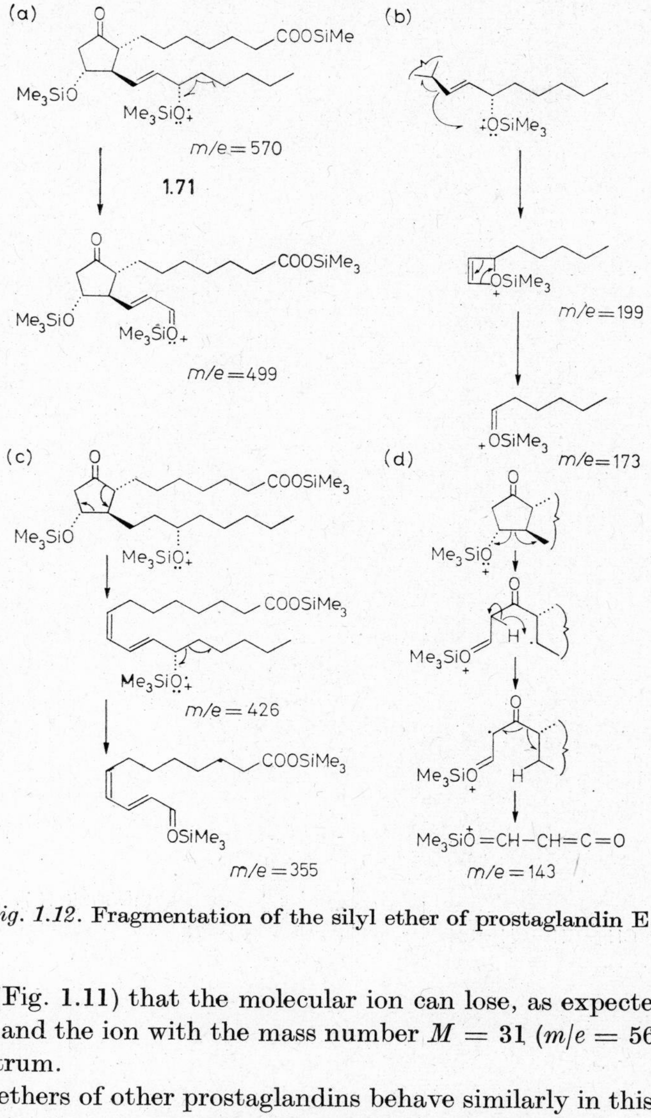

Fig. 1.12. Fragmentation of the silyl ether of prostaglandin E_1

has shown (Fig. 1.11) that the molecular ion can lose, as expected, a methoxy radical and the ion with the mass number $M = 31$ ($m/e = 568$) appears in the spectrum.

The silyl ethers of other prostaglandins behave similarly in this respect to the silyl derivative of prostaglandin E_1 (Fig. 1.13) [68, 69].

Prostaglandins of the F series are amenable to mass spectrometric investigation preferably as their butylboronate derivatives [70–72]. Members of this series can, in the presence of E prostaglandins, be selectively transformed by butylboric acid (involving the C_9 and C_{11} hydroxyls) to cyclic esters — the bis-trimethylsilyl derivatives of which can be conveniently separated from

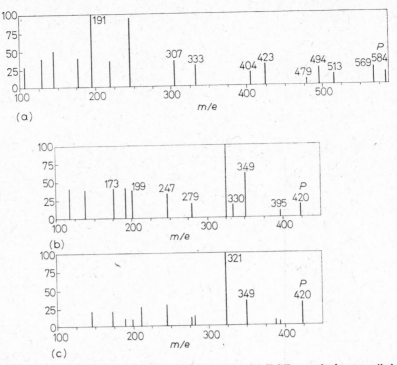

Fig. 1.13. Mass spectra of (a. PGF$_{2\alpha}$, (b) PGA$_2$ and (c) PGB$_2$ methyl ester silyl ethers

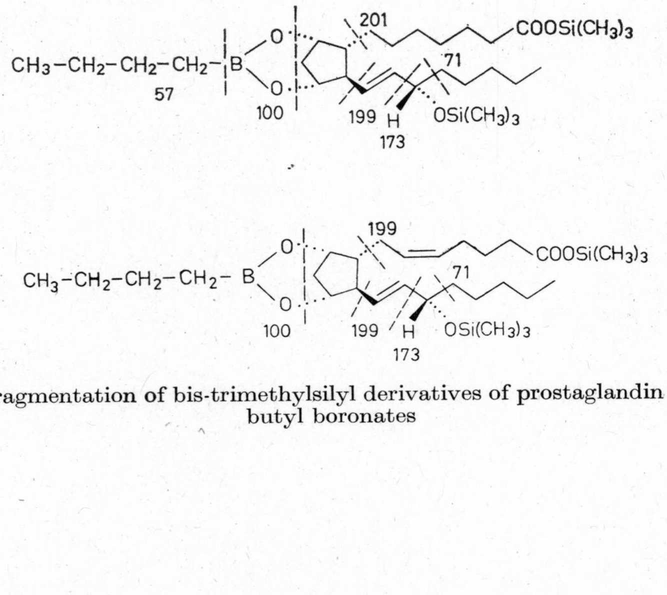

Fig. 1.14. Fragmentation of bis-trimethylsilyl derivatives of prostaglandin F$_{1\alpha}$ and F$_{2\alpha}$ butyl boronates

the unreacted E compound by gas chromatography. The compounds give fairly intensive (10%) molecular ions which undergo relatively simple fragmentation. The base peak represents an ion formed by loss of a pentyl radical *via* homolysis of the $C_{15}-C_{16}$ bond (Fig. 1.14).

The extensive fragmentation of the molecular ions formed from prostaglandins on electron impact can be avoided with the help of *chemical ionization* [73].

The chemical ionization method consists of introducing into the ionization chamber a reagent gas of 0.5 to 1 mm pressure containing the substance under investigation in 0.1% concentration. Under these conditions the electron beam ionizes the reagent gas molecule and the ions formed in the primary process collide with the molecules of the substance to be investigated. As a consequence of the relatively high concentration (i.e. the shorter mean free path) of the reagent gas, its ions lose most of their excitation energy prior to colliding with the substrate molecules by collisions between themselves with the result that they transfer only a small amount of energy to the substrate. The fragmentation of the molecular ion formed by this low-energy secondary process is not significant, so it is possible to determine the molecular weight from the spectrum.

The chemical ionization spectrum of prostaglandin A_1 (**1.30**) was studied with methane of 0.55 mm pressure as reagent gas at 200°C to 220°C evaporation temperature (Fig. 1.15).

CH_5^+ and $C_2H_5^+$ ions generated from methane by the electron beam caused by collision with the prostaglandin molecules partly ionization and partly the formation of adduct ions.

The mass number of the molecular ion ($M = 336$) can be read from the spectrum. Ions with mass numbers $M + 1$ and $M - 1$, and ions $M + 1-18$ ($m/e = 319$) and $M + 1-2 \times 18$ ($m/e = 301$) formed from the first by the loss of one and two molecules of water, give the most intense lines of the spectrum. The intensity of the fragments resulting from the subsequent fragmentation of these ions is negligible.

The adduct ions appear in the spectrum with an intensity comparable to that of the $M + 1$ fragment. The addition of $C_2H_5^+$ leads to $M + 29$ ($m/e = 365$) and of $C_3H_5^+$ to $M + 41$ ($m/e = 377$).

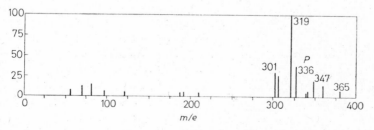

Fig. 1.15. Chemical ionization spectrum of prostaglandin A

The prostaglandins $F_{1\alpha}$, $F_{2\alpha}$, E_1 and E_2 have chemical ionization spectra similar to that of prostaglandin A_1. The $M + 1$ ion formed by chemical ionization always loses one more molecule of water than the number of hydroxyl groups contained in the initial molecule. For instance, prostaglandin $F_{2\alpha}$ contains three hydroxyl groups and a fragment with mass number $M + 1 - 4 \times 18$ appears in its spectrum.

1.3 REACTIONS AND INTERCONVERSIONS

Prostaglandins are weak organic acids which combine with alkalis to form water-soluble hygroscopic salts. When preparing a salt, exactly one equivalent of alkali must be used as the compounds are sensitive to alkali. Crystalline salts which are easy to handle are obtained from prostaglandins E_2 and $F_{2\alpha}$ with tris-(hydroxymethyl)aminomethane [74]. Salt formation is carried out in acetonitrile–water mixtures at 65 °C; the salt crystallizes on cooling.

Monoolefinic prostaglandins (e.g. PGE_1, $PGF_{2\alpha}$) are relatively stable in the crystalline state and can be stored under nitrogen below 5 °C. Representatives with two and three double bonds (e.g. PGE_2, PGE_3) are sensitive and undergo autooxidation in air even at room temperature.

The esters of prostaglandins cannot be prepared by acid-catalyzed esterification since prostaglandins are sensitive to acid. The methyl esters are synthesized in a methylene chloride solution with ethereal diazomethane [75]. The mixed anhydride method can also be applied to the preparation of esters [75]; a tertiary amine is added to the solution of prostaglandin in methylene chloride and the salt is treated with p-toluenesulfonyl chloride. The mixed anhydride is decomposed to the corresponding esters by means of alcohol [76].

Similar difficulties are encountered in the hydrolysis of esters that, in turn, cannot be performed with alkalis because of the sensitivity of the compounds. An enzymatic method using acylase has been developed for the hydrolysis of methyl esters [12].

The trichloroethyl esters of prostaglandins are, on the other hand, easy to decompose. These are prepared in methylene chloride with trichloroethyl alcohol in the presence of pyridine and dicyclohexylcarbodiimide, and cleaved in aqueous acetic acid with zinc [49].

The trimethylsilyl ethers of prostaglandins can be prepared readily using hexamethyldisilazane in tetrahydrofuran solution to which a catalytic amount of trimethylsilyl chloride has been added [75]. The silyl ethers are used mainly for the purification and mass spectrometrical identification of

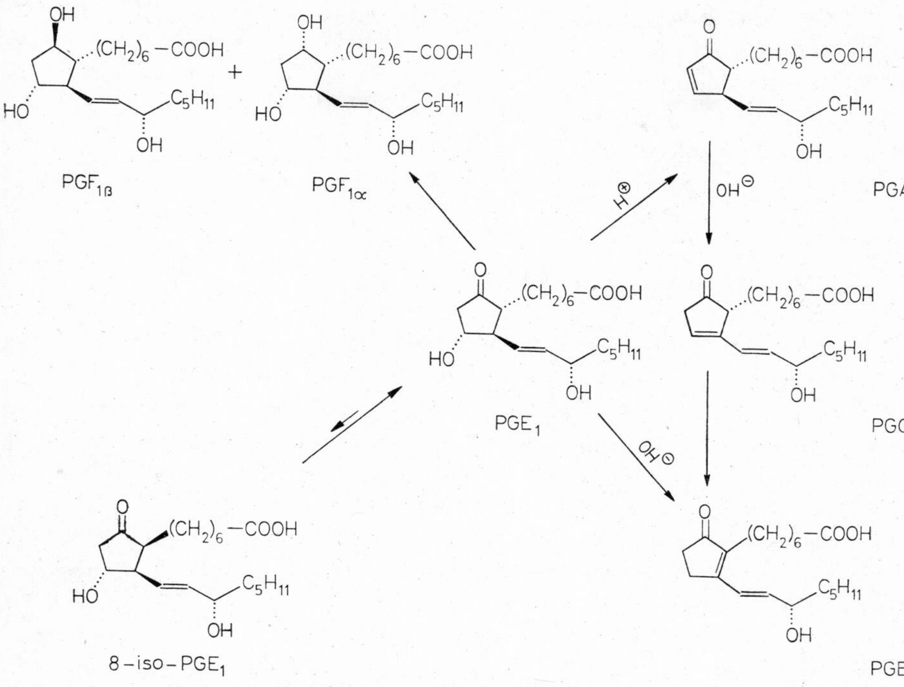

Fig. 1.16. Interconversions of prostaglandins

prostaglandins. Silyl compounds are stable in basic media and readily hydrolyze on the addition of weak acids to the parent prostaglandins.

Prostaglandins are sensitive to both acids and alkalis. Formic acid causes an inversion at C_{15} even at $0°$. The configurational change proceeds presumably through an allyl cation intermediate. The treatment of prostaglandins $F_{1\alpha}$ and E_1 with a mixture of formic acid and sodium formate led to an equilibrium mixture containing 30% of the (15R)-epimers (15-*epi*-PGF$_{1\alpha}$ and 15-*epi*-PGE$_1$, respectively) [49].

Prostaglandins of the E and D series may be epimerized at C_8 by base. For example, when prostaglandin E_1 is treated in ethanol with sodium acetate, an equilibrium mixture containing 15% of 8-iso-PGE$_1$ (Fig. 1.16) is obtained [49]. Prostaglandin D_1 can also be epimerized with activated charcoal [37].

The β-hydroxyketone moiety of E and D prostaglandins are highly susceptible to acids, which cause dehydration. When prostaglandins E_1 and E_2 are heated to $60°C$ in an acetic acid–water mixture, they are converted into prostaglandin A_1 and A_2, respectively (Fig. 1.16); treatment with

4*

alkali transforms them, also by dehydration, into prostaglandin B_1 and B_2 respectively [8, 49].

A-type prostaglandins can be converted, *via* C-type intermediates, into prostaglandins of the B series by means of treatment with a base. The driving force of isomerization is the higher thermodynamical stability of the B-type compounds in which two carbon-carbon double bonds are conjugated with the carbonyl group.

The pH-dependent transformation of prostaglandin E_1 into prostaglandins A_1 and B_1 has been comprehensively investigated. PGE_1 is relatively stable between pH 3 and 7.4; below pH 3 and in the range of pH 7.4–11.5 conversion to prostaglandin A_1 is fast and complete within 6 hours at room temperature. At a higher pH the product is prostaglandin B_1.

The conversion of prostaglandin A into prostaglandin B also takes place in living organisms. Prostaglandin A is converted by the PGA isomerase enzyme system into prostaglandin C from which — by way of a base-catalyzed process — prostaglandin B is formed [77, 78].

Corey and Cyr have recently overcome the problem of converting prostaglandin A_2 (**1.31**) into prostaglandin C_2 [79]. This involved the generation of a so-called γ-extended enolate ion (**1.72**) from prostaglandin A_2 by its reaction with a strong base (potassium t-butoxide) acting by abstraction of the C_{12} hydrogen. Treatment of the reaction mixture with acidic methanol resulted in prostaglandin C_2 (**1.40**).

1.31   **1.72**   **1.40**

The esters of prostaglandin A_2 [(15S)- and (15R)-PGA$_2$ acetate methyl esters] occur in relatively high quantities in a coral species *(Plexaura homomalla)* indigenous to the Caribbean Sea [80, 81]. Since the biological action of prostaglandin A_2 is of less interest than that of the primary prostaglandins, considerable effort has been devoted to the conversions of this naturally occurring compound into prostaglandins E_2 and $F_{2\alpha}$.

Transformation was effected by oxidizing the methyl ester of prostaglandin A_2 acetate (**1.73**) in an alkaline medium with hydrogen peroxide into two stereoisomeric 10,11-epoxy compounds which were reduced, without separating the α- and β-epoxides (**1.74** and **1.75**), with chromium(II) acetate.

Separation of the products by chromatography afforded prostaglandin E_2-acetate methyl ester (**1.76**; 56%) and the 11-*epi*-PGE$_2$-acetate methyl ester (**1.77**; 25%); these were hydrolyzed with an esterase enzyme system to give PGE$_2$ and *epi*-PGE$_2$, respectively [82].

Stereoselectivity of epoxide formation in this sequence was poor, the ratio of α- and β-epoxides being approximately 60 : 40. For the achievement of a higher stereoselectivity difference between the steric accessibility of the two sides of the enone system must be significant.

The cyclopentenone ring of prostaglandin A$_2$ is nearly planar, the C_{8-1} side chain linked to it is directed downwards, the C_{13-20} chain in turn upwards, in relation to the plane of the ring. There is no significant difference between the shielding of the two faces of the ring, thus a reactant can attack the enone system from either of the two faces.

Corey and Ensley envisaged solving the problem by the introduction of a group which, in its preferred conformation, would shield the β-side of the cyclopentenone skeleton [83]. These authors silylized the C_{15} hydroxyl group of prostaglandin A$_2$ with tribenzylsilyl chloride in the presence of one equivalent of 2,6-lutidine. The conformation of the silyl compound (**1.78**) was determined by the presence of the bulky tribenzylsilyloxy group. In the favoured conformation the side chains are staggered and the silyl group is situated on the β-face of the ring (Fig. 1.17). Any deviation from this conformation (e.g. conformers obtained by rotation around the C_{15}-O bond) would greatly increase steric strain.

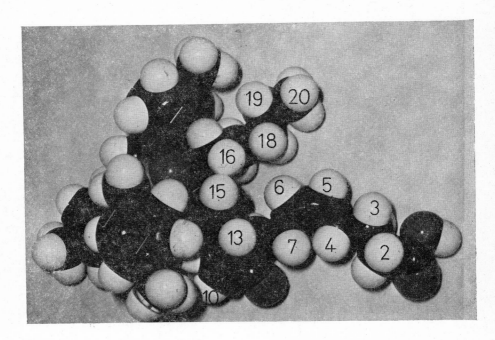

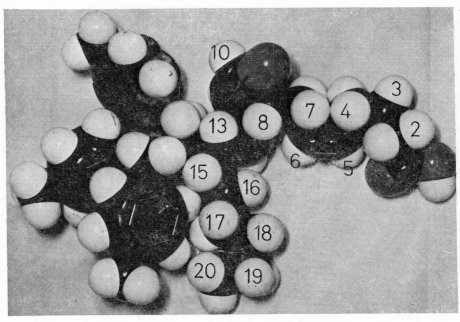

Fig. 1.17. Molecular model of compound **1.78**

When the silyl compound was epoxidized with alkaline hydrogen per-oxide at low temperature ($-40\,^{\circ}$C) 87.5% of α-epoxide (**1.79**) and 12.5% of β-epoxide (**1.80**) were obtained. An increase in the size of the silyl group — by the introduction of tri-p-xilylsilyl group into the molecule — led to the expected increase in stereoselectivity ($\alpha/\beta = 94 : 6$).

Having hydrolyzed the epoxy-silyl ethers (**1.79** and **1.80**) with acetic acid, Corey and Ensley reduced the epoxy compound with aluminium amal-gam to prostaglandin E$_2$ (**1.17**). Since the α-epoxide is reduced considerably faster than its β-stereoisomer and only 6% of the latter is present, it is not necessary to separate the epoxides prior to reduction. Provided that the reaction time is appropriate, only the α-epoxide will be reduced and the PGE$_2$ formed in this manner can be separated by crystallization from the oily β-epoxide.

The C$_9$ carbonyl group of prostaglandins of the E series can be reduced with metal hydrides [84]. Reduction of prostaglandin E$_1$ with sodium boro-hydride leads to two products: prostaglandin F$_{1\alpha}$ and F$_{1\beta}$ (Fig. 1.16) in a ratio of 35 : 65. When prostaglandin E$_2$ is reduced with sodium borohydride again the β-isomer will prevail (**1.15** and **1.26**; $\alpha/\beta = 45 : 55$). The ratio of isomers is somewhat more favourable when the methyl esters of E-type prostaglandins are reduced.

As the pharmacological action of the β-series differs considerably from that of natural prostaglandins, a reduction method furnishing mainly the α-isomer was sought.

The isomer ratio was much improved ($\alpha/\beta = 60 : 40$) when the trimethyl-silyl ether prepared from the methyl ester of prostaglandin E was subjected to sodium borohydride reduction, but final solution was brought about by the application of lithium trialkylborohydrides. Corey and Varma reduced prostaglandin E_2 at low temperature ($-78\,^{\circ}C$) with a reagent (**1.81**) of great space requirement and isolated the almost theoretical amount (98.7%) of prostaglandin $F_{2\alpha}$ [31].

1.81

Prostaglandins of the E series are reduced microbiologically with yeast extract when the F_{α} compounds are obtained with high stereoselectivity [85].

Reduction of the carbonyl group of prostaglandin D_1 (**1.46**) with sodium borohydride leads to a mixture of prostaglandin $F_{1\alpha}$ (**1.22**) and 11-*epi*-PGF$_{1\alpha}$ in the ratio 9 : 1. Prostaglandin D_1 displays an interesting behaviour towards alkali: when treated with sodium hydroxide it is converted by way of double-bond migration into iso-PGD$_1$ (**1.82**) from which, by dehydration, a product of yet unclarified structure is obtained [41].

1.46   **1.82**

Prostaglandins of the F-type can be converted into those of the E-type by a process in which the different reactivities of the three hydroxyl groups in prostaglandin F are utilized. As has already been mentioned when discussing the conformation of this series, the environment of the C_9 hydroxyl is more shielded than the C_{11} and C_{15} hydroxyl groups thereby offering a possibility of selective silylation.

Yankee *et al.* [27] allowed to react the methyl ester of prostaglandin $F_{2\alpha}$ with N-trimethylsilyldiethyl amine at low temperature ($-40\,^{\circ}C$) and oxidized the 11,15-bis-(trimethylsilyl) derivative obtained by means of Collins reagent (chromium(VI) oxide–pyridine complex). 11,15-Bis-(trimethylsilyl)-PGE$_2$ methyl ester was formed which, after acid solvolysis, led to the methyl ester of PGE$_2$.

Prostaglandin E_2 (**1.17**) can be converted into prostaglandin E_1 (**1.16**). In this transformation of the two olefinic bonds, that in the C_5-C_6 position must be saturated. Corey and Varma [31] realized this objective by using a silyl ether of prostaglandin E_2 prepared with a 1 : 1 mixture of isopropyldi-methylchlorosilane and 1,1,3,3-tetramethyl-1,3-diisopropyldisilazane. In the product (**1.83**) the two bulky dimethylisopropylsilyl groups in positions 11 and 15 have the role of shielding the C_{13}-C_{14} double bond. Consequently, when the compound is hydrogenated, the adsorption of the molecule to the palladium catalyst will take place mainly at the C_5-C_6 double bond, leading to the silyl ether of prostaglandin E_1 (**1.84**). After the removal of the silyl groups prostaglandin E_1 is obtained in an excellent yield.

1.83   **1.84**

Prostaglandin $F_{2\alpha}$ can be converted into $PGF_{1\alpha}$ in a similar manner by hydrogenating the 11,15-bis-(tetrahydropyranyl) derivative, prepared from the methyl ester of $PGF_{2\alpha}$, on a palladium catalyst. Removal of the masking tetrahydropyranyl groups from the product gave rise to the methyl ester of prostaglandin $F_{1\alpha}$.

Prostaglandin E_2 (**1.85**; R' and $R'' = O$) can be converted into (5E)-PGE_2 (**1.86**; R' and $R'' = O$). The C_5-C_6 double bond of (Z)-geometry in (**1.85**) is converted into its geometrical isomer when exposed to UV light (350 nm) [41].

1.85   **1.86**

A similar transformation can be performed on prostaglandin $F_{2\alpha}$ (**1.85**; $R' = OH$, $R'' = H$). The product of this reaction (**1.86**; $R' = OH$, $R'' = H$) has also been isolated from *Plexaura homomalla* (*cf.* [80, 81]).

Prostaglandin $F_{2\alpha}$ can be selectively oxidized to its 15-oxo derivative with 2,3-dichloro-5,6-dicyano-1,4-benzoquinone. This reaction is of significance in the transformation of prostaglandins of $(15R)$-configuration into natural prostaglandins [82, 86].

Prostaglandin $F_{2\alpha}$ can be converted to the $F_{2\beta}$ epimer (**1.88**; R^1, R^2, $R^3 = $ $=$ H). This task was efficiently solved by Corey et al. [87]. They started from the 11,15-bis(tetrahydropyranyl) ether (**1.87**; R = H) of the corresponding methyl ester. The sequence involved tosylation, reaction of the tosylate (**1.87**; R = Tos) with potassium superoxide (KO_2), hydrolysis of the methyl ester of the resulting prostaglandin $F_{2\beta}$ derivative (**1.88**; $R^1 = $ H, R^2, $R^3 = $ $=$ THP) with lithium hydroxide to the acid, and finally removal of the protective groups to afford prostaglandin $F_{2\beta}$. (Synthetic applications of potassium superoxide will be further discussed in Chapter 2.)

Inversion at C_{11} of prostaglandin $F_{2\alpha}$, i.e. the preparation of 11-*epi*-prostaglandin $F_{2\alpha}$ (**1.91**; R^1, $R^2 = $ H), was accomplished similarly. The synthesis was commenced by blocking the two α-hydroxyls of prostaglandin $F_{2\alpha}$ methyl ester (**1.89**) as the phenylboronate (**1.90**; R = H) and acetylating the C_{15} hydroxyl. The borate ester group of the acetate (**1.90**, R = Ac) was then removed and the resulting diol (**1.92**, R = H) monotosylated at

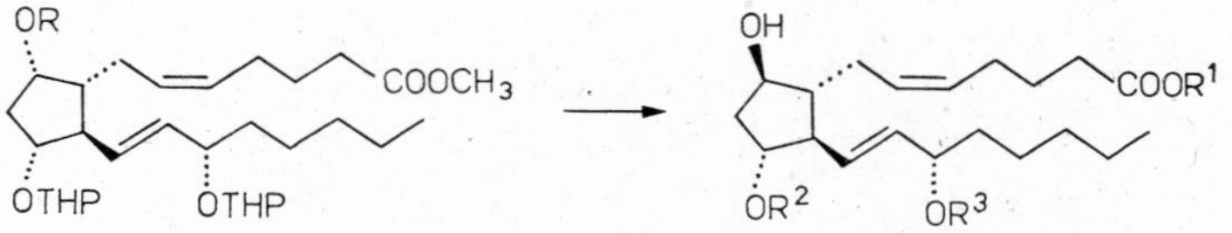

1.87   1.88

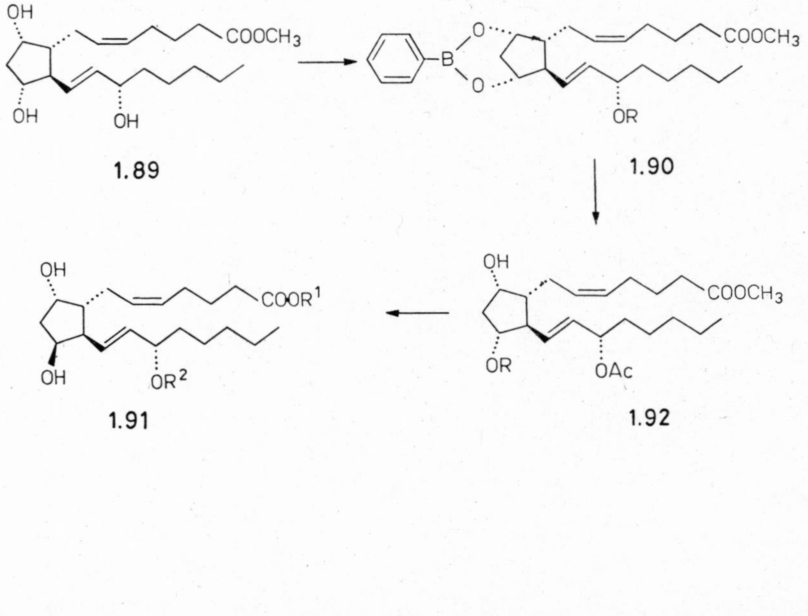

1.89   1.90

1.91   1.92

the C_{11} hydroxyl. The tosylate (**1.92**, R = Tos) was subjected to S_N2 nucleophilic displacement with potassium superoxide and the inverted product (**1.91**, $R^1 = CH_3$, $R^2 = Ac$) hydrolyzed with lithium hydroxide to 11-*epi*-prostaglandin $F_{2\alpha}$.

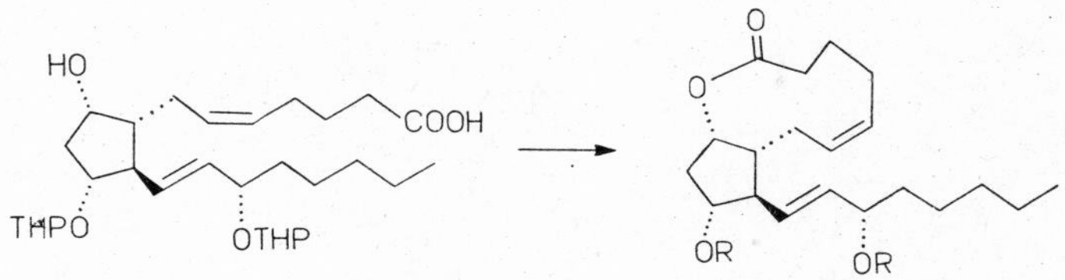

1.93   1.94

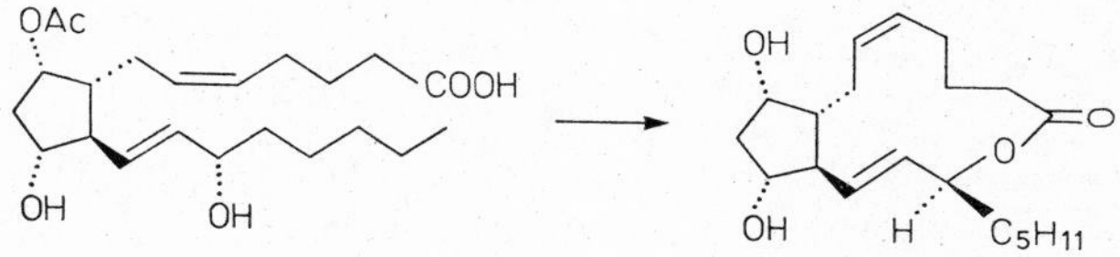

1.95   1.96

Recently Corey and his co-workers reported an interesting transformation of prostaglandin $F_{2\alpha}$ to a macrocyclic lactone [88]. Treatment of the corresponding 11,15-bis(tetrahydropyranyl) ether (**1.93**) with 2,2'-dipyridyl disulfide and triphenylphosphine effected the formation of a ten-membered lactone involving the C_9 hydroxyl (**1.94**). Under similar conditions with 9-acetylprostaglandin $F_{2\alpha}$ (**1.95**) it was the C_{15} hydroxyl which was incorporated into a macrocyclic lactone (**1.96**).

REFERENCES

1. COLBERT, J. C., "Prostaglandins, Isolation and Synthesis." *Chemical Technology Review*, No. 17. Noyes Data Corporation, Park Ridge, New Jersey, 1973.
2. BENTLEY, P. H., "Total Syntheses of Prostanoids." *Chemical Society Reviews*, *2*, 29 (1973).
3. AXEN, U., PIKE, J. E., SCHNEIDER, W. P., "The Total Synthesis of Prostaglandins." *The Total Synthesis of Natural Products*, Vol. I, 81. Wiley-Interscience, New York, 1972.

4. PIKE, J. E., "Total Synthesis of Prostaglandins." *Progress in the Chemistry of Organic Natural Products*, 28, 313 (1970), Springer-Verlag, New York.
5. BAGLI, J. F., "Prostaglandins and Related Compounds." *Annual Reports in Medicinal Chemistry, 1970*, 170, Academic Press, New York.
6. SZEJTLI, J., RÁDÓCZI, I., FINÁLI, I., ERŐS, J., JÉCSAI, Gy., KOVÁCS, G., ILLÉS, P., SZENTMIKLÓSI, P., "Prostaglandins. Scientific and Technical Review." Pharmaceutical and Chemical Works Chinoin, Budapest, 1972.
7. HAMBERG, M., "A Note on Nomenclature." International Conference on Prostaglandins. Vienna, 1972. *Advances in the Biosciences.* 9, 847 (1973), Pergamon Press, Oxford.
8. BERGSTRÖM, S., RYHAGE, R., SAMUELSSON, B., SJÖVALL, J., *J. Biol. Chem.*, 238, 3555 (1963).
9. BERGSTRÖM, S., *Science, 157*, 382 (1967).
10. AXEN, U., "Synthetic Approaches to Prostaglandin." *Annual Reports in Medicinal Chemistry, 1967*, 290, Academic Press, New York, 1968.
11. SAMUELSSON, B., "The Prostaglandins." *Angew. Chem. Int. Ed.*, 4, 410 (1965).
12. RAMWELL, P. W., SHAW, J. E., CLARKE, G. B., GROSTIC, M. F., KAISER, D. G., PIKE, J. E., "Prostaglandins." *Progress in the Chemistry of Fats and Other Lipids*, 9, 231 (1968), Pergamon Press, Oxford.
13. *Chemical Abstracts*, Index Guide, 76, 850 (1972).
14. GRANSTRÖM, E., LANDS, W. E., SAMUELSSON, B., *J. Biol. Chem.*, 243, 4104 (1968).
15. FOSS, P. S., SIH, C. J., TAKEGUCHI, C., SCHNOES, *Biochemistry*, 11, 2271 (1972).
16. HAYASHI, M., TANOUCHI, T., *J. Org. Chem.*, 38, 2115 (1973).
17. "IUPAC Tentative Rules for the Nomenclature of Organic Chemistry. Section E. Fundamental Stereochemistry." *J. Org. Chem.*, 35, 2849 (1970).
18. ELIEL, E. L., "Recent Advances in Stereochemical Nomenclature." *J. Chem. Education*, 48, 163 (1971).
19. NUGTEREN, D. H., VAN DORP, D. A., BERGSTRÖM, S., HAMBERG, M., SAMUELSSON, B., *Nature, 212*, 38 (1966).
20. ABRAHAMSSON, S., *Acta Cryst.*, 16, 409 (1963).
21. DUAX, W. L., EDMONDS, J. W., *Prostaglandins, 3*, 201 (1973).
22. EDMONDS, J. W., DUAX, W. L., *J. Am. Chem. Soc.*, 97, 413 (1975).
23. COOPER, G. F., FRIED, J., *Proc. Nat. Acad. Sci. U.S.A.*, 70, 1579 (1973).
24. LUKACS, G., PIRION, F., GERO, S. D., VAN DORP, D. A., HAGAMAN, E. W., WENKERT, E., *Tetrahedron Lett., 1973*, 515.
25. CHACHATY, C., WOLKOWSKI, Z., PIRION, F., LUKACS, G., *Chem. Commun., 1973*, 951.
26. BRUTCHER F. V., JR., ROBERTS, TH., BARR, S. J., PEARSON, N., *J. Am. Chem. Soc.*, 81, 4915 (1959).
27. YANKEE, E. W., LIN, C. E., FRIED, J., *Chem. Commun., 1972*, 1120.
28. HOYLAND, J. R., KIER, L. B., *J. Med. Chem.* 15, 84 (1972).
29. BROWSTER, D., MYERS, M., ORMEROD, J., OTTER, P., SMITH, A. C. B., SPINNER, M. E., TURNER, S., *J. Chem. Soc. Perkin I, 1973*, 2796.
30. VENTON, D. L., COUNSELL, R. E., SANNER, I. H., *J. Med. Chem.*, 18, 9 (1975).
31. COREY, E. J., VARMA, R. K., *J. Am. Chem. Soc.*, 93, 7319 (1971).
32. SCHAAF, T. K., COREY, E. J., *J. Org. Chem.*, 37, 2921 (1972).
33. COREY, E. J., SCHAAF, T. K., AUBER, W., KOELLIKER, U., WEINSHENKER, N. M., *J. Am. Chem. Soc.*, 92, 397 (1970).
34. BERGSTRÖM, S., SJÖVALL, J., *U.S. Patent* 3 598 858, 1971.
35. BERGSTRÖM, S., DRESSLER, F., RYHAGE, R., SAMUELSSON, B., SJÖVALL, J., *Arkiv för Kemi, 19*, 563 (1962).
36. PIKE, J. E., LINCOLN, F. H., SCHNEIDER, W. P., *J. Org. Chem.*, 34, 3552 (1969).
37. BERGSTRÖM, S., SJÖVALL, J., *U.S. Patent* 3 706 789, 1972.
38. SAMUELSSON, B., *J. Biol. Chem.*, 238, 3229 (1963).
39. COREY, E. J., MANN, J., *J. Am. Chem. Soc.*, 95, 6832 (1973).
40. COREY, E. J., MOINET, G., *J. Am. Chem. Soc.*, 95, 6831 (1973).
41. FOSS, P. S., SIH, C. J., TAKEGUCHI, C., SCHNOES, H., *Biochemistry, 11*, 2271 (1972).
42. SLATES, H. L., ZELAWSKI, Z. S., TAUB, D., WENDLER, N. L., *Chem. Commun., 1972*, 304.

43. KLUGE, A. F., UNTCH, K. G., FRIED, J. H., *J. Am. Chem. Soc.*, *94*, 9256 (1972).
44. ABRAHAM, N. A., *Tetrahedron Lett.*, *15*, 1393 (1974).
45. VAN DORP, D. A., *Ann. N. Y. Acad. Sci.*, *180*, 181 (1971).
46. BUNDY, G. L., DANIELS, E. G., LINCOLN, F. H., PIKE, J. E., *J. Am. Chem. Soc.*, *94*, 2124 (1972).
47. GANDOLFI, C., DORIA, G., GAIO, P., *Tetrahedron Lett.*, *1972*, 4303.
48. COREY, E. J., TERASHIMA, S., RAMWELL, P. W., JESSUP, R., WEINSHENKER, N. M., FLOYD, D. M., CROSBY, G. A., *J. Org. Chem.*, *37*, 3043 (1972).
49. PIKE, J. E., LINCOLN, F. H., SCHNEIDER, W. P., *J. Org. Chem.*, *34*, 3552 (1969).
50. FRIED, J., LIN, C. H., *J. Med. Chem.*, *16*, 429 (1973).
51. CRABBÉ, P., GARCIA, G. A., RINS, C., *J. Chem. Soc. Perkin I*, *1973*, 810.
52. SCOTT, A. I., *Interpretation of the Ultraviolet Spectra of Natural Products*. MacMillan, New York 1964.
53. DANIELS, E. G., KRUEGER, W. C., KUPIECKI, F. P., PIKE, J. E., SCHNEIDER, W. P., *J. Am. Chem. Soc.*, *90*, 5894 (1968).
54. KORVER, O., *Rec. Trav. Chim.*, *88*, 1070 (1969).
55. MIYANO, M., DORN, C. R., *J. Am. Chem. Soc.*, *95*, 2664 (1973).
56. SAMUELSSON, B., *J. Am. Chem. Soc.*, *85*, 1878 (1963).
57. HAMBERG, M., SAMUELSSON, B., *Biochim. Biophys. Acta*, *106*, 215 (1965).
58. COCKERILL, A. F., DAVIES, G. L. O., HARDEN, R. C., RACKHAM, D. M., "Lanthanide Shift Reagents for Nuclear Magnetic Resonance Spectroscopy." *Chem. Rev.*, *73*, 553 (1973).
59. MCCREARY, M. D., LEWIS, D. W., WERNICK, D. L., WHITESIDES, G. M., "The Determination of Enantiomeric Purity Using Chiral Lanthanide Shift Reagents." *J. Am. Chem. Soc.*, *96*, 1038 (1974).
60. GARCIA, G. A., DIAZ, E., CRABBÉ, P., *Chem. and Ind.*, *1973*, 585.
61. CRABBÉ, P., *Tetrahedron*, *30*, 1979 (1974).
62. JENNY, E. F., SCHÄUBLIN, P., FRITZ, H., FUHRER, H., *Tetrahedron Lett.*, *1974*, 2235.
63. HORVÁTH, Gy., *Biomed. Mass Spectrom.*, *2*, 190 (1975).
64. MIDDLEDITCH, B. S., DESIDERIO, D. M., *J. Org. Chem.*, *38*, 2204 (1973).
65. HORVÁTH, Gy., "Recent Applications of Mass Spectrometry in Pharmaceutical Research. Prostaglandins." *Progress in Drug Research*, *18*, 427 (1974).
66. CRAIN, P. F., DESIDERIO, D. M., MCCLOSKEY, J. A., "Mass Spectrometry of Prostaglandins." *Methods in Enzymology*, *35*, 359 (1975).
67. VANE, F., HORNING, M. G., "Separation and Characterization of the Prostaglandins by Gas Chromatography and Mass Spectrometry." *Anal. Letters*, *2*, 357 (1969).
68. GRÉEN, K., "Quantitative Mass Spectrometric Analysis of Prostaglandins." *International Conference on Prostaglandins, Vienna, 1972, Advances in the Biosciences*, *9*, 91 (1973), Pergamon Press, Oxford.
69. MIDDLEDITCH, B. S., DESIDERIO, D. M., *Prostaglandins*, *2*, 115 (1972).
70. OSWALD, E. O., PARKS, D., ELING, T., CORBETT, B. J., *J. Chromat.*, *93*, 47 (1974).
71. PACE-ASCIAK, C., WOLFE, L. S., *J. Chromat.*, *56*, 129 (1971).
72. KELLY, R. W., *Anal. Letters.*, *45*, 2079 (1973).
73. DESIDERIO, D. M., HÄGELE, K., *Chem. Commun.*, *1971*, 1074.
74. MOROZOWICH, W. (to Upjohn Co.), *U. S. Patent* 3 657 327, 1972.
75. LINCOLN, F. H., PIKE, J. E. (to Upjohn Co.), *U.S. Patent* 3 651 116, 1972.
76. *Belgian Patent* 776 294
77. JONES, R. L., *J. Lipid Res.*, *13*, 511 (1972).
78. JONES, R. L., CAMNOCH, S., "Purification, Properties, and Biological Significance of Prostaglandin A Isomerase." *International Conference on Prostaglandins, Vienna, 1972, Advances in the Biosciences*, *9*, 61 (1973), Pergamon Press, Oxford.
79. COREY, E. J., CYR, C. R., *Tetrahedron Lett.*, *1974*, 1761.
80. WEINHEIMER, A. J., SPROGGINS, R. L., *Tetrahedron Lett.*, *1969*, 5183.
81. SCHNEIDER, W. P., HAMILTON, R. D., RHULAND, L. E., *J. Am. Chem. Soc.*, *94*, 2122 (1972).
82. BUNDY, G. L., SCHNEIDER, W. P., LINCOLN, F. H., PIKE, J. E., *J. Am. Chem. Soc.*, *94*, 2123 (1972).
83. COREY, E. J., ENSLEY, H. E., *J. Org. Chem.*, *38*, 3187 (1973).

84. RAMWELL, P. W., SHAW, J. E., CLARKE, G. B., GROSTIC, M. F., KAISER, D. G.,
    PIKE, J. E., *Progress in the Chemistry of Fats and Other Lipids*, *9*, Part 2, Chapter 7,
    Pergamon Press, Oxford, 1968.
85. SCHNEIDER, W. P., MURRAY, H. C., *J. Org. Chem.*, *38*, 397 (1973).
86. ÄNGGÅRD, E., SAMUELSSON, B., *J. Biol. Chem.*, *239*, 4091 (1964).
87. COREY, E. J., NICOLSON, K. C., SHIBASAKI, M., *Chem. Commun.*, *1975*, 658.
88. COREY, E. J., NICOLSON, K. C., MELVIN, L. S., *J. Am. Chem. Soc.*, *97*, 653 (1975).
89. CROSSLEY, N. S., "Prostaglandins." *Chemistry and Industry*, 1976, (Apr.) 334.
90. DE CLERCQ, P., SAMSON, M., TAVERNIER, D., VANDEWALLE, M., Manuscript in
    preparation and HAVER, D., SAMSON, M., VANDEWALLE, M., *Tetrahedron*, *33*,
    255, (1977)
91. HORVÁTH, Gy., *Biomed. Mass Spectrom.*, *3*, 4 (1976).
92. HORVÁTH, Gy., *Biomed. Mass Spectrom.*, *3*, 127 (1976)

2. STEREOCONTROLLED SYNTHESIS
OF PROSTAGLANDINS, I

2.1 COREY'S STEREOCONTROLLED SYNTHESES
OF PROSTAGLANDINS

The synthesis of prostaglandin E_1 was published in 1968 by E. J. Corey [1], who had been investigating this problem with his group at Harvard University since 1964. This was soon followed by two other total syntheses [2, 3], and the concentrated efforts of the Harvard group have resulted, to date, in no less than six different routes for the synthesis of prostaglandins [4]. From these we will report here only that which is at present deemed to be the best and suitable for the preparation of the whole series of natural prostaglandins.

2.1.1 Synthesis of Prostaglandin $F_{2\alpha}$

As described in Chapter 1, a common feature of E- and F-type prostaglandins is the substitution of the cyclopentane ring in positions 8α, 11α, and 12β, the F-series being differentiated by an additional 9α-hydroxyl.* Members with different numerical subscripts in both series differ only in their degree of unsaturation. Consequently, the construction of a cyclopentane derivative containing all four substituents in the correct steric arrangement, with functions in positions 8 and 12 being suitable for the elaboration of the side chains, would provide a key intermediate from which the preparation of all the natural prostaglandins would become possible. A further requirement which this intermediate has to fulfil is a suitable protection of the hydroxyl to be found ultimately in position 11, since otherwise this functional group would be eliminated in the end product.

It was the lactol aldehyde **2.1** which was selected by Corey and his co-workers as a common intermediate eligible for the synthesis of all natural

---

* If not otherwise stated for the sake of clarity, atomic positions in prostaglandin intermediates will be designated by numbers referring to the prostane skeleton.

prostaglandins. On the one hand this compound contains the substituents of the cyclopentane ring in the correct steric disposition and, on the other, the C_1-C_5 and C_{13}-C_{20} chains of prostaglandins can easily be elaborated with the aid of the two aldehyde functions.

2.1

The fourfold substitution of cyclopentane with different groups permits the formation of eight diastereomeric racemates, of which **2.1**, the key intermediate of the synthesis, is but one. Consequently, in every step of the synthetic sequence in which a new chiral centre is created, only one of the stereoisomers produced is useful for further transformations. This means that an economic synthesis can be achieved only if one avoids the formation of stereoisomers by means of a sequence of highly stereoselective steps.

Corey *et al.* based the preparation of the lactol aldehyde **2.1**, and its transformation to prostaglandins on such stereoselective reactions. An additional advantage of their approach was that resolution was carried out at an early stage of the synthesis thereby avoiding the processing of the unwanted enantiomers throughout the rest of the sequence.

The synthesis raised difficulties of uncommon magnitude which could be surmounted only by invoking the latest achievements of organic chemistry and by the development of a number of novel preparative methods by the Harvard group. Familiarity with these methods is indispensable for an understanding of the synthetic operations. In addition to getting acquainted with this remarkable synthesis, a more detailed discussion of these methods may give some stimulation for readers interested in organic chemistry to apply these new techniques to their own particular areas of interest.

With these points in mind, the stereocontrolled synthesis of prostaglandins will be described from the viewpoint of the historic process of its development. Novel methods applied in the individual steps and the mechanism of these reactions will be treated in detail. The most advanced version of the synthesis is summarized in Fig. 2.1 (p. 70).

One of the starting materials [5] is cyclopentadiene obtained by thermolysis of the inexpensive commercial chemical dicyclopentadiene. Sodium cyclopentadienide (**2.2**) was formed from the monomer with sodium metal and allowed to react at low temperature ($-55°$) with chloromethyl methyl-

ether. The product, 5-methoxymethyl-1,3-cyclopentadiene (**2.3**) underwent
cupric fluoroborate catalyzed Diels–Alder reaction with 2-chloroacrylonitrile
to afford two stereoisomeric norbornene derivatives differing in the orientation (*exo vs. endo*) of the nitrile group and chlorine (**2.4**, only one stereo-
isomer shown).

In the customary laboratory batches the addition gave excellent yields
exceeding 90%. Scaling up, however, involved considerable difficulties due
to the prolonged reaction time causing transformation of 5-methoxymethyl-
-1,3-dicyclopentadiene (**2.3**) to its 1-methoxy isomer (**2.6**). This isomerization is catalyzed both by bases and acids [6, 7].

Rapid isomerization of alkyl cyclopentadienes has been observed before
Kresze *et al.* observed that 5-methyl-1,3-cyclopentadiene, the primary
product from the reaction of methyl iodide with cyclopentadienyl sodium,
suffered rearrangement to 1-methyl-1,3-cyclopentadiene on distillation [7].
It was just this tendency to isomerization which necessitated the catalysis of the Diels–Alder reaction. Cupric fluoroborate, however, is not a catalyst of the addition proper, but acts rather as a Lewis acid enhancing the
dienophilic character of 2-chloroacrylonitrile by increasing electron attraction by the nitrile group.

Depending on the temperature and medium, 10–40% of by-products were formed in the cupric fluoroborate catalyzed reaction, from which the Diels–Alder adduct of 1-methoxymethyl-1,3-cyclopentadiene and 2-chloroacrylonitrile (**2.9**), further bicyclo[3.2.0]-heptene derivatives, arising from [2+2] cycloaddition of the reactants (**2.10**), have been isolated.

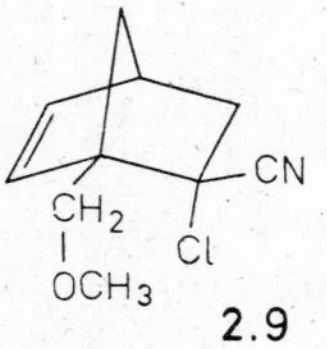

2.9 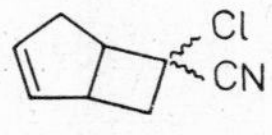   2.10

Though a change from the sodium salt to the less basic cyclopentadienyl lithium as well as from the chloro ether to the more reactive bromodimethyl ether improved the yields [8], a breakthrough was only brought about by the use of the thallium(I) salt of cyclopentadiene. This permitted to carry out the alkylation reaction at −20° and with short reaction times; thus the formation of isomeric products was efficiently suppressed. An additional advantage of the thallium(I) salt is its easy preparation in aqueous media using thallium(I) sulfate and sodium hydroxide, further that it can be stored in air for longer periods.

The Diels–Alder adduct (**2.4**) was hydrolyzed with potassium hydroxide in dimethyl sulfoxide to a cyanohydrin (**2.11**) that decomposed instantaneously in the strongly alkaline medium to the norbornenone (**2.12**). The latter was the first distillable product of the sequence; its yield calculated on cyclopentadiene was 50–55%.

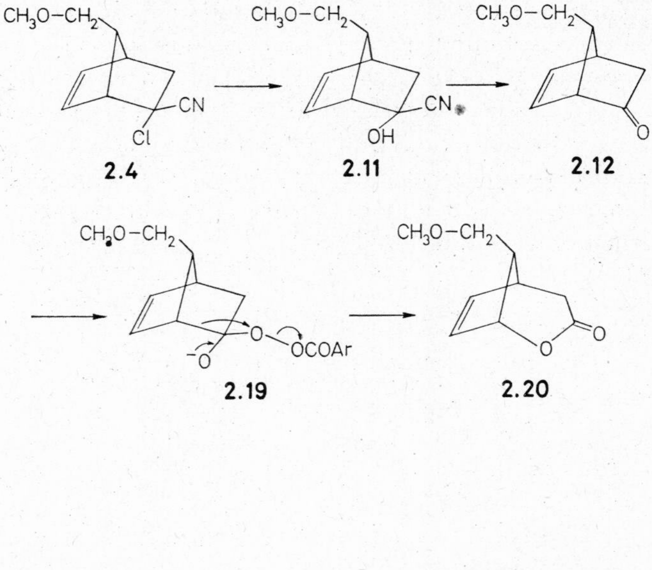

2.4   2.11   2.12

2.19   2.20

A simple version based on the oxidative decarboxylation of an appropriate carboxylic acid (**2.13**) has been published by Trost and Tamaru [9] for the preparation of the norbornenone (**2.12**). The cyclopentadiene derivative (**2.3**) was first allowed to react with acrylic acid, a strong dienophile, and the product (**2.13**) treated with lithium diisopropylamide to give a dianion; this was then made to react with dimethyl disulfide to obtain the α-methylthio acid (**2.14**). Treatment of the sulfide with N-chlorosuccinimide furnished a ketal that was hydrolyzed with acid to the norbornenone (**2.12**).

The following mechanism may be envisaged for the oxidative decarboxylation step. N-Chlorosuccinimide transforms the α-methylthio acid (**2.14**) to an S-chloro derivative (**2.15**) that decomposes rapidly with the loss of carbon dioxide to the S-methylsulfonium ion (**2.16**); addition of alcohol affords in succession a mixed ketal (**2.17**) and a ketal (**2.18**).

The method is suitable for the conversion of carboxylic acids into ketones containing one carbon atom less.

2.3 2.13

2.14 2.12

2.14 2.15 2.16

2.17 2.18 2.12

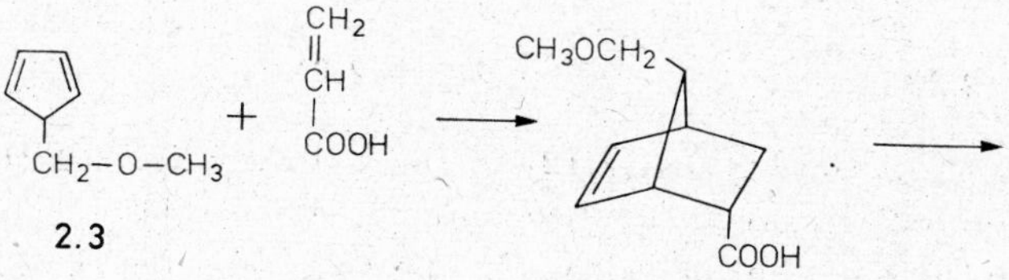

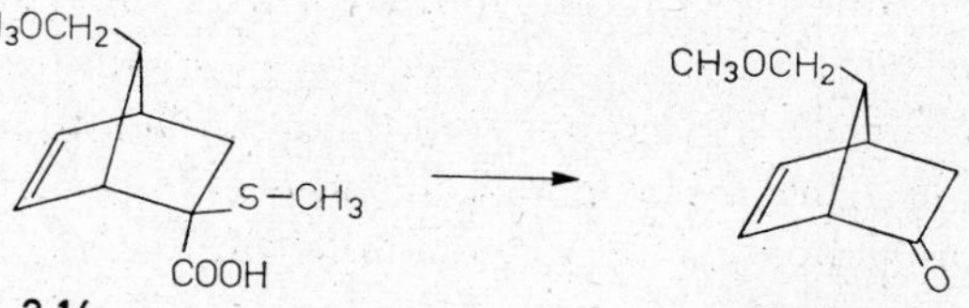

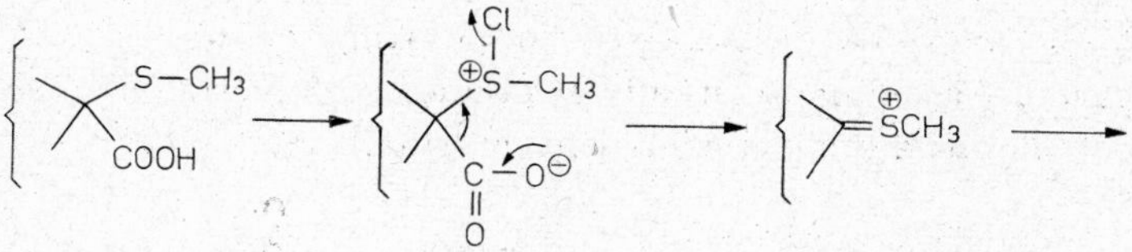

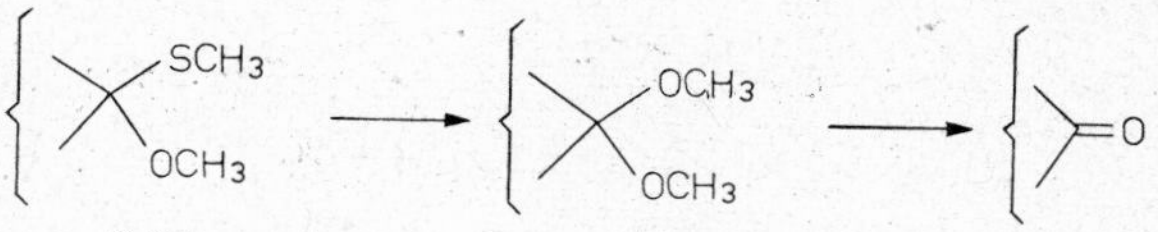

Baeyer–Villiger oxidation of this ketone with *m*-chloroperbenzoic acid yielded the lactone (**2.20**). The regiospecificity of this reaction can be explained by considering the structure of the primary adduct formed by nucleophilic addition (**2.19**). In this intermediate the migrating group is expected to be the one which can more easily accommodate a partial positive charge (*cf.* Beckmann-rearrangement). Accordingly, of the two α-carbons the more heavily substituted one will participate in the 1,2-rearrangement.

The lactone obtained on oxidation was hydrolyzed with sodium hydroxide to the hydroxy acid (**2.21**), which was then resolved with ephedrine. The use of (+)-ephedrine resulted in the crystallization of the salt of the (+)-hydroxy acid needed for the synthesis of the natural product.

2.20   **2.21**

The conversion of the ketone (**2.12**) to the hydroxy acid (**2.21**) was substantially simplified by Weinshenker and Stephenson [10], who oxidized the ketone in ethereal solution with alkaline hydrogen peroxide. Acidification of the solution gave an almost quantitative yield of the racemic hydroxy acid.

Subsequently the optically active hydroxy acid was subjected to iodo-lactonization, a reaction which can be performed with an alkaline solution of iodine solubilized with potassium iodide [11]. The aqueous solution of potassium triiodide contains some hypoiodic acid which dissociates to hydroxyl anion and iodo cation. Electrophilic addition of the latter onto the carbon–carbon double bond of the hydroxy acid leads to an equilibrium with the cyclic halonium ion (**2.22**); the latter is then opened by an intra-molecular attack of the carboxylate anion. Ring closure is stereospecific since the carboxylate anion can only approach the reaction centre from the same side of the quasi-planar cyclopentane ring.

2.21   **2.22**   **2.23**

2.24   **2.25**

Next, the free hydroxyl of the iodolactone (**2.23**, R = H) was protected by acetylation, and the acetate (**2.23**, R = COCH$_3$) was deiodinated with tri-n-butyltin hydride in a reaction initiated by azobisisobutyronitrile [67]. The product (**2.24**) was demethylated by boron tribromide, acting as a strong Lewis acid, to obtain the lactone alcohol (**2.25**).

Though this sequence fulfils to a high degree the requirements of a rational synthesis as specified earlier, i.e. stereoselectivity of the reactions, early resolution and protection of the hydroxyl groups of the ring, it involves some preparative difficulties. Right at the beginning, in the Diels–Alder addition a fourfold excess of 2-chloroacrylonitrile has to be applied. Protection of one of the hydroxyls by acetylation was unfavourable inasmuch as it had to be removed later by base-catalyzed hydrolysis. Ether cleavage gave only moderate yields since the reaction was not really regiospecific and resulted in the formation of 10–30% of bromomethyl derivative [12].

An improved version of the synthesis (Fig. 2.1) comprises the alkylation of the thallium(I) salt of cyclopentadiene with chloromethyl benzyl ether and treatment of the product (**2.26**) with 2-chloroacryloyl chloride. The reactivity of this dienophile is comparable to that of maleic anhydride, its cycloaddition proceeds readily even without a catalyst and gives the norbornene (**2.27**) in nearly quantitative yields. The product was converted by means of sodium azide to the acylazide (**2.36**) and then by Curtius rearrangement to the isocyanate (**2.37**), followed by hydrolysis to yield ultimately the norbornenone (**2.28**). This sequence is carried out in "one pot" thereby obviating the isolation of intermediates; the yield of the ketone is 90% (from cyclopentadiene).

2.27   **2.36**   **2.37**

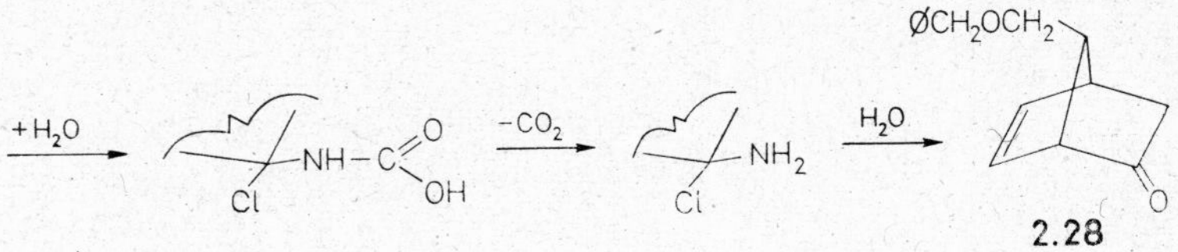

From this point the synthesis proceeds as with the methyl ether, i.e. the ketone is oxidized with m-chloroperbenzoic acid to the lactone (**2.29**) and the lactone ring is opened to give the hydroxy acid (**2.30**). Resolution of the latter was in this case effected with amphetamine, and the optically active acid was subjected to iodolactonization.

Resolution of the hydroxy acid can be achieved efficiently with (+)-1-(p-nitrophenyl)-2-amino-1,3-propanediol, a by-product of chloramphenicol production [13].

An important novel feature of the modified route is the protection of the hydroxyl group of the iodolactone (**2.31**) by acylation with p-phenyl-

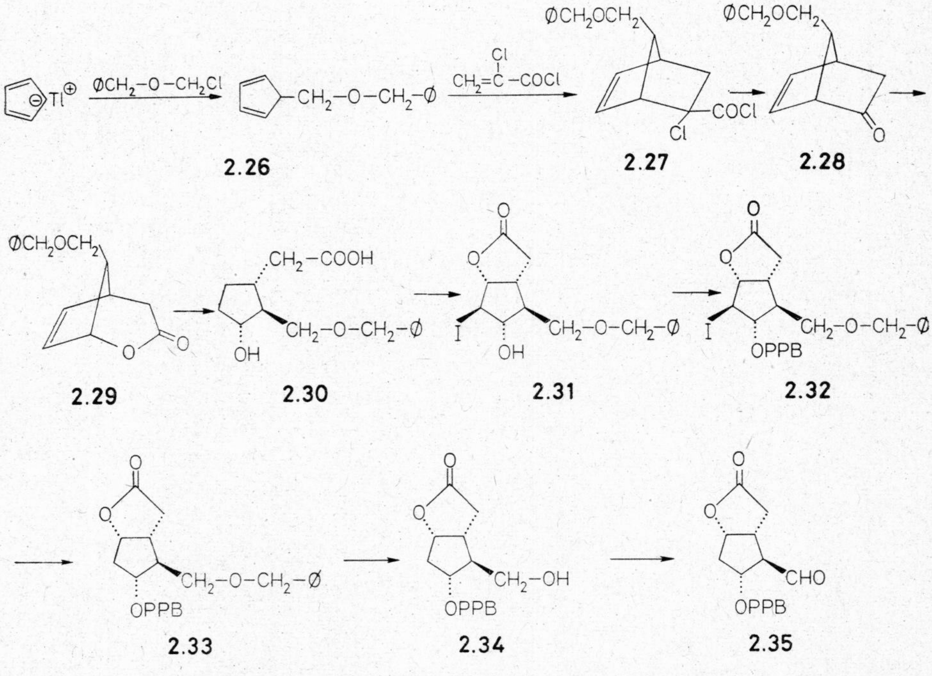

Fig. 2.1. Corey's stereocontrolled synthesis of prostaglandins. Generation of the lactone aldehyde intermediate

benzoyl chloride to obtain (**2.32**). The use of this reagent is superior in several ways to acetylation employed previously. Owing to its high molecular weight, derivatives crystallize readily; its characteristic ultraviolet absorption facilitates the analytical examination of intermediates; further, it plays a decisive part in the stereoselective reduction of the C_{15} carbonyl group (see later Fig. 2.3).

The possibility of using trialkylsilyl groups for hydroxyl protection has been extensively studied by Corey and Venkateswarlu [14]. The simple trimethylsilyl ethers that can be made by the reaction of alcohols with trimethylsilyl chloride are unsuited for this purpose because of rapid solvolysis in protic solvents in the presence of acids or bases. Increasing the size of the alkyl groups results in a decrease in the solvolysis rate of silyl ethers. Compared with that of the trimethylsilyl ether, the cleavage of the dimethyl-isopropyl and dimethyl-t-butyl analogues is slower by a factor of 10^3 and 10^4, respectively. The presence of a dimethyl-t-butyl-trimethylsilyloxy group allows the effecting of Grignard and Wittig reactions as well as Jones oxidation (chromic acid in acetone). It can easily be introduced by dimethyl-t-butylsilyl chloride in dimethyl-formamide in the presence of imidazole as catalyst and, as an extra advantage, it can be removed under practically neutral conditions by means of tetrabutylammonium fluoride.

Returning to the main line of the synthesis, the next step is the deiodination of the iodolactone (**2.32**) with tri-n-butyltin hydride. This reduction can be also performed giving excellent yields using chromium(II) acetate combined with a proton donor (e.g. ethanedithiol) [15] or sodium borohydride in DMSO [68].

Cleavage of the benzyloxy group of the deiodinated lactone (**2.33**) by palladium-catalyzed hydrogenation occurs in nearly 100% yields.

Conversion of the resulting alcohol (**2.34**) to the crucial lactone-aldehyde intermediate (**2.35**) of prostaglandins was initially accomplished at Harvard by Collins oxidation (chromium trioxide and pyridine), but the preparative difficulties inherent in this procedure prompted the development of a novel and generally applicable method of oxidizing primary and secondary alcohols to aldehydes [16, 17].

Conversion of a thioether (**2.38**), preferably the readily accessible thioanisole, by treatment with chlorine or N-chlorosuccinimide gave an S-chloro derivative (**2.39**) which underwent nucleophilic displacement with the alcohol to furnish the salt of an O-alkyl sulfoxide (**2.40**). On treatment with triethylamine the sulfoxide decomposed via an oxysulfonium ylide (**2.41**) to the required carbonyl compound and the original thioether.

This method has been successfully employed for the oxidation of the lactone-alcohol (**2.34**) [18]. The whole series of reactions should be performed below 0°C. At this temperature the formation of by-products is negligible and the lactone-aldehyde (**2.35**) can be isolated in quantitative yield.

$$CH_3-\overset{|}{\underset{R}{S}}\;+\;Cl_2\;\longrightarrow\;CH_3-\overset{\oplus}{\underset{R}{S}}-Cl\;\;Cl^{\ominus}\;\xrightarrow{\;R'-CH_2-OH\;}\;R'-CH_2-O-\overset{CH_3}{\underset{R}{\overset{\oplus}{S}}}\;Cl^{\ominus}$$

2.38   **2.39**   **2.40**

$$\xrightarrow{Et_3N}\;\left[\;R'-\overset{H}{\underset{H}{C}}\cdots O-\overset{\oplus}{\underset{R}{S}}\cdots CH_2^{\ominus}\;\right]\;\longrightarrow\;R'-CHO\;+\;CH_3-\overset{|}{\underset{R}{S}}$$

2.41

The dimethyl sulfoxide–chlorine complex can also be used with advantage for the oxidation of secondary and tertiary 1,2-diols to α-ketoles [16]. The easy cleavage of the carbon–carbon bond of the $HO-C-C-OH$ unit by oxidants (e.g. periodate, MnO_2) is well known and interferes with their oxidation to α-ketoles. The specificity of the dimethyl sulfoxide–chlorine complex can be explained by an energetical preference for the five-membered cyclic transition state (**2.41**) leading to the ketole as compared with that required for diol cleavage (**2.42**), which is seven-membered.

2.42

In the next stage of the synthesis the carbon atoms C_{13}-C_{20} (the "lower" chain of postaglandins) must be introduced, with the olefinic bond in (*E*)-configuration. As mentioned earlier, this problem was solved by using a modified Wittig-reaction.

Product geometry in the Wittig condensation, i.e. the reaction of carbonyl compounds with phosphoranes obtained from phosphonium salts with bases, is controlled among other factors by the structure of the phosphorane [19]. Phosphoranes can be divided roughly into two classes. One of them, the unstabilized phosphoranes, in the β-position to the phosphorus have no group capable of conjugative interaction. Characteristic of the condensation of such phosphoranes is a fast and kinetically controlled nucleophilic addition in the first step to yield an *erythro*-betaine (**2.43**), from which by phosphine oxide elimination, an olefin of (*Z*)-geometry (**2.45**) is generated in the second step.

With the stabilized phosphoranes, which have in the β-position a group (e.g. CO) that can enter conjugation, the first addition step is a slow equilibrium process leading to the thermodynamically more stable *threo*-betaine (**2.44**), which eliminates the elements of a phosphine oxide to form an (*E*)-olefin (**2.46**).

Recently [20], oxaphosphetanes formed by $[\pi^2s + \pi^2a]$ cycloaddition have been supposed to be intermediates in the reaction of reactive phosphoranes.

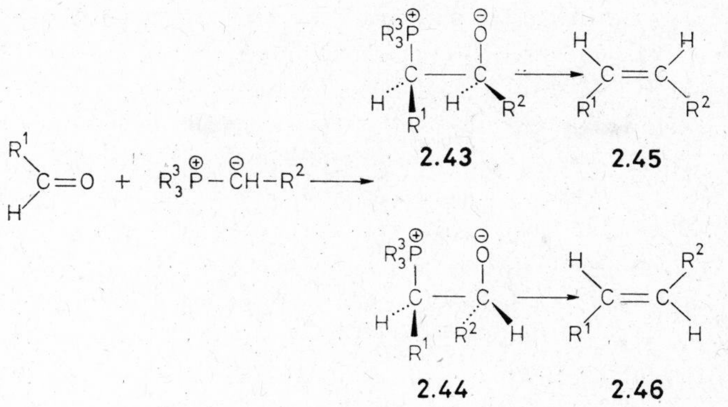

$$2.43 \qquad 2.45$$

$$2.44 \qquad 2.46$$

For the elaboration of the "lower" chain of prostaglandins, the lactone aldehyde (**2.35**) was made to react with the anion (**2.47**), generated from dimethyl 2-oxoheptylphosphonate with a base, to yield a ketone (**2.48**) containing the (E)-enone system (Fig. 2.2).

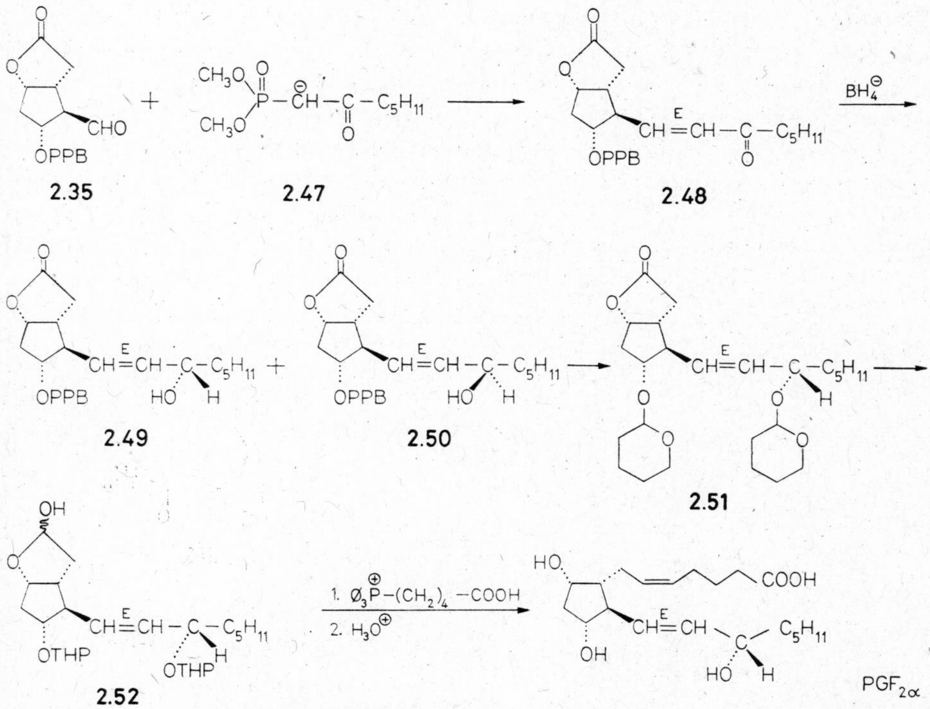

2.35   2.47   2.48

2.49   2.50   2.51

2.52   PGF$_{2\alpha}$

Fig. 2.2. Corey's stereocontrolled synthesis of prostaglandins. Conversion of the lactone aldehyde intermediate to PGF$_{2\alpha}$

At this point the synthetic scheme requires the creation of a new chiral centre at C_{15} by reduction of the carbonyl group. In natural prostaglandins this is of (S)-configuration. Reduction of the ketone (**2.48**) with sodium borohydride proceeds with poor stereoselectivity and also in the undesired sense, giving about 60% of the (R)-alcohol (**2.50**) contaminated with material arising from the saturation of the carbon–carbon double bond. The use of zinc borohydride suppressed this side reaction but did not alter appreciably the ratio of stereoisomers (1 : 1). Corey and his co-workers undertook a very thorough study in order to improve the stereoselectivity of the reduction. A different approach to the transformation of the lactone aldehyde (**2.35**) into an (S)-alcohol (**2.49**) has been realized by the same group and will be reported in detail in connection with the synthesis of prostaglandin $F_{3\alpha}$.

Stereoselective reductions of carbonyl groups can generally be achieved using alkyl borohydrides containing bulky groups. These reactions are steric approach-controlled: nucleophilic attack of the bulky alkylborohydride anion takes place preferably on the less hindered face of the molecule. In an earlier investigation Corey *et al.* reduced prostaglandin E_2 to prostaglandin $F_{2\alpha}$ with lithium trialkylborohydrides (LiR_3BH) [21]. The attack of the reducing agent on the carbonyl at C_9 comes from the less hindered face of the molecule which is the one opposite to the α-oriented C_1-C_7 side chain and gives exclusively the 9α-hydroxy epimer ($PGF_{2\alpha}$).

Stereoselective reduction of the intermediate (**2.48**) containing an α,β-unsaturated ketone moiety is more problematic since attack of the nucleophile on the β-carbon of the enone system is also possible leading by 1,4-reduction, *via* the enol form (**2.53**), to saturation of the double bond (**2.54**) [22, 23].

2.48   **2.53**   **2.54**

In the reductions using lithium trialkylborohydrides the ratio of products arising from 1,2- (**2.49** + **2.50**) and 1,4-reduction (**2.54**) was 2.5 : 1. Later it was found that 1,4-reduction can be suppressed by the addition of a Lewis base, e.g. hexamethylphosphorotriamide in excess.

A source of difficulties is the fact that the molecule has several conformations of nearly equal energy. In the intermediate product (**2.48**) the hydrogen
attached to carbon-12 of the *quasi*-planar cyclopentane ring is *trans*-copla-
nar with the hydrogen on carbon 13, and the four atoms of the enone system
lie in the plane defined by these four atoms. The α,β-unsaturated ketone
segment in turn can assume the conformations *s-cis* and *s-trans* by rotation
around the carbon–carbon single bond (Fig. 2.3, **2.48a** and **2.48b**). Since the

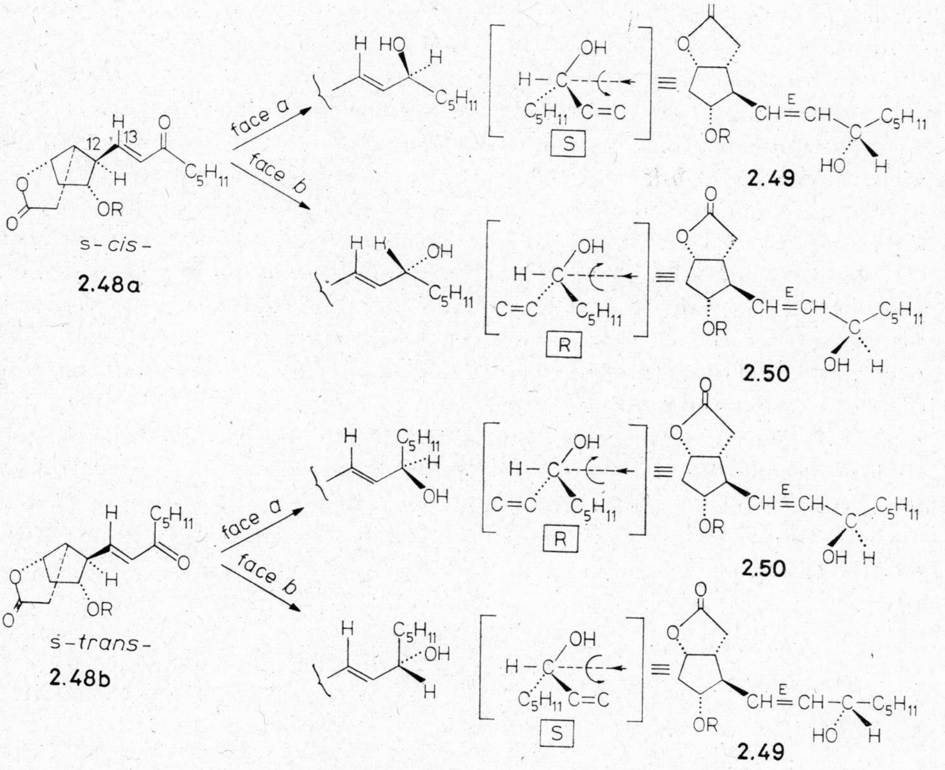

Fig. 2.3. Conversion of the enone to alcohol

energy barrier separating them is only a few kcal/mole, these two conformers convert into each other easily. *s-Cis* and *s-trans* forms can, however,
be distinguished by the carbonyl frequencies in the infrared, the former
(**2.48a**) absorbing at 1695 cm^{-1} in contrast to the latter (**2.48b**) at 1675 cm^{-1}.

Let us now deduce from the conformation of the ketone (Fig. 2.3) the
configuration of the alcohol obtained by reduction. Placing the enone

moiety into the plane of the paper, it can be envisaged that a perpendicular attack of the reducing agent on the carbonyl group may take place either from below this plane (face a) or from above it (face b). Configuration is assigned to the resulting alcohols by applying the Cahn–Ingold–Prelog sequence rules [24].

With the s-cis conformer (**2.48a**), the approach of the reactant from face a gives rise to an alcohol of (S)-configuration (**2.49**) (group sequence: OH > C = C > C_5H_{11} > H), whereas attack from face b results in the formation of an (R)-alcohol (**2.50**). Conversely, with the enone in the s-$trans$ conformation (**2.48b**) the approach from face a gives a product with an (R)-configuration and that from face b one of (S)-configuration.

It follows that formation of the desired (S)-alcohol involves, with the different conformations, an approach from opposite faces: a-face attack with the s-cis and b-face attack with the s-$trans$ conformation. In other words, stereoselective reduction not only requires the shielding of one of the faces, but also the fixation of the molecule in one of its conformations.

Several attempts have been made by Corey et $al.$ to improve the stereoselectivity of the reduction by introducing different kinds of blocking groups for the protection of the C_{11} hydroxyl. It has turned out that the acetyl, pelargonyl and dimethyl-isopropylsilyl groups are without effect on the S/R ratio. Substantial progress was attained by the introduction of the p-phenylbenzoyl group mentioned earlier. Reduction of the p-phenylbenzoyloxy ketone (**2.48**) with lithium trialkylborohydrides at extremely low temperatures (below $-120°$) gave predominantly the (15S)-alcohol (**2.49**). Stereoselectivities attained with various reducing agents of the R^1, R^2, $R^3BH^-Li^+$ type are summarized in Table 2.1.

Table 2.1

Stereoselectivity in Reductions of the p-Phenylbenzoyloxy Ketones (**2.48**) with Lithium Trialkylborohydrides ($R^1R^2R^3BH^-Li^+$)

$R^1R^2R^3$	15S/15R
dicyclohexyl-t-butyl	59/41
dicyclohexyl-trityl	64/36
triphenyl	67/33
diisopinocamphenyl-methyl	68/32
diisobutyl-t-butyl	74/26
di-sec-butyl-t-butyl	80/20
tri-sec-butyl	78/22

It can be seen from the Table that stereoselectivity improves with increasing size of the alkyl groups.

The best result, a $15S/15R$ ratio of 82 : 12, was achieved with the boronate (**2.55**) in which the boron atom became part of a cycle.

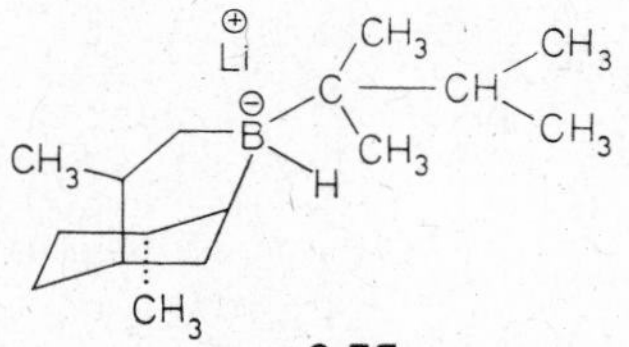

2.55

The borohydrides employed can be prepared from trialkylboranes with t-butyllithium or from dialkylboranes with alkyl lithium. One of the reagents listed above, lithium tri-sec-butylborohydride and the corresponding potassium derivative are marketed as L- and K-Selectride®, respectively.

Dialkylboranes are unsuitable for the reduction of (**2.48**) since, owing to their strong electrophilic character, they give rise, by 1,4-reduction, mainly to the 13,14-dihydro compound (**2.54**).

The effect of the p-phenylbenzoyl group on the conformation of the ketone (**2.48**) can be assessed by inspection of the molecular models. In one of the favoured conformers with the enone system in the s-cis conformation, the two side chains can enter into attractive van der Waals interaction along their entire length (**2.56**). The C—O—CO—Ar section of the ester being in the s-cis conformation, four atoms of the benzoyl group come into proximity with the four atoms of the enone system thereby permitting the establishment of π–π interactions between them. The best fit requires the C—O—CO—Ar sequence to be tilted out by 30° from its energetically most favoured coplanar disposition.

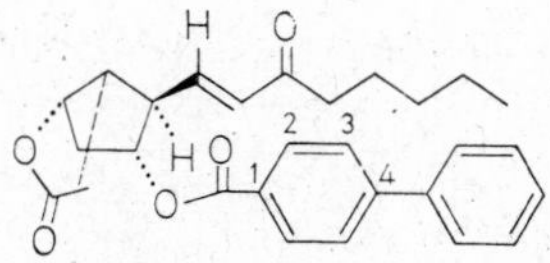

2.56

The construction of a similar model for the s-$trans$ conformer reveals that in this case the two π-systems cannot be brought sufficiently close to each other.

The hypothesis of $\pi-\pi$ interaction can be easily supported since the exchange of p-phenylbenzoyl to p-butylbenzoyl left the isomeric ratio unchanged (Table 2.2), whereas with 4-phenyl-1,3-cyclohexadiene carboxylic acid as acylating agent stereoselectivity increased owing to stronger $\pi-\pi$ interactions with the more polarizable π-electron system of this group.

Table 2.2

Correlation of Stereoselectivity with the Structure of the Blocking Group in Reductions of the 11-O-Acyl Ketones (**2.48**) with the Boronate (**2.55**)

Blocking group (R)	15S/15R
$p-C_6H_5-C_6H_4-CO$	82/18
$p-Bu-C_6H_4-CO$	82/18
	84/16
$p-C_6H_5-C_6H_4-CH_2-CO$	70/30
$C_6H_5-NH-CO$	89/11
$p-C_6H_5-C_6H_4-NH-CO$	92/8

An attempt at improving the stereoselectivity was based on the concept that in the case of the p-phenylbenzoyl group the tendency of the C—O—CO—Ar sequence for coplanarity counteracted the development of a conformation optimal for stereoselective reduction, which was, as mentioned, off-coplanar. To eliminate this effect, the p-phenylphenylacetyl analogue was prepared which satisfied the condition of coplanarity in respect of the ester moiety, but unfortunately this was negated by a substantial steric interaction between the methylene hydrogens and the hydrogen at C_{11} of the cyclopentane skeleton; the net result was a considerable drop in stereoselectivity.

A real advance was, however, brought about by the introduction of carbamic ester as the protecting group. Reduction of the p-phenylcarbamoyl analogue of (**2.48**) gave 92% of the (15S)-epimer. This series of investigations is an enlightening example for the utilization of the directing effect of a group attached to a site relatively remote from the reaction centre.

Recently Corey *et al.* found a direct way for converting the acetate (Fig. 2.3; **2.50**, R = Ac) of (15R)-configuration to the (15S)-epimer (**2.49**, R = Ac) [25]. This was realized by means of potassium superoxide (KO_2) — an extremely active nucleophile.

The superoxide radical anion ($O_2^{\cdot -}$) can be generated either by electrochemical reduction of oxygen or from an alkali superoxide. Potassium and sodium superoxides (KO_2 and NaO_2, respectively) are inexpensive commercial chemicals. In organic synthesis where they now find application as single-electron reducing agents or as strong nucleophiles, their use had earlier been limited by insolubility in aprotic solvents and fast decomposition in protic ones (e.g. $2\ KO_2 + H_2O \rightarrow 2\ K^+ + OH^- + OOH^- + O_2$). Recently it has been discovered that their solubility in organic solvents (dimethyl sulfoxide, dimethoxyethane, benzene, etc.) can be greatly enhanced by the addition of catalytic amounts of the macrocyclic polyether dicyclohexyl-18-crown-6 (**2.57**).

2.57   **2.58**

Potassium superoxide solvated by the polyether (**2.58**) is an exceptionally active and efficient oxygen nucleophile. With halogen compounds it gives a mixture of dialkyl peroxide and alcohol. Using a larger excess (2–3 molar equivalents) of potassium superoxide, only the alcohol can be isolated. The mechanism of the reaction is probably as follows:

$$O_2^{\cdot -} + R - X \rightarrow R - O - O^{\cdot} + X^-$$
$$R - OO^{\cdot} + O_2 \rightarrow R - OO^- + O_2{}^+$$
$$R - O - O^- + R - X \rightarrow R - O - O - R + X^-$$

The first step, a nucleophilic substitution, results in an inversion of configuration. The formation of the alcohol is a consequence of the reduction of the hydroperoxide anion formed in the second step.

Mesylates and tosylates of alcohols undergo similar reactions which also involve the inversion of configuration.

The reactivity of halides towards substitution by potassium superoxide decreases in the following order: benzyl > primary alkyl > *sec.* alkyl > *tert.* alkyl > aryl, and for alkyl halides: iodide > bromide > chloride.

With secondary alkyl halides, substitution is accompanied by elimination; with tertiary halides the latter becomes predominant [26, 27].

For the inversion of configuration at C_{15} the mesylate of the alcohol (**2.50**, R = Ac) was used as substrate. Reaction with four equivalents of potassium superoxide in the presence of equivalents of dicyclohexyl-18-crown-6 polyether in a mixture of dimethyl sulfoxide, dimethylformamide and dimethoxyethane gave a product which contained some 15-hydroperoxy compound. After decomposition of the hydroperoxide with triphenylphosphin and relactonization of the portion which had hydrolyzed by ethyl chloroformate, treatment with lithium hydroxide finally gave the (15S)-alcohol (Fig. 2.3, **2.49**, R = Ac) in 75% yield.

The synthesis was continued (Fig. 2.2) by liberating the C_{11} hydroxyl of (**2.49**) by alkaline hydrolysis followed by blocking both hydroxyl groups by tetrahydropyranylation (**2.51**) and reduction of the lactone function at low temperature with diisobutyl aluminium hydride to a lactol (**2.52**). The latter was then subjected to Wittig reaction with the phosphorane generated from triphenyl-4-carboxybutylphosphonium salt with dimsyl sodium. The phosphorane being of the non-stabilized type, the newly formed double bond was of (Z)-geometry. Removal of the blocking groups from the product by acid hydrolysis concluded the synthesis of optically active prostaglandin $F_{2\alpha}$.

2.1.2 *Synthesis of Prostaglandin* $F_{3\alpha}$

As mentioned earlier, Corey and his associates also realized an alternative scheme for the stereospecific elaboration of the C_{13}-C_{20} side chain which circumvented the highly stereospecific but technically rather difficult reduction discussed before. This approach required the synthesis of a phosphonium salt which already contained a hydroxyl group in the required (S)-configuration (Fig. 2.4, **2.68**) [28, 29].

For the synthesis of this phosphonium salt (**2.68**), (S)-($-$)-malic acid (**2.59**, R = H) served as the starting material; this was converted with diazomethane to the methyl ester (**2.59**, R = Me) and subsequently reduced with potassium borohydride to (S)-($-$)-butanetriol (**2.60**). The acetonide (**2.61**) of the triol was subjected to Collins oxidation to give the aldehyde (**2.62**), which was condensed with triphenylpropylidenephosphorane. The product of the Wittig reaction (**2.63**) was saturated by catalytic hydrogenation (**2.64**), hydrolyzed to the diol (**2.65**) and transformed to the monotosylate (**2.66**). Exchange of the tosyl group for iodine with sodium iodide afforded (**2.67**) which gave, with triphenylphosphine at low temperature, the required phosphonium salt (**2.68**). The corresponding phosphonate (**2.74**), generated from this salt with alkyl lithium, was allowed to react with the lactone-aldehyde (**2.73**) to give, in one step, the alcohol of (S)-configuration (**2.75**).

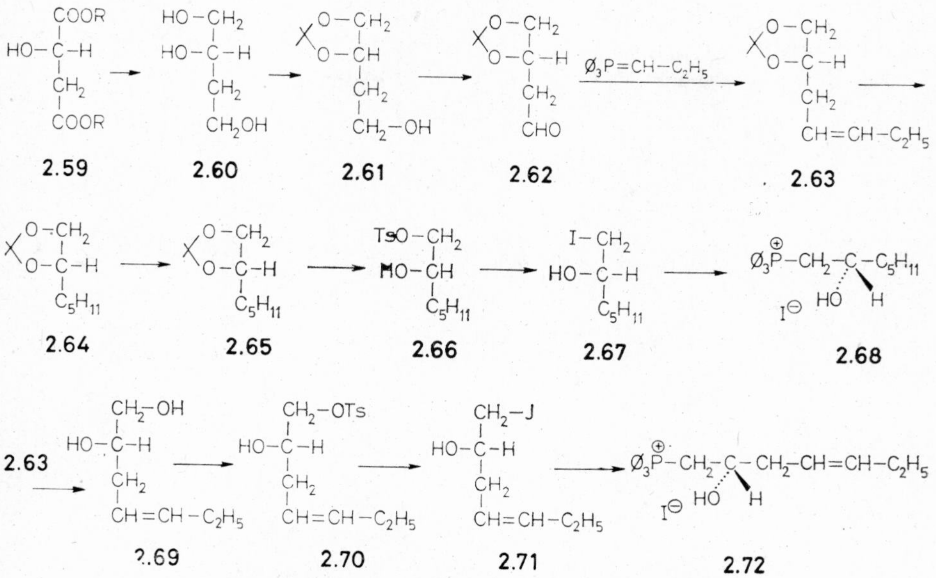

Fig. 2.4. Synthesis of intermediates **2.68** and **2.72,**

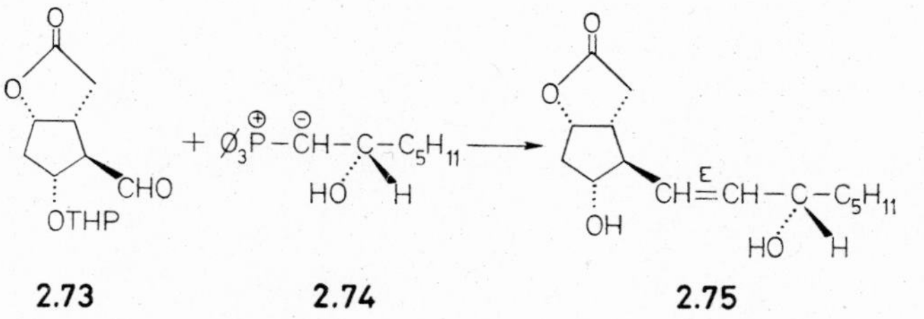

The sequence could be adapted for the synthesis of prostaglandin $F_{3\alpha}$. This required the hydrolysis of the product of the Wittig reaction (Fig. 2.4, **2.63**) to (Z)-4-heptene-1,2-diol (**2.69**), that was first monotosylated (**2.70**) and the tosylate then transformed to the iodoalcohol (**2.71**). This iodoalcohol, when repeatedly reacted with triphenylphosphine, gave the (S)-(+)-phosphonium salt (**2.72**). The phosphorane derived from (**2.72**) was coupled with the lactone-aldehyde (**2.73**) to yield the dihydroxylactone (**2.76**, R = H). Reduction of the corresponding bis-tetrahydropyranyl derivative (**2.76**, R = THP) with diisobutylaluminium hydride converted the lactone to a lactol (**2.77**). Reaction of the lactol with a phosphorane obtained from

6 R.D.C.

triphenyl-4-carboxybutylphosphonium salt and subsequent acidic hydrolysis led ultimately to optically active prostaglandin $F_{3\alpha}$.

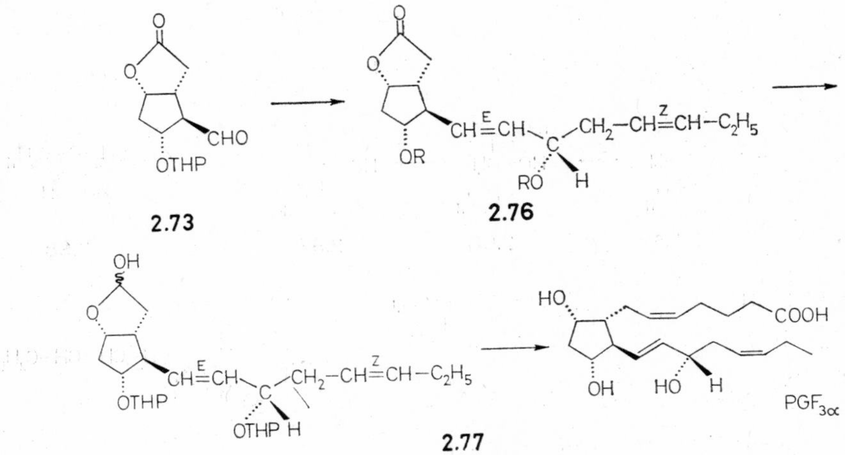

2.73   2.76

2.77

The syntheses described above solved in principle the construction of the
"lower" chain in a stereospecific manner. A realization of these sequences
in our laboratory revealed that some of the steps involved considerable
practical difficulties. During the long time (up to 2 weeks) required for the
formation of the phosphonium salt (2.68), elimination of the hydroxyl
group was observed, which resulted in contamination of the product by
triphenylphosphine oxide. The reaction could not be accelerated by heating, since at higher temperatures (e.g. in benzene at the boiling point) phosphine oxide formation became predominant.

A promising way of eliminating this side reaction seemed to be the
preparation of an iodo compound having a suitably protected hydroxyl.
In order to realize this new version, we oxidized the readily accessible 1-hep-
tene to racemic heptane-1,2-diol, which was resolved by means of the
amphetamine salt of its hemiphthalate ester. From the (S)-$(-)$-heptane-
-1,2-diol (2.78) a dioxolane (2.79) was prepared using ethyl orthoacetate;
this was then cleaved in a regiospecific reaction with trityl iodide to 2-acet-
oxy-1-iodoheptane (2.81). In the first elementary step of this reaction a
1,3-dioxanilium cation (2.80) was generated by cleavage of the ethoxyl
group of the 1,3-dioxolane by the triphenylmethyl cation formed in the
dissociation of trityl iodide. Reaction of the cation with trityl iodide gave
with concomitant opening of the ring the iodoacetate (2.81) [30, 31].

Reaction of this compound with triphenylphosphine gave excellent yields of the phosphonium salt (**2.82**) within a few hours; the corresponding phosphorane obtained by treatment with three moles of n-butyllithium reacted with the lactone-aldehyde (**2.73**) to give the dihydroxylactone (**2.75**) of Corey's synthesis.

2.1.3 *Synthesis of Prostaglandin* $F_{1\alpha}$

With the synthesis of prostaglandin $F_{1\alpha}$, the order followed earlier for the introduction of the side chains was reversed, i.e. first the C_1-C_5 unit was attached to a cyclopentane derivative and the hydroxyoctyl chain was constructed thereafter [32].

In the first step the hydroxylactone (**2.83**, R = H, Fig. 2.5) was protected as the tetrahydropyranyl ether (**2.83**, R = THP) followed by reduction with diisobutylaluminium hydride. The lactol obtained (**2.84**) was subjected to Wittig condensation with a phosphorane prepared from triphenyl-4-carboxybutylphosphonium salt, the resulting acid (**2.85**, $R^1 = R^2 = H$) treated with diazomethane to give the ester (**2.85**, $R^1 = H$, $R^2 = CH_3$), and this was acetylated (**2.85**, $R^1 = Ac$, $R^2 = CH_3$). Hydrogenation in the presence of palladium catalyst until the uptake of two moles of hydrogen removed the benzyl group and also saturated the C_5-C_6 double bond.

The alcohol (**2.86**) was oxidized with Collins reagent (chromium trioxide–pyridine) to an aldehyde (**2.87**), which was then allowed to react with the anion formed from dimethyl-2-oxoheptylphosphonate. This gave rise to an (E)-enone (**2.88**), which on reduction with zinc borohydride furnished a 1 : 1 mixture of the epimeric alcohols. Separation of the epimers followed by alkaline and acid hydrolysis of the (15S)-alcohol completed the synthesis of $F_{1\alpha}$.

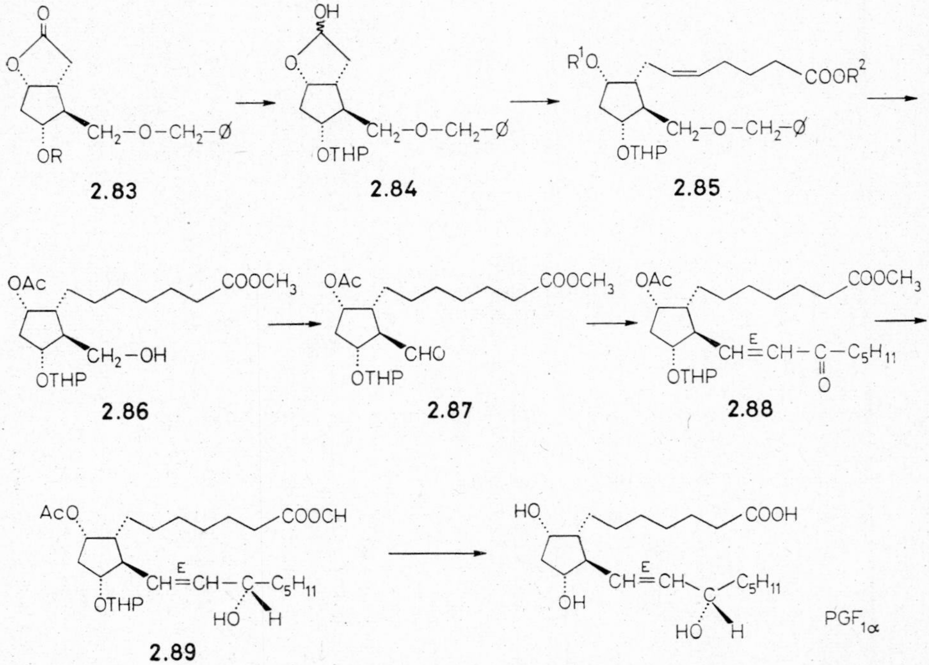

Fig. 2.5. Synthesis of prostaglandin $F_{1\alpha}$

The alcohol of the unnatural (15R)-configuration was recycled to the synthesis by reoxidation with manganese dioxide to the ketone (2.88).

2.1.4 Synthesis of Prostaglandin A_2

Although the acid-catalyzed dehydration of prostaglandins E provided easy access to members of the A series, the marked hypotensive effect of prostaglandin A_2 prompted the Harvard group to devise an alternative route providing this compound, which would utilize an early intermediate of their general synthesis [33, 34, 35] (Fig. 2.6).

For this purpose the mesylate of the optically active iodolactone (2.31) was converted to the unsaturated lactone (2.90) by elimination of the mesyl-oxy group and iodine. Treatment with acetic anhydride–boron trifluoride effected simultaneous ether cleavage and acetylation. The acetate (2.91) was reduced with diisobutylaluminium hydride to the lactol alcohol (2.92). The lactol function was protected by forming the methyl acetal, which was oxidized with Collins reagent to the aldehyde (2.93) and then con-

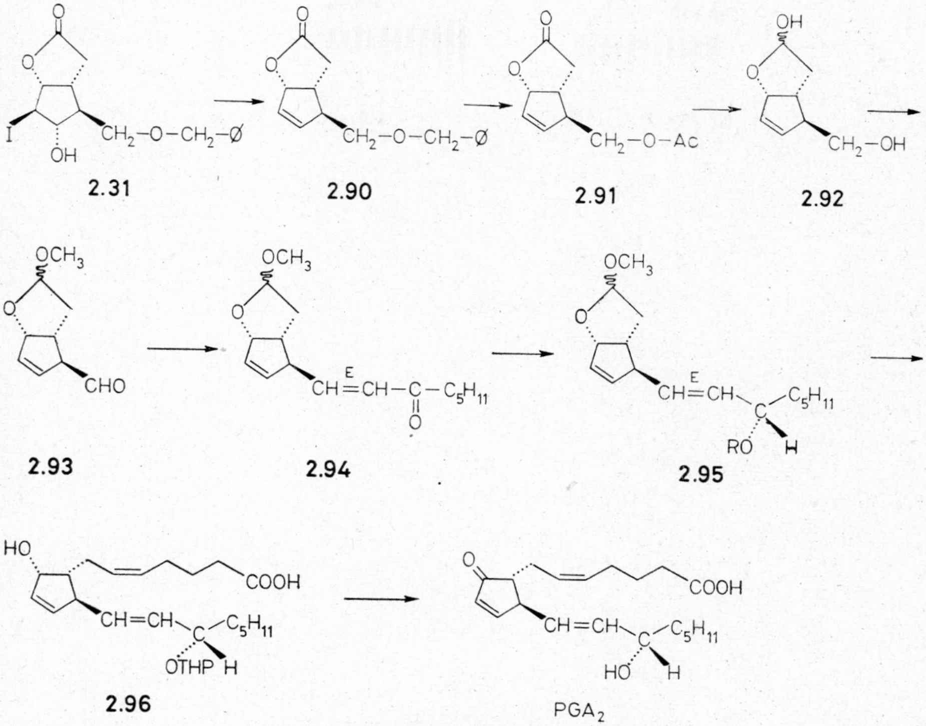

Fig. 2.6. Synthesis of prostaglandin A$_2$

densed with sodium dimethyl-2-oxoheptylphosphonate. Reduction of the
ketone (**2.94**) and separation of the epimeric alcohols was followed by conversion of the (15S)-component (**2.95**, R = H) to the tetrahydropyranyl
derivative (**2.95**, R = THP). Wittig condensation with triphenyl-4-carboxy-
butylidenephosphorane furnished a hydroxy acid (**2.96**) that was oxidized
with chromium trioxide to the 9-oxo-acid; acid-catalyzed hydrolysis of the
protecting group led finally to prostaglandin A$_2$.

Corey and Terashima conducted a detailed investigation in order to
achieve the conversion of the hydroxy-lactone (**2.97**, R = H) to the unsaturated lactone intermediate (**2.90**) of prostaglandin A$_2$ synthesis [36]. Treatment of the corresponding tosylate (**2.97**, R = tosyl) with organic salts of
tetrabutylammonium cation resulted in two reactions. An S$_N$2 substitution gave rise to an acyloxy compound (**2.98**) of inverted configuration,
whereas elimination by the E$_2$ mechanism afforded the required unsaturated
lactone (**2.90**). The product ratio was controlled by the nature of the nucleophile, i.e. the anion of the ammonium salt.

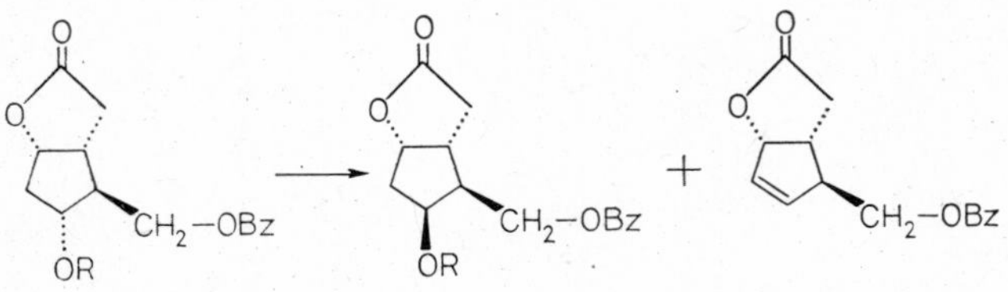

2.97   2.98   2.90

Tetrabutylammonium acetate in acetone at room temperature gave the acetate (**2.98**, R = CH_3CO) and (**2.90**) in a ratio of 1.2 : 1; with the formate the ratio was 3 : 1 and, finally, the oxalate induced only elimination and permitted the isolation of the unsaturated lactone (**2.90**) in 82% yield. The acceleration of elimination by oxalate ions can be rationalized by a two-centre (bidentate) attack. The mono-oxalate anion (**2.100**) arising from the collapse of the transition state (**2.99**) is stabilized by hydrogen bonding and this effect manifests itself already in the transition state.

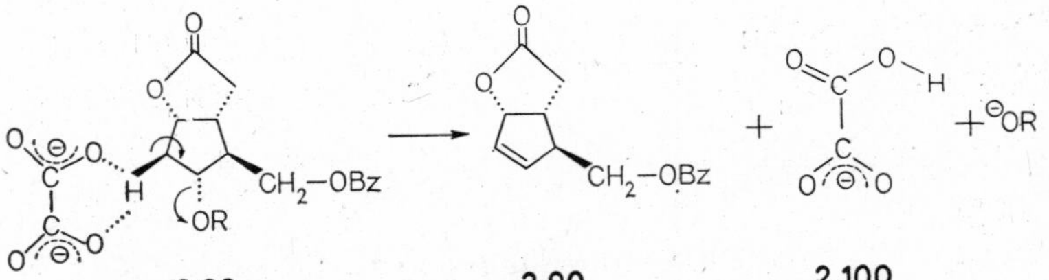

2.99   2.90   2.100

An alternative approach to the key intermediate leading to prostaglandin A_2 has been developed by Ranganathan et al. [37, 38]. Nitroethylene (**2.101**) was used this time as the dienophile in the Diels–Alder reaction of methoxy-methylcyclopentadiene (**2.3**). The nitronorbornene (**2.102**) formed thereby in 90% yield was converted to a salt with sodium hydroxide. The nitrone liberated from the salt rapidly rearranged to a mixture of the lactone (**2.104**, 32%) and the cyclic hydroxamic acid ester (**2.105**, 33%). With nitrous acid the latter could be transformed to the lactone as well.

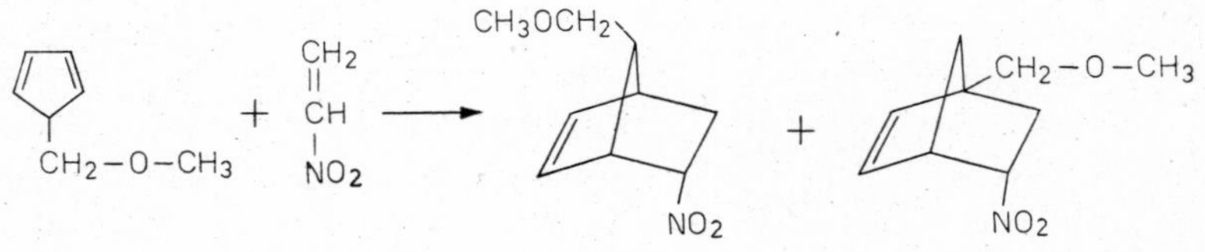

2.3   2.101   2.102   2.103

2.102 ⟶

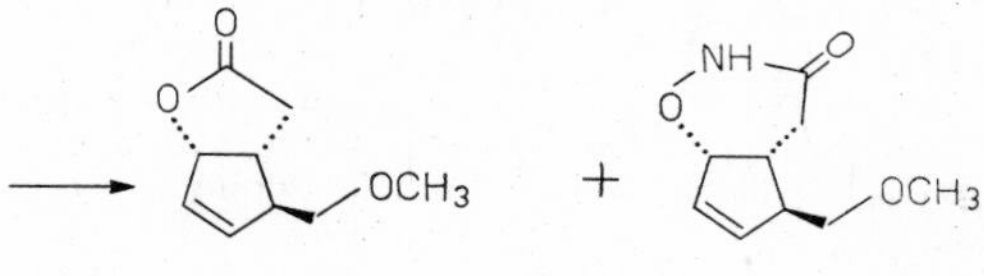

2.104   +   2.105

An advantage of this procedure is that the preparation of the lactone requires only two steps; this is partly offset by the highly toxic and lachrymatory properties of nitroethylene and its tendency to polymerize. Rearrangement of the nitrobornene (**2.102**) follows presumably the following pathway [65].

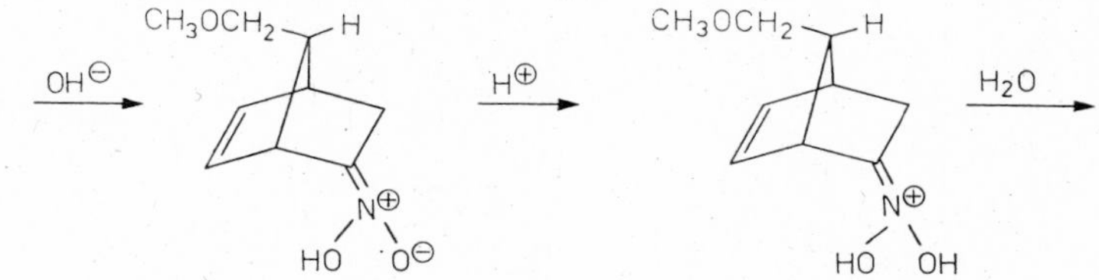

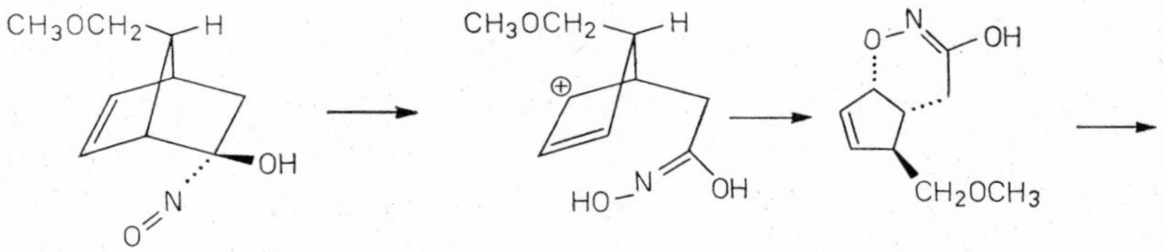

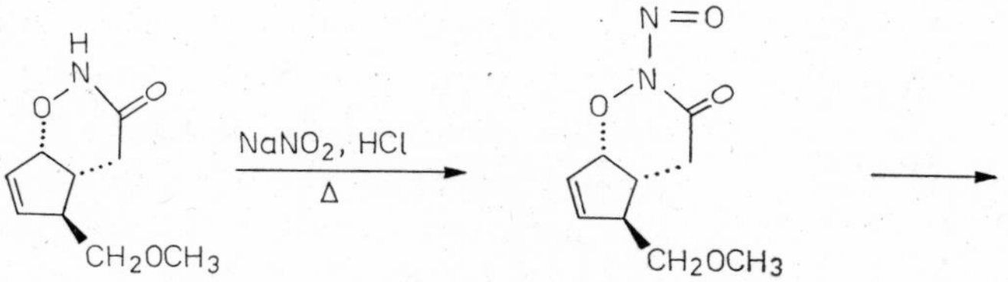

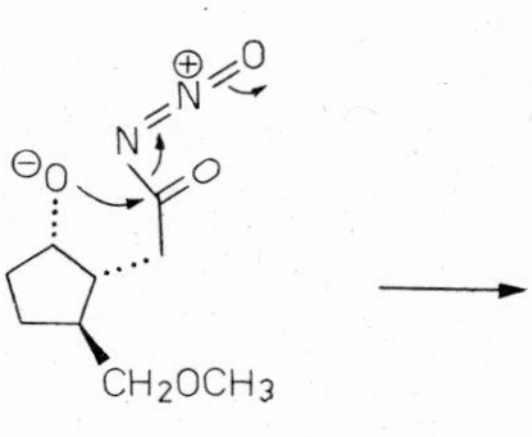

The same authors also solved the problem of converting the lactone to an intermediate of prostaglandin $F_{2\alpha}$ synthesis. For this purpose the lactone (**2.104**) was first treated with hypobromic acid generated from N-bromoacetamide in aqueous acetone; the Br^+ cation approached the π-electron system from the convex, i.e. *exo* side of the molecule. Attack of the hydroxyl anion on the cyclic bromonium ion intermediate (**2.106**) proceeded with inversion giving rise to the bromolactone (**2.107**, R = H). Acetylation (**2.107**, R = Ac) and hydrogenation in the presence of nickel catalyst completed the sequence leading to the lactone (**2.108**) suitable for prostaglandin $F_{2\alpha}$ synthesis.

| | 2.104 | | 2.106 | | 2.107 |

2.108

2.1.5. *Synthesis of Prostaglandin C_2*

As described above, the transformation of prostaglandins of the A series to those of the B series proceeded *via* intermediates of type C. Recent pharmacological studies have shown that the isomerization of PGA to PGC is catalyzed by an isomerase enzyme system found in the blood of mammals. As the hypotensive effect of PGC is more pronounced than that of PGA [39, 40, 41], the total synthesis of C-type prostaglandins became of considerable interest. This task was solved by the Harvard group in 1973 [42].

As starting material for prostaglandin C_2 (an intermediate prostaglandin A_2 synthesis), the unsaturated lactol (**2.109**) was selected. The scheme required the translocation of the endocyclic double bond to the C_{11}-C_{12} position characteristic of the C series. Isomerization of (**2.109**) can give rise to two products in which the endo- and exocyclic double bonds are conjugated. From the two isomers the one belonging to the B series is energetically more favoured, therefore under acidic or basic conditions A-type prostaglandins are rapidly transformed to B-type compounds. The only chance of obtaining an isomer of the C-type is if this intermediate can be stabilized in some form.

This objective was realized by reacting the lactol (**2.109**) with triferrododecacarbonyl [$Fe_3(CO)_{12}$], which both induced the migration of the double bond and trapped the 1,3-diene system formed in the primary process as a stable complex (**2.110**). The complex was then made to react with the phosphorane generated from triphenyl-4-carboxybutylphosphonium salt and the condensation product (**2.111**) was subjected to Collins oxidation. The reagent effected the required oxidation at C–9 and destroyed at the same time the diene–iron tricarbonyl complex. Hydrolysis of the product gave prostaglandin C_2.

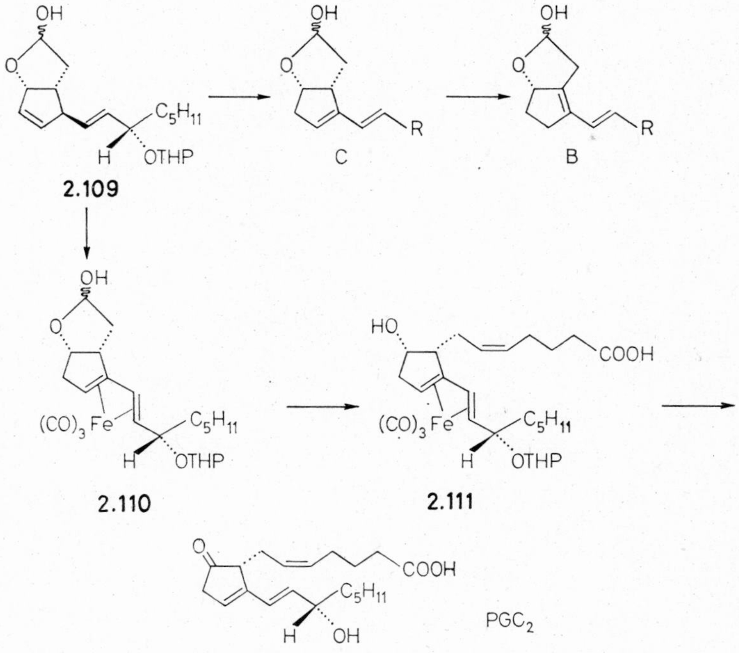

2.2 OTHER ROUTES FOR THE PREPARATION OF COREY'S LACTONE-ALDEHYDE INTERMEDIATE

The fact that all the natural prostaglandins became accessible from the lactone aldehyde intermediate (**2.35**) of Corey's stereoselective synthesis, stimulated research directed towards the development of novel procedures for the preparation of this compound based on inexpensive starting materials and avoiding exotic reagents. From the numerous approaches along this line only two will be discussed here, *viz.* those based on ring contraction of cyclohexane derivatives, and the one starting from norbornene.

Corey's sequence for the synthesis of the lactone aldehyde comprised reactions of the "point type". Reactions can be denoted to be of this type if good yields can be achieved only under strictly controlled conditions (temperature, moisture content, etc.) [43]. In industrial operations, however, reactions of the plateau type are preferred, i.e. those which permit considerable variation in reaction parameteres without appreciably impairing the yields.

2.2.1 *Routes Based on Ring Contraction of Cyclohexane Derivatives.*
Woodward's Synthesis of Prostaglandins

There are several advantages inherent in syntheses based on the ring contraction of cyclohexane derivatives. The latter are readily available, their chemistry has been thoroughly investigated and the stereochemistry of operations on the ring can be controlled adequately. The key step of the syntheses, namely ring contraction, is stereospecific. *Trans*-2-aminocyclohexanol derivatives have been selected as substrates for this important

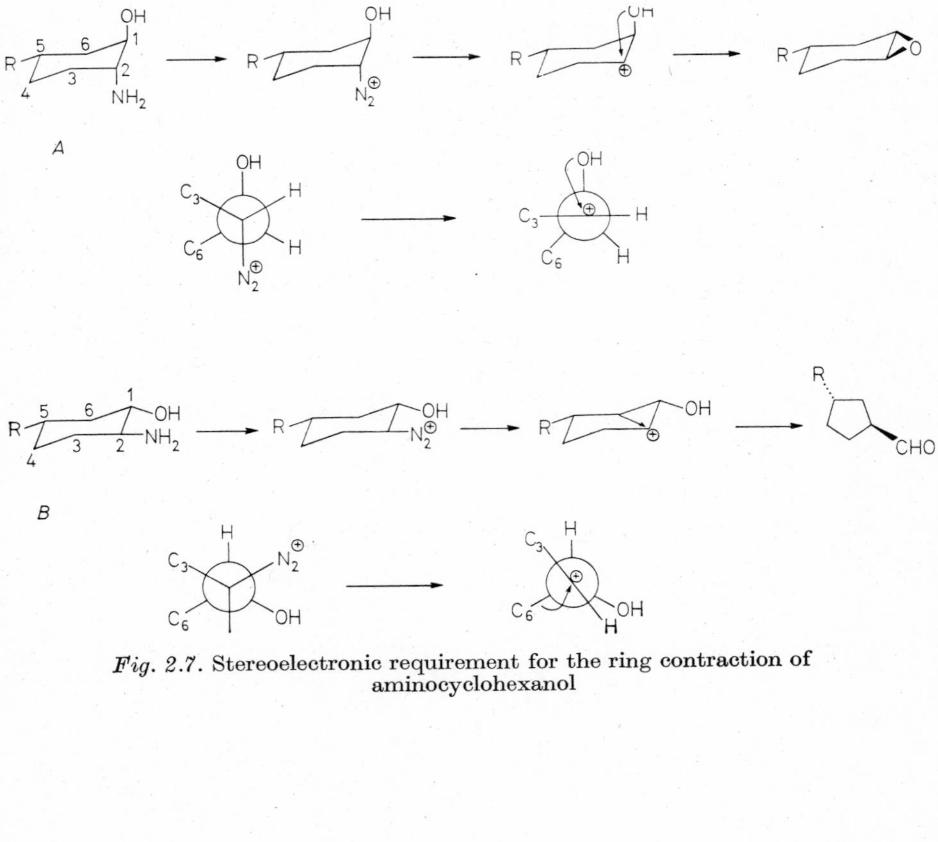

Fig. 2.7. Stereoelectronic requirement for the ring contraction of aminocyclohexanol

reaction. Nitrogen elimination from the labile diazonium salt obtained by treatment of the amino alcohol with nitrous acid gave rise to a carbenium cation that can be stabilized in two ways (Fig. 2.7). In the case of a *trans-diaxial* disposition of the amino and hydroxyl groups as in *A*, stereoelectronic factors in the resulting cation give preference to an intramolecular attack of the hydroxyl and thus a 1,2-epoxide is formed.

In the other possible arrangement of a *trans*-2-aminocyclohexanol (*B*), both the amino and hydroxyl groups are *equatorial*, and in the intermediate carbenium cation the non-bonded electron pair of the oxygen is unfavourably oriented for intramolecular nucleophilic attack. At the same time the stereoelectronic requirements for participation are satisfied by the C_6-C_1 bond and, as a consequence, the carbenium cation is stabilized by ring contraction to give a cyclopentyl-aldehyde.

In order to direct deamination towards ring contraction, i.e. the transformation of a cyclohexane to a cyclopentane, the *trans*-1,2-aminoalcohol has to be constructed in such a way as to secure the *diequatorial* arrangement of the amino and hydroxyl groups.

2.112   2.113   2.114   2.115

2.116   2.117   2.118

2.119   2.120   2.121

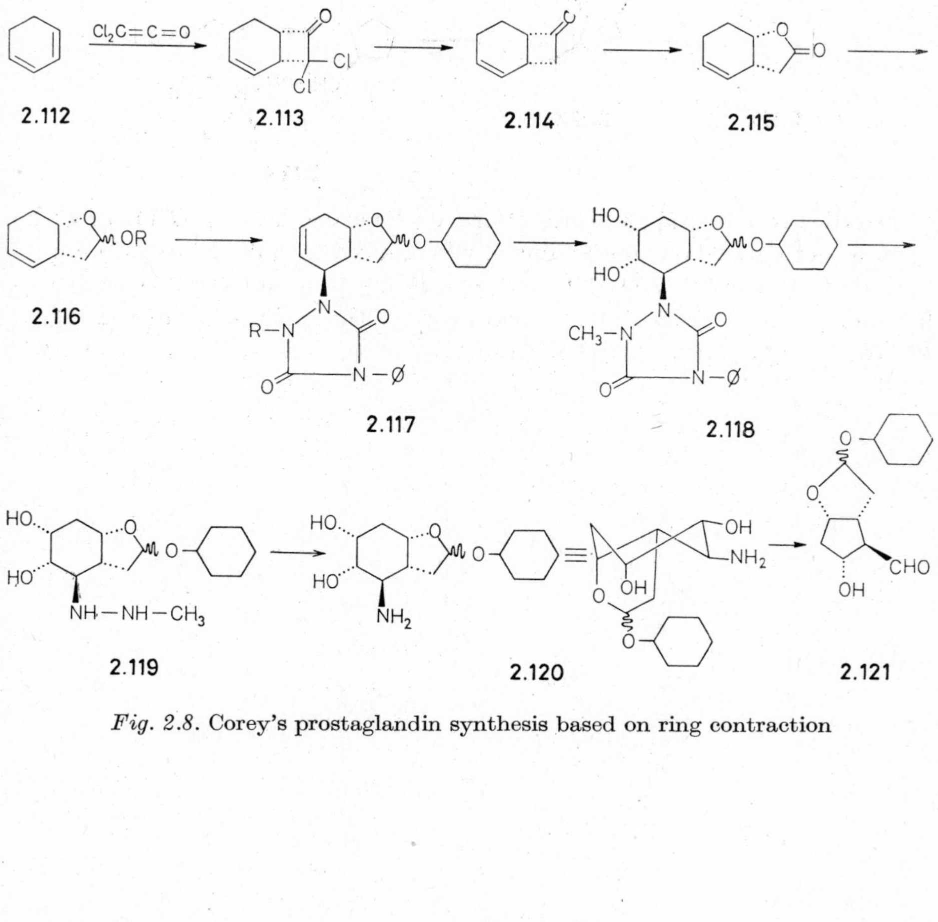

Fig. 2.8. Corey's prostaglandin synthesis based on ring contraction

The first synthesis of the lactol-aldehyde based on the principle of ring contraction was achieved by Corey *et al.* (Fig. 2.8) [44, 45]. The starting material was benzene from which 1,3-cyclohexadiene (**2.112**) was prepared with calcium hexamine [$Ca(NH_3)_6$]. [2+2] addition of the diene to dichloro-ketene, readily prepared from dichloroacetyl chloride with triethylamine, gave the bicyclooctenone (**2.113**). Reductive elimination of the chlorine atoms by zinc in acetic acid and Baeyer–Villiger oxidation of the product (**2.114**) with alkaline hydrogen peroxide furnished the cyclohexenylacetic acid derivative (**2.115**).

The lactone (**2.115**) was already a suitable substrate for ring contraction. This reaction was effected in Corey's version by treatment with thorium(III) nitrate in perchloric acid and sodium perchlorate, leading to an s.c. semi-pinacol rearrangement to give the cyclopentyl aldehyde (**2.122**).

This compound could be converted — as described earlier — to 11-deoxy-prostaglandin $F_{2\alpha}$ (**2.123**).

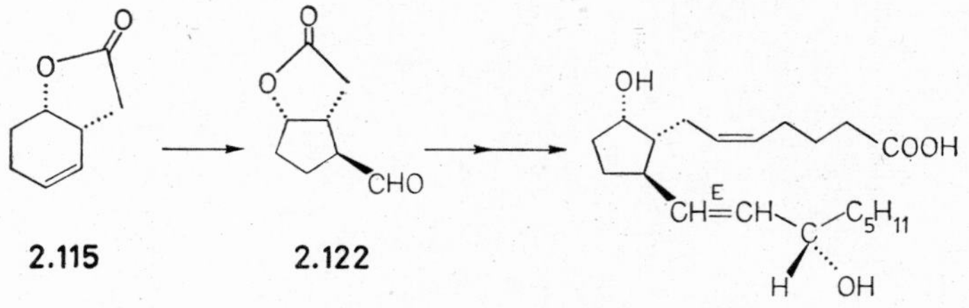

2.115   2.122

2.123

In order to elaborate the use of the cyclohexene-lactone (**2.115**) for the synthesis of natural prostaglandins, it was reduced with diisobutylaluminium hydride to the lactol (**2.116**), R = H; this was allowed to react with cyclo-hexanol in the presence of borontrifluoride etherate to obtain the acetal (**2.116**, R = cyclohexyl). Reaction of the latter with 4-phenyl-1,2,4-triazo-lin-3,5-dione (**2.124**), an extremely strong electrophile, was stereospecific and involved an attack on the double bond from the less hindered β-face of the molecule and proceeded with a simultaneous transposition of the double bond.

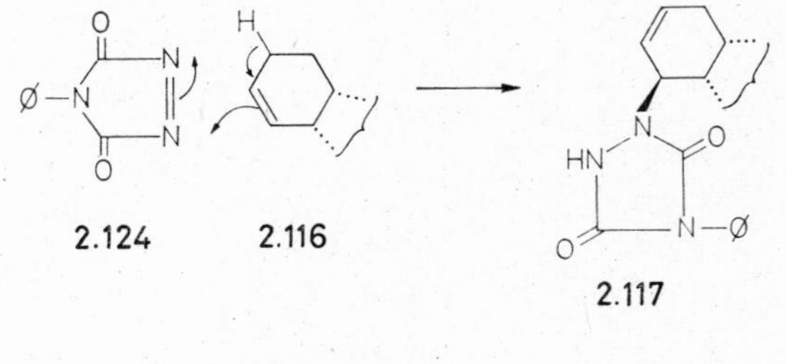

2.124   2.116

2.117

Because of the extreme sensitivity of the adduct (**2.117**, R = H) to acids it was methylated with dimethyl sulfate to the N-methyl derivative (**2.117**, R = CH₃) prior to oxidation with osmium tetroxide to a *cis*-diol (**2.118**). Hydrolysis of the diol with dilute sodium hydroxide led to a disubstituted hydrazine (**2.119**) in which the N—N bond was cleaved by hydrogenation over platinum(IV) oxide.

Of the two possible chair conformers of the resulting aminodiol (**2.120**) (*A* and *B*), the one with three *equatorial* (OH, NH₂ and C—CH₂) and two *axial* (OH and C—O) substituents, (that is, *A*) was more stable by com-parison with *B*, which contained three *axial* substituents. Similar effects were operative in the cation formed by nitrogen elimination from the diazo-tized amine, consequently a predominance of products derived from con-former *A* with an *equatorial* amine group could be anticipated to emerge from its rearrangement. In fact, diazotation of the aminoalcohol (**2.120**) furnished the ring-contracted lactol-aldehyde (**2.121**) in 60% yield.

R. B. Woodward *et al.* published in 1973 a version of the synthesis of prostaglandin F₂α [46, 66] comprising essentially a novel route to Corey's lactone-aldehyde intermediate. It was based on an inexpensive starting material and combined relatively simple reactions to a highly stereoselective sequence (Fig. 2.9).

The synthesis was launched by hydrogenating phloroglucinol (**2.125**) on nickel catalyst to *cis*-1,3,5-cyclohexanetriol (**2.126**). The triol was allowed to react with glyoxylic acid monohydrate (OHC—CO₂H · H₂O) in the presence of polystyrenesulfonic acid catalyst (Amberlite-15) to afford the tricyclic acetal-lactone (**2.127**). This reaction involved the unfavoured *axial* conformation (**2.126a**) of the triol which imparted some steric strain on the ring system. As a consequence, the lactone moiety could be smoothly reduced with sodium borohydride. The diol from this reduction (**2.128**, R = H) was first converted to the dimesylate (**2.128**, R = SO₂CH₃) and then, by potassium hydroxide-induced elimination, to the bicyclic olefin (**2.129**)

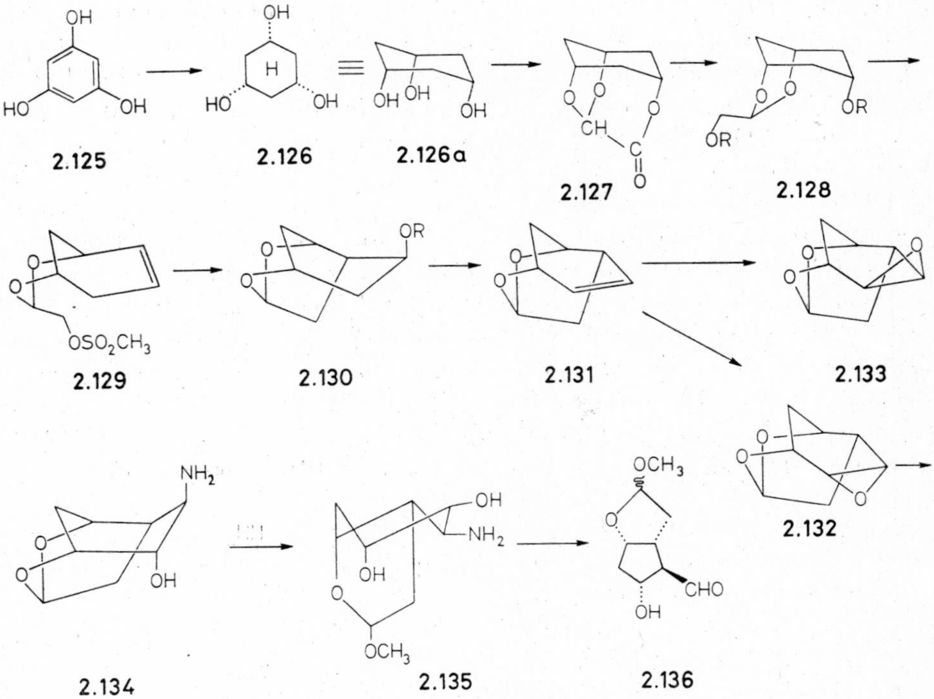

Fig. 2.9. Woodward's synthesis of prostaglandins

which was solvolyzed with potassium carbonate in aqueous 1,2-dimethoxy-ethane to yield the tricyclic alcohol (**2.130**, R = H).

This cyclization followed the known pattern of electrophilic addition to olefins and was introduced by the formation of a cation by heterolysis of the mesyloxy group commencing with an attack on the double bond, followed in the second elementary step by the attachment of the nucleophilic partner, i.e. the hydroxyl group. The reaction was both regio- and stereospecific and resembled the iodolactonization described in Section 2.1.1.

The racemic alcohol was resolved *via* its (+)-camphoric acid ester. The required levorotatory alcohol was converted to the tricyclic olefin (**2.131**) by repeating the procedure of mesylation (to **2.130**, R = SO$_2$CH$_3$) and elimination with potassium hydroxide.

The next objective of the synthesis was the elaboration of an α-epoxide (**2.132**). The range of the potential oxidizing agents was rather limited owing to the extreme sensitivity of the olefin (**2.131**) to acids. Weak peracids, e.g. *m*-chloroperbenzoic acid, were, however, of no avail since they gave rise to the unwanted β-epoxide (**2.133**). The optimal reagent was that formed *in situ* from benzonitrile (**2.137**) and hydrogen peroxide in the presence of potassium hydrogen carbonate in methanol. The actual oxidant under these conditions was an extremely reactive peroxy-carboximide

2.137   2.138   2.139

(**2.139**) which provided the α-epoxide (**2.132**) as the major product (62%).

After chromatographic separation the β-epoxide (**2.133**) could be recycled to the synthesis by lithium aluminium hydride reduction to the tricyclic alcohol (**2.130**, R = H).

The synthesis was pursued by ammonolysis of the α-epoxide (**2.132**) by means of heating it with ammonium hydroxide in a sealed tube to give the aminoalcohol (**2.134**). Owing to the *trans-diaxial* disposition of the amino and hydroxyl groups on the rigid ring system, the latter was unsuited for ring contraction, but fortunately when treated with anhydrous methanolic hydrogen chloride the opening of one of the rings by partial methanolysis took place to form a bicyclic acetal (**2.135**). This was now flexible and in its preferred conformation the amino group occupied *equatorial* position (*cf.* **2.120**), permitting its transformation by diazotation to the lactol-aldehyde (**2.136**) in high yield (80%).

This key intermediate was used in the synthesis of Woodward *et al.*, without the protection of the C_{11}-hydroxyl. The lactol-aldehyde (**2.136**) was first made to react with the stabilized phosphorane derived from tributyl-2-oxoheptylphosphonium salt and then the resulting ketone (**2.140**) was reduced with zinc borohydride.

2.140   2.141

After having separated the epimeric alcohols, the one with (15S)-con-figuration (**2.141**) was carried along the lines established by Corey and his associates in two steps to prostaglandin $F_{2\alpha}$.

2.2.2 *Preparation of the Lactone-aldehyde from Norbornadiene*

The possibility of preparing the lactone-aldehyde intermediate of Corey's synthesis (**2.35**) from inexpensive norbornadiene was investigated in several laboratories. Procedures of industrial relevance were published by Peel and Sutherland [47], as well as by Corey *et al.* [48]. There are many common features in the two routes, essential differences emerge only in the later stages.

Corey's group used the Prins reaction and reacted norbornadiene (**2.142**) with paraformaldehyde in formic acid containing sulfuric acid as catalyst (Fig. 2.10). The dihydroxy compound formed was formylated *in situ* by formic acid enabling undesired side reactions to be avoided.

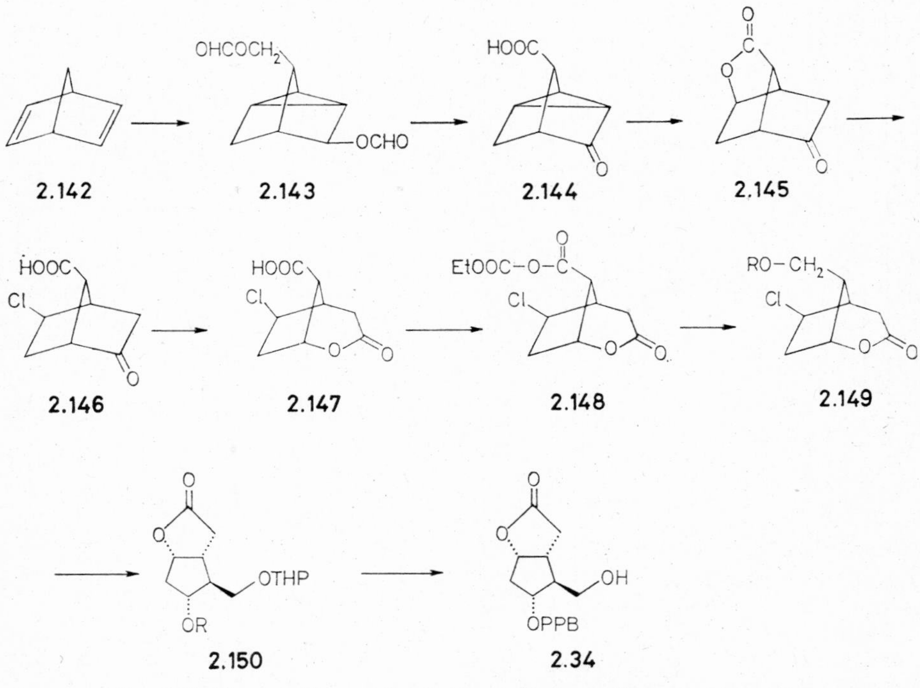

Fig. *2.10*. Preparation of the lactone-aldehyde from norbornadiene

Jones oxidation of the diformate (**2.143**) gave a crystalline keto-acid (**2.144**) that was resolved as its (*S*)-1-phenylethylamine salt. The dextro-rotatory acid was subjected to electrophilic ring opening by perchloric acid. As might have been anticipated, this affected the cyclopropyl-ketone system of the molecule in a regio- and stereoselective manner, because both the site and direction of the attack were predetermined by the *anti*-orientation of the carboxyl group permitting approach only from one side of the cyclopropane ring.

The lactone thus obtained (**2.145**) gave, on treatment with hydrogen chloride, a chloroacid (**2.146**) that was converted to a chlorolactone (**2.147**) by Baeyer–Villiger oxidation. The carboxyl group was converted with ethyl chloroformate to a mixed anhydride (**2.148**) in order to facilitate its selective reduction with sodium borohydride to the lactone-alcohol (**2.149**, R = H). Treatment of the corresponding tetrahydropyranyl ether (**2.149**, R =THP) with alkaline hydrogen peroxide effected the opening of the six-membered lactone ring giving rise to the formation of a five-membered one (**2.150**, R = H) by S_Ni-type substitution of the chlorine atom. After protection of the C_{11}-hydroxyl by *p*-phenylbenzoylation (**2.150**, R = PPB) and removal of the tetrahydropyranyl group, the sequence ended up in the familiar lactone-alcohol intermediate (**2.34**).

Up to the chlorolactone (**2.147**), the route followed by Peel and Sutherland [47] was essentially the same as Corey's approach. Treatment of the corresponding bromolactone (**2.147**, bromine instead of chlorine) with hydroxylamine in collidine effected a translactonization similar to that of (**2.149**) to furnish the hydroxy-acid (**2.151**). The carboxyl was then blocked temporarily as the *p*-bromophenacylester (**2.152**, R = H), followed by acylation of the hydroxyl group with *p*-phenylbenzoyl chloride and cleavage of the phenacyl ester moiety of the benzoate (**2.152**, R = PPB) with zinc in acetic acid. Reduction of the free acid (**2.153**) with diborane afforded Corey's lactone-alcohol (**2.34**).

2.151   2.152

2.153   2.34

A recent variant of the preparation of Corey's aldehyde (Fig. 2.11, **2.35**) according to Brown *et al.*, adopting the crucial reactions of the original route, started with acetoxyfulvene (**2.154**) [49]. Uncatalyzed Diels–Alder addition of α-chloroacrylonitrile (**2.7**) on acetoxyfulvene (**2.154**) was followed by hydrolysis of the resulting norbornene derivative (**2.155**, only one epimer shown) with hydrochloric acid. First, the *anti*-aldehyde (**2.156**) was formed

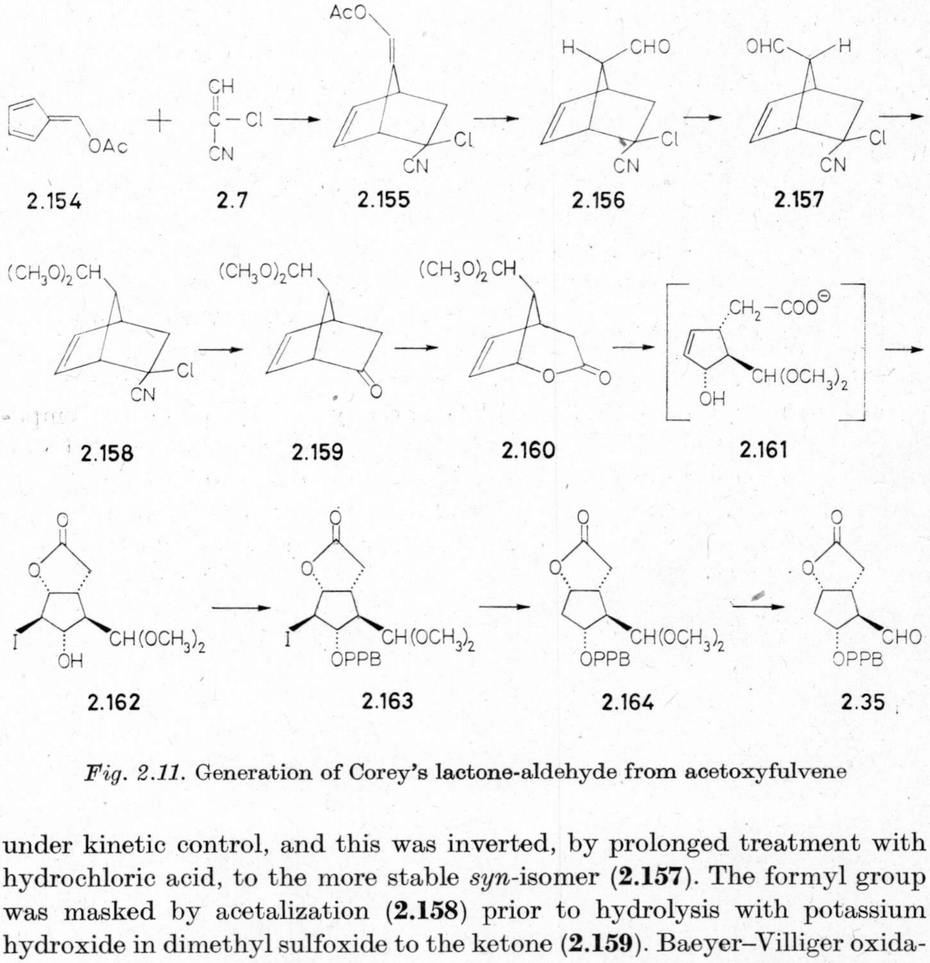

Fig. 2.11. Generation of Corey's lactone-aldehyde from acetoxyfulvene

under kinetic control, and this was inverted, by prolonged treatment with hydrochloric acid, to the more stable *syn*-isomer (**2.157**). The formyl group was masked by acetalization (**2.158**) prior to hydrolysis with potassium hydroxide in dimethyl sulfoxide to the ketone (**2.159**). Baeyer–Villiger oxidation to the lactone (**2.160**), iodolactonization, *p*-phenylbenzoylation of the iodolactone (**2.163**), reduction with tri-*n*-butyltin hydride and acidic hydrolysis of the acetal ester (**2.164**) completed this new synthesis of Corey's lactone-aldehyde obtained as the *p*-phenylbenzoate ester (**2.35**).

The advantage of the above route as compared with Corey's synthesis was that it avoided the use of the extremely toxic thallium salts. This was, however, more than offset by a cumbersome multistep resolution procedure requiring the preparation of the hemiphthalate ester of the alcohol obtained by sodium borohydride reduction of the ketone (**2.159**), resolution by means of (+)-amphetamine, hydrolysis of the levorotatory ester and finally reoxidation of the alcohol to the ketone.

A modification of the sequence based on acetoxyfulvene has been reported recently by Brown and Lilley [50] (Fig. 2.12). Their concept was to introduce the "lower" chain (C_{13}–C_{20}) first and to elaborate the remaining three substituents associated with the cyclopentane ring by known transformations thereafter. Thus the protection of the C_{11}-hydroxyl became unnecessary.

Accordingly, the *syn*-aldehyde (**2.157**) was first condensed with the lithium salt of dimethyl 2-oxoheptylphosphonate to the enone (**2.165**); this was then reduced with aluminium isopropoxide to a 1 : 1 mixture of the epimeric

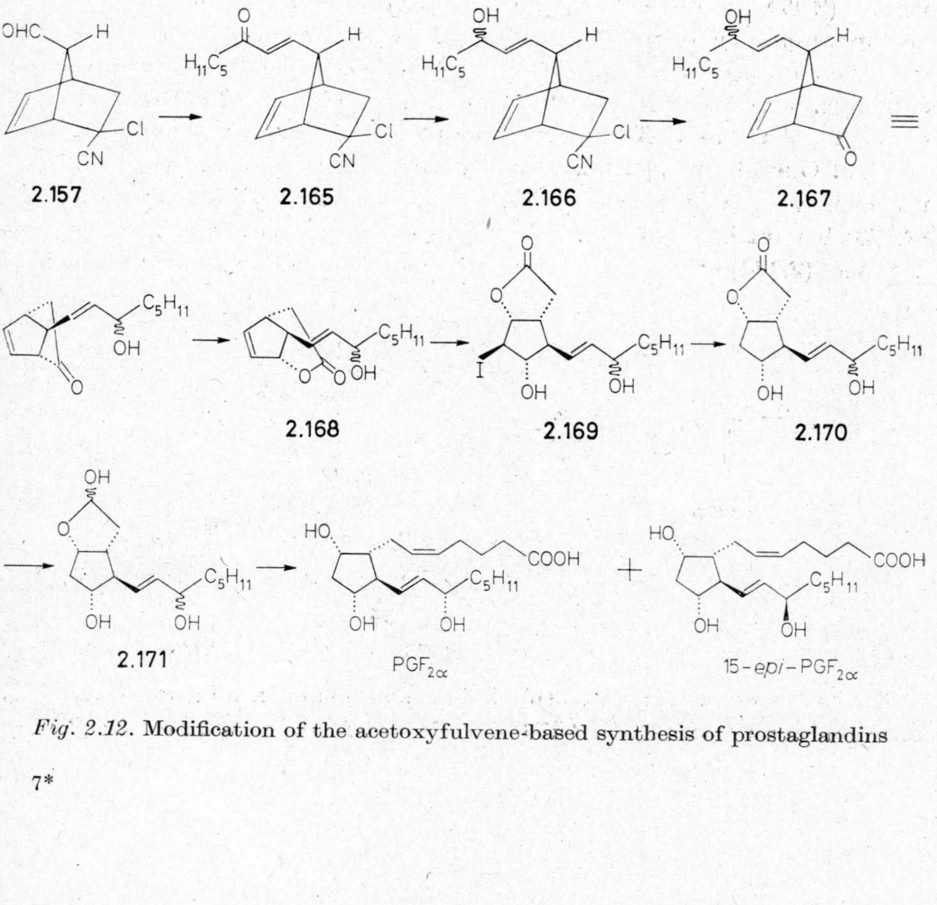

Fig. 2.12. Modification of the acetoxyfulvene-based synthesis of prostaglandins

alcohols (**2.166**). Hydrolysis of the mixture with potassium hydroxide in dimethyl sulfoxide and oxidation of the ketone (**2.167**) with alkaline hydrogen peroxide yielded the lactone (**2.168**). This was opened to the hydroxyacid, subjected in succession to idoolactonization (**2.169**), reduction first with tributyltin hydride to remove iodine (**2.170**) and then with diisobutylaluminium hydride to give a lactol (**2.171**), which was finally subjected to Wittig condensation with 4-carboxybutyltriphenylphosphorane. The product, a 1 : 1 mixture of racemic prostaglandin $F_{2\alpha}$ and racemic 15-*epi*-prostaglandin $F_{2\alpha}$ was separated by chromatography.

2.3 SYNTHESIS OF COREY'S DIHYDROXYLACTONE INTERMEDIATE *VIA* BICYCLOHEXANE DERIVATIVES

Cyclopropylcarbinyl derivatives are known to solvolyze readily and may give rise to remarkable products by skeletal rearrangements [51].

Studying, for example, the solvolysis of 6-tosyloxymethyl-bicyclo[3.1.0]-hexane (**2.171a** and **b**) Wiberg and Ashe [51] came to the conclusion that in the first step a cyclopropylcarbinyl cation was formed.

This cation may be stabilized in different ways depending on whether the starting material was the *exo*-(**2.171a**) or the *endo*-isomer (**2.171b**). Acetolysis of the *exo*-compound afforded, for example two acetates in about equal proportion. One of them (**2.172**) retained the bicyclohexane structure of the parent tosylate, whereas the other proved to be a 2-vinylcyclopentyl acetate (**2.173**). The main product, however, was the tosylate of *trans*-2-vinylcyclopentanol (**2.174**) arising by internal return of the ion pair formed in the first step:

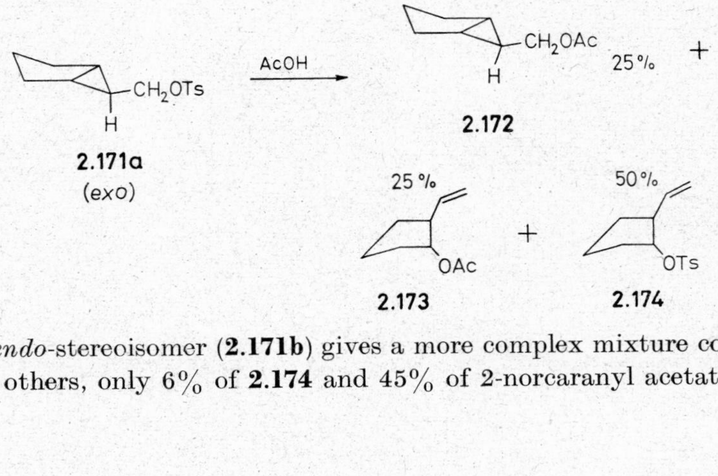

The *endo*-stereoisomer (**2.171b**) gives a more complex mixture containing, among others, only 6% of **2.174** and 45% of 2-norcaranyl acetate (**2.175**):

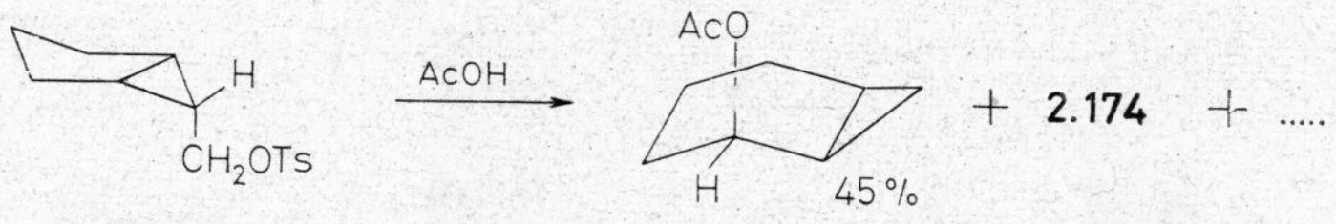

2.171b
(*endo*)

2.175

Formally, the rearrangement leading to a 2-norcaranyl ion requires the attack of the C_2-C_5 bond of the cyclopropyl ion on CH_2^+. This is feasible with the *endo*-isomer leading to (**2.179**), but with the *exo*-cation the same would give rise to the highly strained *trans*-norcaranyl system (**2.176**):

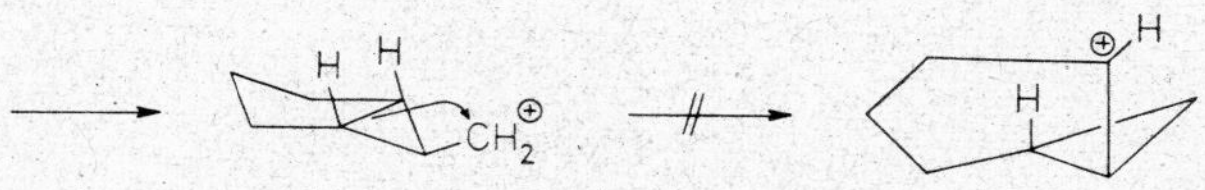

This explanation may be an oversimplification but probably accounts for the main features of the solvolysis.

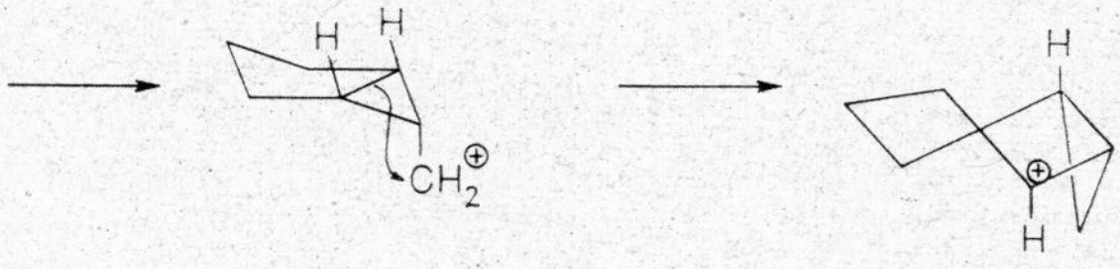

Rearrangement of cyclopropylcarbinyl cations to vinylcyclopentyl derivatives opened a way for the utilization of this reaction in the synthesis of prostaglandins.

In a preliminary communication [52], Just and Simonovitch claimed that a reaction mixture of unspecified composition, containing among others the bicyclohexanone (**2.178**), furnished on treatment with hydrogen peroxide and sodium formate in formic acid the impure racemic prostaglandin E_1.

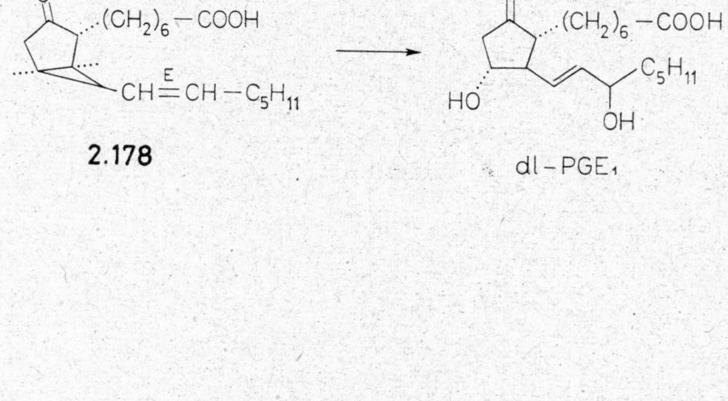

2.178

dl-PGE₁

Although these results could not be verified employing the conditions originally specified [53], a joint team of Upjohn Co. and the above-mentioned authors were able to demonstrate that congeners of (**2.178**) could be converted to racemic prostaglandin $F_{1\alpha}$ [54, 55].

Reaction of the tetrahydropyranyl ether of 3-cyclopentenol (**2.179**; Fig. 2.13) with carbethoxycarbene generated from ethyl diazoacetate afforded a mixture of the *endo*- and *exo*-bicyclohexane derivatives, the *endo*-component of which epimerized to the *exo*-stereoisomer on refluxing with sodium methoxide in methanol. Reduction of the *exo*-ester (**2.180**) to the corresponding alcohol followed by reoxidation to an aldehyde and Wittig condensation with the ylide prepared from n-hexyltriphenylphosphonium bromide gave a mixture of (*Z*)- and (*E*)-olefins. Chromatographic separation, hydrolysis of the (*E*)-isomer and oxidation of the alcohol function yielded a ketone (**2.181**), which on alkylation with methyl-ω-iodoheptanoate (**2.182**) in the presence of potassium-*t*-butoxide in dimethoxyethane gave rise to a product from which the epimeric monoalkyl derivatives (**2.183**) and (**2.184**) could be isolated in 10% and 25% yield, respectively. Reduction of the

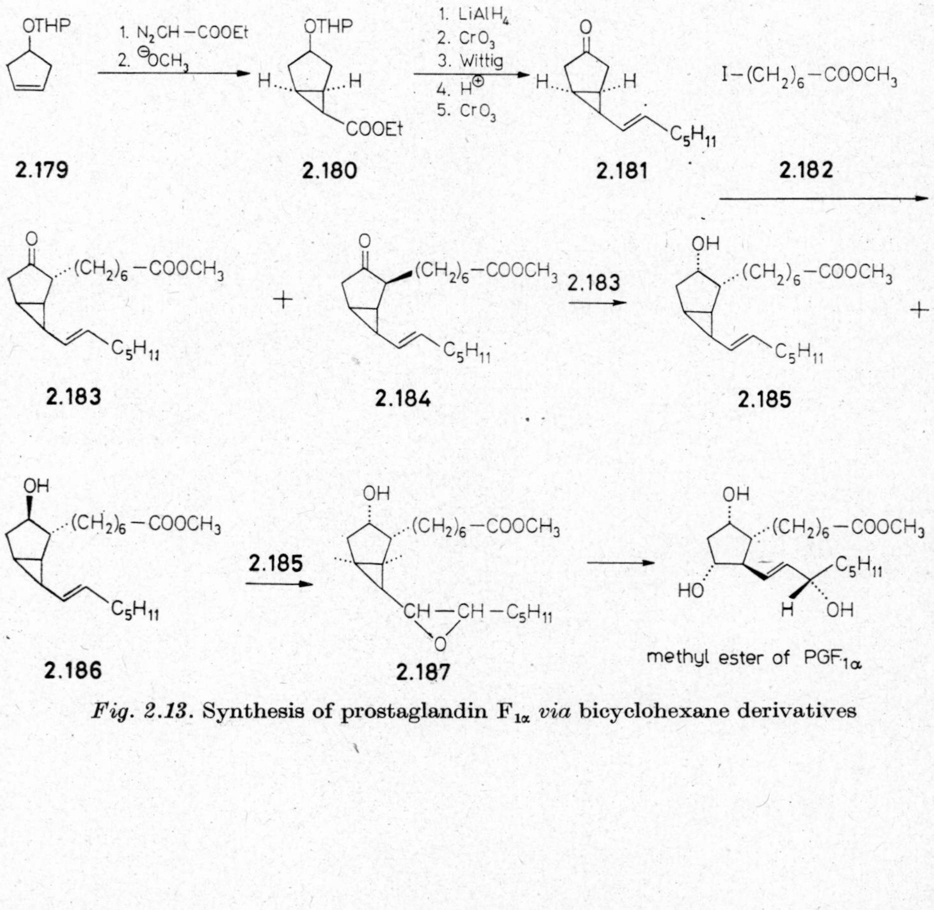

Fig. 2.13. Synthesis of prostaglandin $F_{1\alpha}$ *via* bicyclohexane derivatives

exo-epimer (**2.183**) gave the epimeric alcohols (**2.185** and **2.186**). The 9α-hydroxyepimer obtained in 10% yield when epoxidated under especially mild conditions afforded, in a nonstereospecific reaction, a mixture of epoxides (**2.187**). Solvolysis of the mixture with formic acid at room temperature followed by selective hydrolysis of the formate ester led to a complex mixture from which crystalline (±)-prostaglandin $F_{1\alpha}$ methylester could be isolated in 2–3% yield. The main product was an unrearranged glycol. The poor overall yield renders this sequence unsuitable for practical purposes.

Further work by the Upjohn group demonstrated that the opening of the epoxide ring can be effected in much higher yields using strictly anhydrous formic acid [56]. At the same time an efficient approach to prostaglandins $F_{2\alpha}$ and E_2 was developed based on a bicyclohexane intermediate.

Norbornadiene (**2.142**) was oxidized to the bicyclic aldehyde (**2.188**) which was converted, without purification, by means of neopentylglycol in the presence of a trace of acid, to the crystalline acetal (**2.189**) (yield 61%, from norbornene).

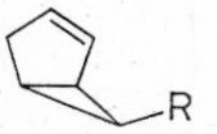

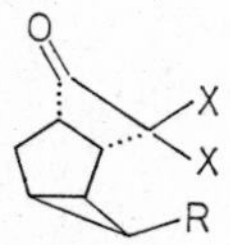

2.188 R=CHO	**2.190**	X=Cl; R=CH(OCH$_2$)$_2$ C(CH$_3$)$_2$
2.189 R=CH(OCH$_2$)$_2$ C(CH$_3$)$_2$	**2.191**	X=H; R=CH(OCH$_2$)$_2$ C(CH$_3$)$_2$

Addition of dichloroketene to the acetal (**2.189**) gave a dichlorocyclobutanone derivative (**2.190**, 81%) that could be dehalogenated with zinc and ammonium chloride in methanol to give (**2.191**) in almost quantitative yield.

At first sight it was surprising that this addition was both regio- *and* stereospecific, yet a similar specificity was observed earlier by Corey *et al.* [57] in the case of a likewise addition on *endo*-6-methoxybicyclo[3.1.0]-2-hexene:

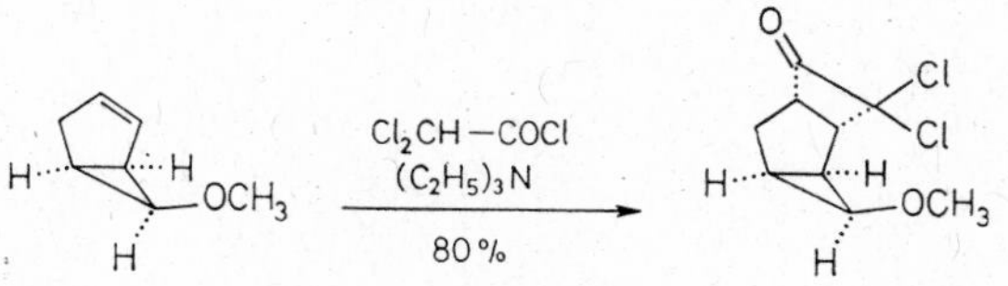

Steric control may account for the formation of the four-membered ring in *anti*-disposition to the cyclopropane ring. Regiospecificity can be rationalized by assuming that, owing to the electron releasing character of the *endo-*

methoxy group, transition states (*a*) or (*b*) derived by attachment of the carbonyl group of dichloroketene to C_3 are of lower energy than those originating from a primary attack at C_2, since in the former case a better stabilization is attained for the positive charge appearing at the other carbon of the former double bond:

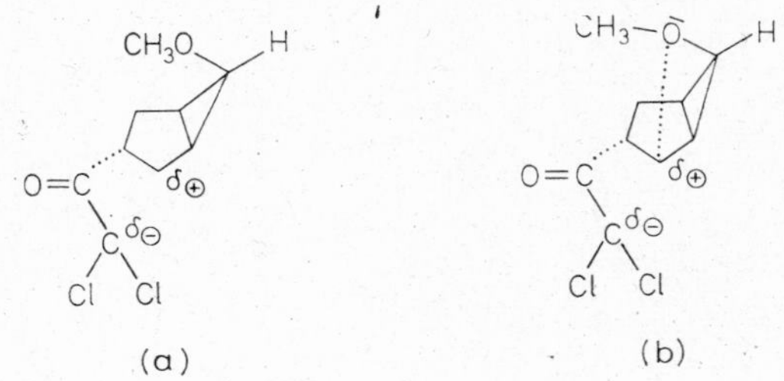

(a)   (b)

Apparently, the same factors are involved in the addition of dichloroketene to (**2.189**). It should be noted that the addition of ketenes to olefins are expected to conform to the conservation of orbital symmetry [58].

The resolution of (**2.191**) was solved in an elegant way [59]. Reaction of the ketone with l-ephedrine for 24 hours in boiling benzene in the presence of a trace of *p*-toluenesulfonic acid provided a pair of diastereomeric oxazolidines (**2.192**), which could be efficiently separated by crystallization from methanol. Hydrolysis with a mixture of tetrahydrofuran–water–acetic acid at room temperature afforded optically active (**2.191**).

Resolution was followed by Baeyer–Villiger oxidation with *m*-chloroperbenzoic acid to obtain the lactone-acetal (**2.193**) in 90% yield (from oxazolidine). Hydrolysis of (**2.193**) furnished the free aldehyde (**2.194**; 95%); this was subjected to Wittig condensation to give the olefin (**2.195**; 93%).

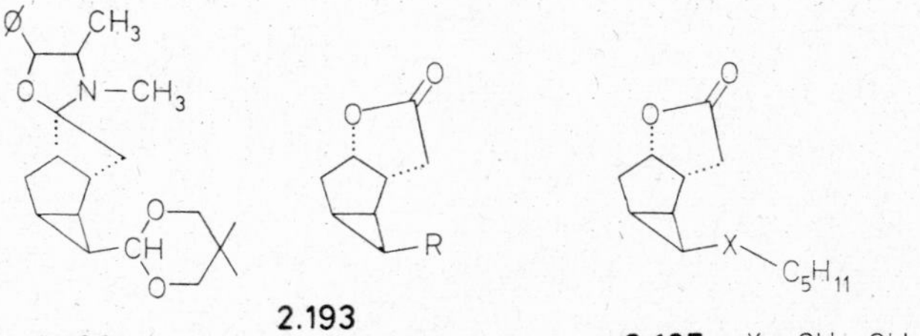

2.192

2.193
$R=CH(OCH_2)_2 C(CH_3)_2$

2.194   R=CHO

2.195   X=CH=CH

2.196   X=CH—CH
                    \O/

Oxidation of this olefin with *m*-chloroperbenzoic acid in a suspension of potassium bicarbonate in methylene chloride gave the epoxide (**2.196**) in nearly quantitative yields. Hydrolysis of the latter with a mixture of acetone, water and formic acid resulted, however, in a mixture which contained 75% of glycols (**2.197**) and only 25% of the required rearranged diols (**2.198** and **2.199**).

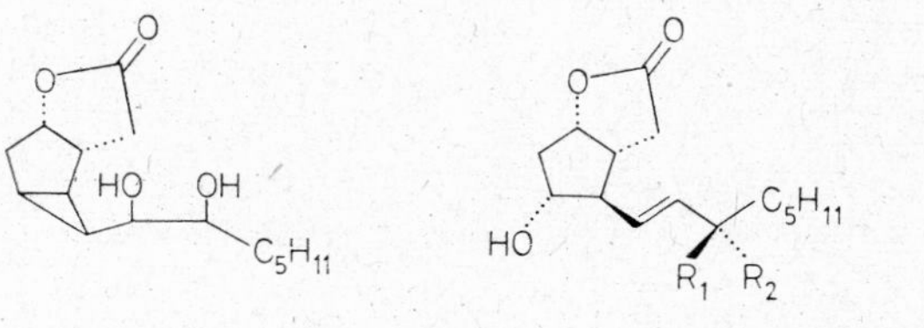

2.197   2.198 $R_1 = H$; $R_2 = OH$

2.199 $R_1 = OH$; $R_2 = H$

Reprocessing of this mixture with carefully dried formic acid and thereafter with methanolic potassium carbonate increased the proportion of the diols.

Recently the Upjohn group succeeded in performing the diol rearrangement (**2.197** → **2.198** and **2.199**) in a stereospecific manner with excellent yields [64]. The clue was that this rearrangement triggered by formic acid was sensitive to water. It was assumed that first a monoformate (**2.200**) was formed from the diol (**2.197**), followed by cyclization to an orthoester (**2.201**), which rearranged to the allyl acohol derivative (**2.198** and **2.199**).

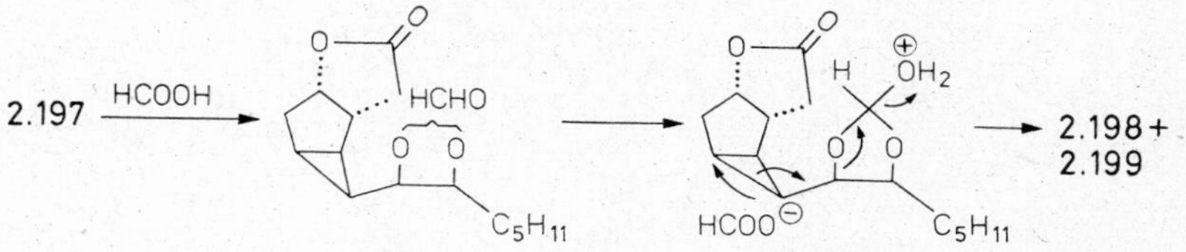

2.200   2.201

In support of this proposal the orthoester of the diol was prepared using methyl orthoformate. This compound (**2.202**) gave, in fact, with formic acid smoothly the allyl alcohols (**2.198** and **2.199**) (70% yield within less than 5 minutes).

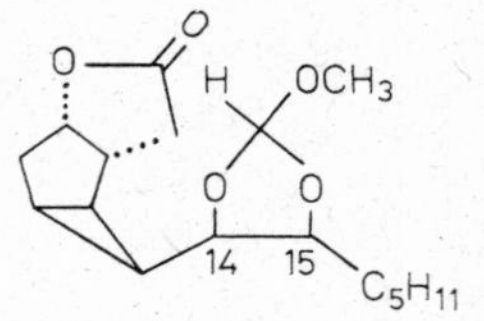

2.202

The rearrangement does not affect the C_{15}-O bond, i.e. configuration at this centre is retained. In order to confirm this, a mixture of the stereoisomeric glycols (**2.203**) and (**2.204**) was prepared from the allene (**2.195**) by osmium tetroxide oxidation. After chromatographic separation these were converted in a stereospecific manner to prostaglandin intermediates with $15S$ and $15R$ configuration (**2.207** and **2.208**). In this sequence instead of orthoformates the more stable orthopropionates (**2.205** and **2.206**) were used.

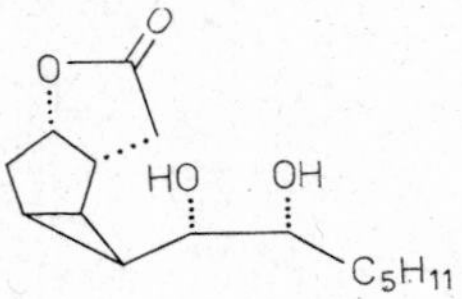

2.203

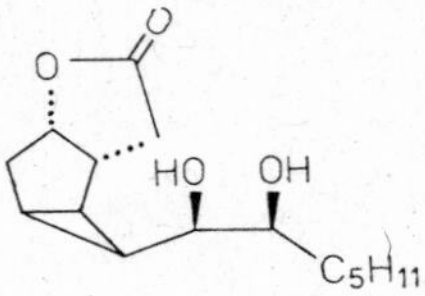

2.204

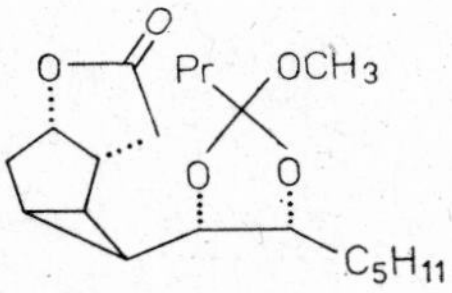

2.205

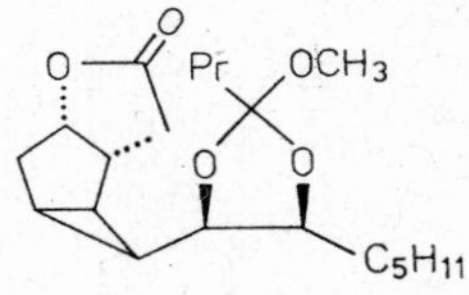

2.206

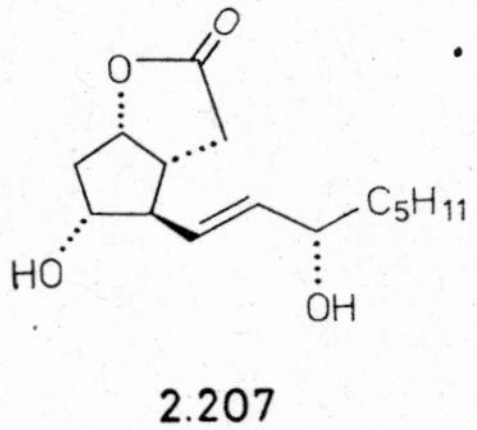

2.207

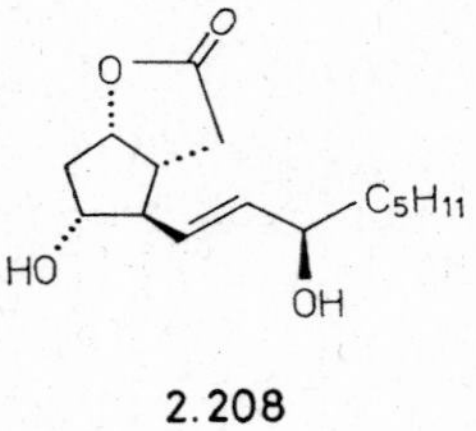

2.208

Chromatography resulted in the isolation of the desired (15S)-diol (**2.198**) in 25% yield. The remaining mixture of glycols (**2.199**) and the (15R)-diol (**2.199**) could be repeatedly treated with dry formic acid. Two recyclizations raised the yield of the required diol (**2.198**) to a total of 45% (from the epoxide, **2.196**).

The (15S)-diol (**2.198**) is identical with an intermediate of Corey's synthesis described earlier and can be accordingly converted to prostaglandin $F_{2\alpha}$ or E_2.

The Upjohn group also investigated an alternative way for opening of the cyclopropane ring. The underlying concept was that the cyclopropylcarbinyl cation formed in the first step was stabilized by the adjacent oxygen atoms and this interaction competed with the delocalization of the positive charge over the cyclopropyl system and thereby with the participation of the latter in solvolysis. In fact, the unsubstituted cyclopropane derivative (**2.171**) undergoes facile rearrangement. Since it is known that the neighbouring group effect of tosyloxy groups on carbonium ions is small [60], the rearrangement of a number of substituted 1,2-glycols was studied [55, 61].

Solvolysis of the bis-mesylate of the glycol (**2.199a**) in aqueous acetone at room temperature gave only 5% of ($\pm$)-prostaglandin E_1 together with an equal amount of its C_{15}-epimer.

All four possible stereoisomers of the glycol (**2.199a**) were also prepared, but none of them gave better yields than 4–8% of racemic prostaglandin E_2, nor more than 10–15% for the whole rearrangement (i.e. including the two C_{15}-epimers). The only identified by-product was the monomesylate (**2.209**) and this could be recycled by remesylation.

2.199a

(4 isomers; 2 *threo* and 2 *erythro*;
the latter were separated)

⟶ methyl ester of dl-PGE₁

2.209

Purification of the glycols (**2.199**) yielded a minor isomer that gave on solvolysis (as the dimesylate) two to three times higher yields than the others. This substance proved to be the C_{13} *endo-* isomer of the major products and it might have been formed either initially or by isomerization in one of the subsequent transformations. This observation prompted the design of a new synthesis with the object of preparing an *endo-*bicyclohexane derivative (Fig. 2.14) [62].

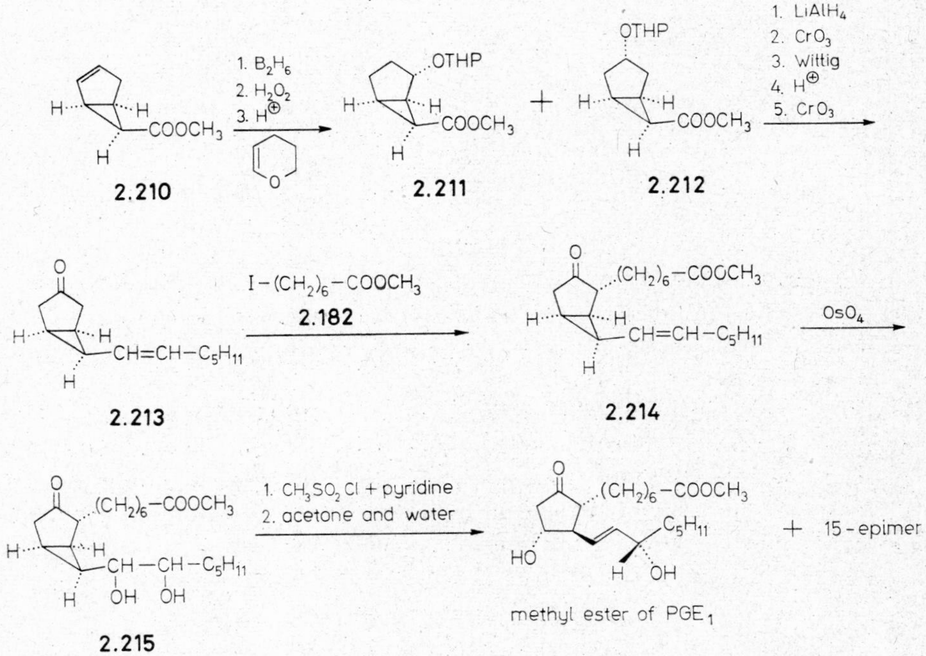

Fig. 2.14. Synthesis of prostaglandin E_1 *via* bicyclohexane derivatives

Methyl *endo-*bicyclo[3.1.0]-2-hexene-6-carboxylate (**2.210**) — readily accessible from norbornadiene — was hydroborated and oxidized to yield a mixture of the alcohols (**2.211** and **2.212**). Protection of the hydroxyl was followed by reduction with lithium aluminium hydride and oxidation to an aldehyde. Wittig condensation of the latter, removal of the tetrahydropyranyl protecting group, oxidation of the hydroxyl function to a ketone and separation from the 2-oxo isomer afforded (**2.213**); this was monoalkylated with methyl ω-iodoheptanoate to (**2.214**) and converted to a mixture of glycols (**2.215**) by hydroxylation with osmium tetroxide. Solvolysis of the corresponding mesylate gave (±)-prostaglandin E_1 methyl ester in 19% yield.

In respect of yield, the pure isolated stereoisomers of the glycol (**2.215**) showed little variance, suggesting that their solvolysis was not a synchronous process.

Interestingly, high stereoselectivity was experienced in respect of the product which was exclusively the 11α-isomer with a (13Z) double bond.

Along similar lines, prostaglandins E_2 and $F_{2\alpha}$ could also be prepared (Fig. 2.15) [63].

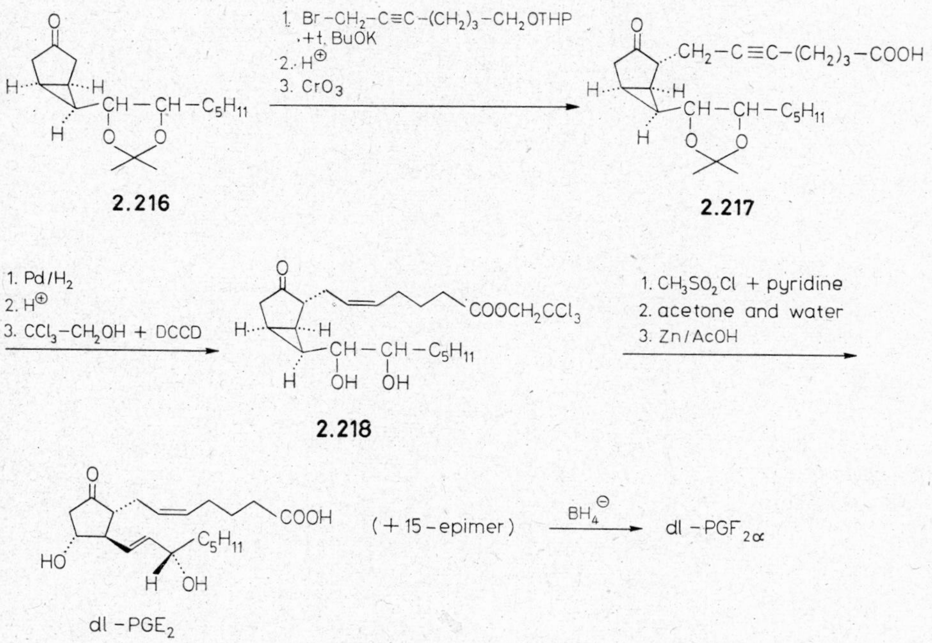

Fig. 2.15. Synthesis of prostaglandins E_2 and $F_{2\alpha}$ *via* bicyclohexane derivatives

This required the transformation of the *endo*-olefin (**2.213**) to the isopropylidene glycol (**2.216**), which was alkynylated in tetrahydofuran with 1-bromo-7-tetrahydropyranyloxyhept-2-yne in the presence of potassium-*t*-butoxide. Cleavage of the ether grouping and oxidation led to the acid (**2.217**) and then, by catalytic hydrogenation of the triple bond, to a (Z)-olefin. Removal of the isopropylidene group under acidic conditions and esterification with trichloroethanol followed. The bis-mesylate of the product (**2.218**) gave on solvolysis (±)-prostaglandin E_2 trichloroethyl ester in 15%

yield together with the same amount of the C_{15}-epimer. Reductive removal of the trichloroethyl group with zinc in acetic acid furnished ($\pm$)-prostaglandin E_2, and by further reduction with sodium borohydride ($\pm$)-prostaglandins $F_{2\alpha}$ and $F_{2\beta}$ were formed.

Racemic prostaglandin E_3 could be prepared following the same scheme [62], with the variation that the component of the Wittig condensation was prepared in this case in good yield from 3-hexyn-1-ol and triphenylphosphine with the aid of N-bromo-succinimide. Reaction of the ylide with the appropriate aldehyde gave the intermediate (**2.219**). Hydrolysis of the tetrahydropyranyloxy group, oxidation of the alcohol and alkylation of the resulting ketone with methyl 7-bromo-5-heptynoate furnished the olefins (**2.220**); these were oxidized with osmium tetroxide to a mixture of glycols. Mesylation, solvolysis and hydrogenation of the product, ($\pm$)-*bis*-dehydroprostaglandin E_3 (**2.221**) over Lindlar catalyst in the presence of quinoline concluded the synthesis of ($\pm$)-prostaglandin E_3.

2.219   2.220

2.221

REFERENCES

1. COREY, E. J., ANDERSEN, N. H., CARLSON, R. M., FAUST, J., VEDEJS, E., VLATTAS, I., WINTER, R. E. K., *J. Am. Chem. Soc.*, 90, 3245 (1968).
2. COREY, E. J., VLATTAS, I., ANDERSEN, N. H., HARDING, K., *J. Am. Chem. Soc.*, 90, 3247 (1968).
3. COREY, E. J., VLATTAS, I., HARDING, K., *J. Am. Chem. Soc.*, 91, 535 (1969).
4. COREY, E. J., *Ann. N. Y. Acad. Sci.*, 180, 24 (1971).
5. COREY, E. J., WEINSHENKER, N. M., SCHAAF, T. K., HUBER, W., *J. Am. Chem. Soc.*, 91, 5675 (1969).
6. DE PUY, C. H., STORY, P. R., *J. Am. Chem. Soc.*, 82, 627 (1960).
7. KRESZE, G., SCHULZ, G., WALZ, H., *Ann.*, 666, 45 (1963).
8. COREY, E. J., KOELLIKER, U., NEUFFER, J., *J. Am. Chem. Soc.*, 93, 1489 (1971).
9. TROST, B. M., TAMARU, Y., *J. Am. Chem. Soc.*, 97, 3528 (1975).

10. WEINSHENKER, N. M., STEPHENSON, R., *J. Am. Chem. Soc.*, *94*, 3741 (1972).
11. VAN TAMELEN, E. E., SHAMMA, M., *J. Am. Chem. Soc.*, *76*, 2315 (1954).
12. GANDOLFI, C., DORIA, G., GAIO, P., *Tetrahedron Lett.*, *1972*, 2063.
13. SZÁNTAY, Cs., NOVÁK, L., KOVÁCS, G., MÉSZÁROS, Z., (Chinoin Pharm. and Chem. Works), "Process for the resolution of 1-hydroxy-2-benzyloxymethyl-3-carboxy-methyl-4-cyclopentene to optical antipodes." *Hung. Pat.* 167.102
14. COREY, E. J., VENKATESWARLU, A., *J. Am. Chem. Soc.*, *94*, 6190 (1972).
15. SZÁNTAY, Cs., NOVÁK, L., GOMBOS, Zs., SIMONIDESZ, V., INSTITORISZ, L., (Chinoin, Pharm. and Chem. Works), "Process for the production of prostaglandin intermediates." *Hung. Appl.*, (Budapest, 1974).
16. COREY, E. J., KIM, C. U., *Tetrahedron Lett.*, *1973*, 919.
17. COREY, E. J., KIM, C. U., *Tetrahedron Lett.*, *1974*, 287.
18. COREY, E. J., KIM, C. U., *J. Org. Chem.*, *38*, 1233 (1973).
19. REUCROFT, J., SAMMES, P. G., *Quart. Rev.*, *25*, 135 (1971).
20. VEDEJS, E., SNOBLE, K. A. J., *J. Am. Chem. Soc.*, *95*, 5778 (1973).
21. COREY, E. J., VARMA, R. K., *J. Am. Chem. Soc.*, *93*, 7919 (1971).
22. COREY, E. J., ALBONICO, S. M., KOELLIKER, U., SCHAAF, T. K., VARMA, R. K., *J. Am. Chem. Soc.*, *93*, 1491 (1971).
23. COREY, E. J., BECKER, K. B., VARMA, R. K., *J. Am. Chem. Soc.*, *94*, 8616 (1972).
24. CAHN, R. S., INGOLD, C. K., PRELOG, V., *Experientia*, *12*, 81 (1956).
25. COREY, E. J., NICOLAU, K. C., SHIBASAKI, M., MACHIDA, Y., SHINER, Ch. S., *Tetrahedron Lett.*, *1975*, 3183.
26. FILIPPO, J. S., CHUEN-ING CHERN, VALENTINE, J. S., *J. Org. Chem.*, *40*, 1678 (1975).
27. JOHNSON, R. A., NIDY, E. G., *J. Org. Chem.*, *40*, 1680 (1975).
28. COREY, E. J., SHIRAHAMA, H., YAMAMOTO, H., TERASHIMA, S., VENKATESWARLU, A., SCHAAF, T. K., *J. Am. Chem. Soc.*, *93*, 1490 (1971).
29. COREY, E. J., *Ann. N. Y. Acad. Sci.*, *180*, 24 (1971).
30. NOVÁK, L., ROHÁLY, J., TOMBOR, A., SZÁNTAY, Cs., "Notes on the stereocontrolled synthesis of prostaglandins." Lecture held at the Hungarian Chemical Society Meeting, Pécs, 1973.
31. NOVÁK, L., ROHÁLY, J., SZÁNTAY, Cs., "Synthesis of 15-methylprostaglandins." Lecture held at the Congressus Pharmaceuticus Hungaricus, Budapest, September, 1974.
32. SCHAAF. T. K.. COREY. E. J., *J. Org. Chem.*, *37*, 2921 (1972).
33. COREY, E. J., GRIECO, P. A., *Tetrahedron Lett.*, *1972*, 107.
34. COREY, E. J., ENSLEY, H. E., *J. Org. Chem.*, *38*, 3187 (1973).
35. COREY, E. J., MOINET, G., *J. Am. Chem. Soc.*, *95*, 6831 (1973).
36. COREY, E. J., TERASHIMA, S., *Tetrahedron Lett.*, *1972*, 111.
37. RANGANATHAN, S., RANGANATHAN, D., MEHROTA, A. K., *J. Am. Chem. Soc.*, *96*, 5261 (1974).
38. RANGANATHAN, S., RANGANATHAN, D., MEHROTA, A. K., *Tetrahedron Lett.*, *1975*, 1215.
39. JONES, R. L., *J. Lipid Res.*, *13*, 511 (1972).
40. JONES, R. L., CAMMOCK, S., *Advances in the Biosciences*, *9*, 61 (1973).
41. KELLY, R. C., SCHLETTER, I., JONES, R. L., *Prostaglandins*, *4*, 653 (1973).
42. COREY, E. J., MOINET, G., *J. Am. Chem. Soc.*, *95*, 7185 (1973).
43. BREWSTER, D., MYERS, M., ORMEROD, J., OTTER, Ph., SMITH, A. C. B., SPINNER, M. E., TURNER, S., *J. Chem. Soc. Perkin I*, *1973*, 2796.
44. COREY, E. J., RAVINDRANATHAN, T., *Tetrahedron Lett.*, *1971*, 4753.
45. COREY, E. J., SNIDER, B. B., *Tetrahedron Lett.*, *1973*, 3091.
46. WOODWARD, R. B., GOSTELI, J., ERNEST, I., FRIARY, R. J., NESTLER, G., RAMAN, H., SITRIN, R., SUTER, Ch., WHITESELL, J. K., *J. Am. Chem. Soc.*, *95*, 6853 (1973).
47. PEEL, R., SUTHERLAND, J. K., *Chem. Commun.*, *1974*, 151.
48. BINDRA, J. S., GRODSKI, A., SCHAAF, Th. K., COREY, E. J., *J. Am. Chem. Soc.*, *95*, 7522 (1973).
49. BROWN, E. D., CLARKSON, R., LEENEY, T. J., ROBINSON, G. E., *Chem. Commun.*, *1974*, 642.
50. BROWN, E. D., LILLEY, T. J., *Chem. Commun.*, *1975*, 39.
51. WIBERG, K. B., ASHE, A. J., *J. Am. Chem. Soc.*, *90*, 63 (1968).
52. JUST, G., SIMONOVITCH, C., *Tetrahedron Lett.*, *1967*, 2093.

53. HOLDEN, K. G., HWANG, B., WILLIAMS, K. R., WEINSTOCK, J., HARMAN, M., WEISBACH, J. A., *Tetrahedron Lett.*, *1968*, 1569.
54. SCHNEIDER, W. P., AXEN, U., LINCOLN, F. H., PIKE, J. E., THOMPSON, J. L., *J. Am. Chem. Soc.*, *90*, 5895 (1968).
55. JUST, G., SIMONOVITCH, Ch., LINCOLN, F. H., SCHNEIDER, W. P., AXEN, U., SPERO, G. B., PIKE, J. E., *J. Am. Chem. Soc.*, *91*, 5364 (1969).
56. KELLY, R. C., VANRHEENEN, V., SCHLETTER, I., PILLAI, M. D., *J. Am. Chem. Soc.*, *95*, 2746 (1973).
57. COREY, E. J., ARNOLD, Z., HUTTON, J., *Tetrahedron Lett.*, *1970*, 307.
58. WOODWARD, R. B., HOFFMANN, R., *Angew. Chem. Internat. Ed.*, *8*, 847 (1969).
59. KELLY, R., VANRHEENEN, V., *Tetrahedron Lett.*, *1973*, 1709.
60. WINSTEIN, S., GRUNWALD, E., INGRAHAM, L. L., *J. Am. Chem. Soc.*, *70*, 821 (1948).,
61. SCHNEIDER, W. P., AXEN, U., LINCOLN, F. H., PIKE, J. E., THOMPSON, J. L., *J. Am. Chem. Soc.*, *91*, 5372 (1969).
62. AXEN, U., THOMPSON, J. L., PIKE, J. E., *Chem. Commun.*, *1970*, 602.
63. SCHNEIDER, W. P., *Chem. Commun.*, *1969*, 304.
64. KELLY, R. C., VANRHEENEN, V., *Tetrahedron Lett.*, *1976*, 1067.
65. RANGANATHAN, S., RANGANATHAN, D., IYENGAV, R., *Tetrahedron*, *32*, 961 (1976).
66. ERNEST, I., "A Prostaglandin Synthesis (Strategy and Reality)." *Angew. Chem.*, 244 (1976).
67. COREY, E. J., SUGGS, J. W., *J. Org. Chem.*, *40*, 2554 (1975).
68. KOVÁCS, G., RÁDÓCZI, J.. SIMONIDESZ, V., SZÉKELY, I., "Process for the Production of Prostglandin Intermediates." *Hung. Appl.*, (Budapest, 1975).

3. STEREOCONTROLLED SYNTHESIS
OF PROSTAGLANDINS, II

This chapter deals with prostaglandin syntheses based on cyclopentane derivatives. These fall into two categories: the key step may be a 1,4-addition, or it may be the transformation of a 3,4-epoxycyclopentane.

In the first group, the starting step of the synthesis is the 1,4-addition of a nucleophile by which the enolate of a β-substituted cyclopentanone is formed. This is decomposed subsequently with acid to a disubstituted cyclopentanone, predominantly the 8,12-*trans* stereoisomer (**3.1**). This intermediate can be then transformed to prostaglandins by additional reactions.

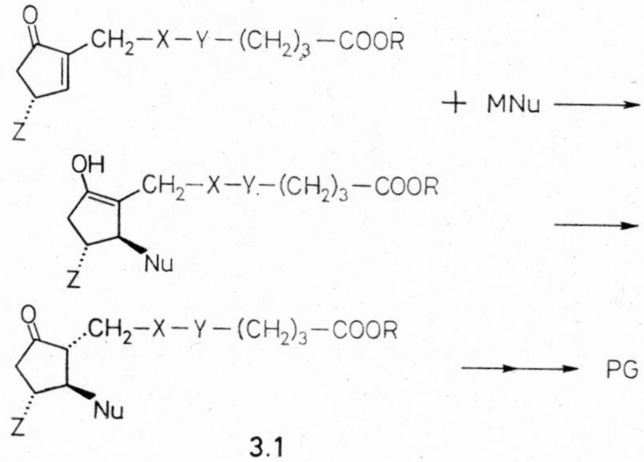

3.1

The crucial reaction of the second approach is the ring opening by nucleophilic bimolecular substitution of an epoxide (**3.2**) easily accessible from cyclopentene derivatives. This process is, in general, both regio- and stereospecific and the product may be converted to prostaglandins by a limited number of transformations.

3.2

Before discussing the individual syntheses in detail, it is appropriate to review the methods available for the preparation of the cyclopentenone derivatives needed as starting materials for the first approach.

3.1 SYNTHESIS OF CYCLOPENTENONE DERIVATIVES

In view of the fact that the cyclopentenone moiety is a characteristic structural unit of several biologically active compounds, among them of retrolons, the ester components of insecticidal pyrethrins, and of *cis*-jasmon, an important perfume component, research on these compounds has become quite intensive in recent years. The discovery of prostaglandins further stimulated these investigations since those belonging to the A, B and C series are themselves cyclopentenone derivatives, or such derivatives are potential prostaglandin intermediates.

A great number of methods have been developed for the synthesis of the cyclopentenone system [1], of which we only refer to those relevant for the synthesis of prostaglandins.

3.1.1 *Synthesis of Cyclopentenones from Cyclopentanones*

The first prostaglandin synthesis starting from a cyclopentanone was accomplished by Bagli and Bogri [2, 3]. The cyclopentanone carboxylic ester (**3.3**) that can be readily obtained from diethyl adipate was allowed to react as the potassium salt in toluene with ethyl ω-bromoheptanoate, and the product, a diester (**3.4**), was brominated in chloroform at low temperature. The bromo-diester (**3.5**) gave, on refluxing with 20% sulfuric acid for 48 hours, 2-(6-carboxyhexyl)-2-cyclopentenone (**3.7**).

Treatment of the bromo compound with 20% sulfuric acid effected not only ester hydrolysis and decarboxylation of the β-keto-acid moiety but also led to the elimination of hydrogen bromide to give (**3.6**), followed by acid-catalyzed migration of the double bond resulting in the more stable enone system of (**3.7**).

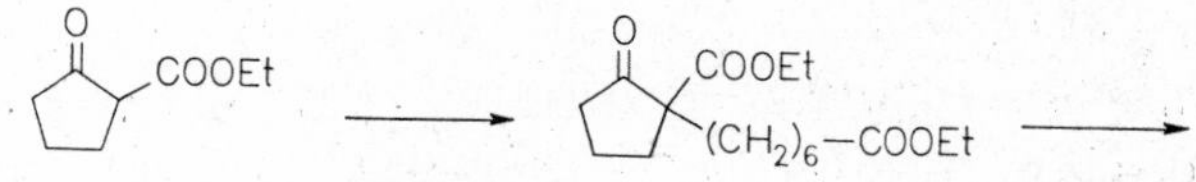

3.3   3.4

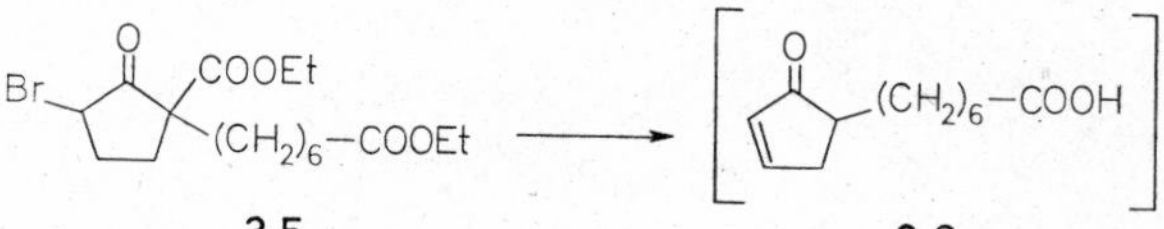

3.5   3.6

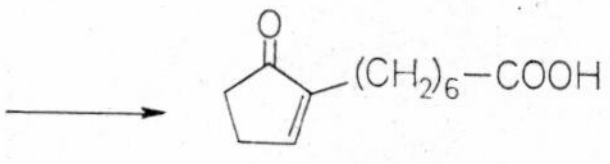

3.7

Yields were not reported, but probably they were poor owing to the notorious instability of 2-halocyclopentanones.

Unsatisfactory yields promoted later investigators to avoid intermediates of the α-bromoketone type. Alvarez *et al.* for example, subjected first the diester (**3.4**) to hydrolysis and decarboxylation, then prepared the enol acetate (**3.9**) of the monoester (**3.8**); the former was brominated with N-bromosuccinimide in tetrahydrofuran and finally the bromoester (**3.10**) was heated with lithium carbonate in pyridine to obtain 2-(6-methoxycarbonylhexyl)--2-cyclopentenone (**3.11**) [4].

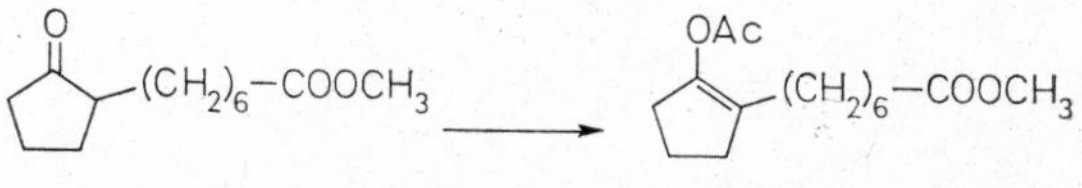

3.8   3.9

3.10   3.11

A convenient version for the preparation of the ester (**3.11**) from 2-carbethoxycyclopentanone was developed in a cooperation programme between the Technical University of Budapest and Chinoin Pharmaceuticals [5–7]. Alkylation was carried out without prior preparation of the enolate salt, simply by refluxing the methyl ester corresponding to (**3.3**) with ω-bromo-

8*

heptanoic acid methyl ester in dry acetone in the presence of potassium carbonate. The diester (3.12) was then transformed to the cyclopentanone (3.8) by hydrolysis with hydrochloric acid and decarboxylation. Bromination of (3.8) in ethylene glycol at low temperature afforded directly the more stable ethylene ketal of the α-bromoketone.

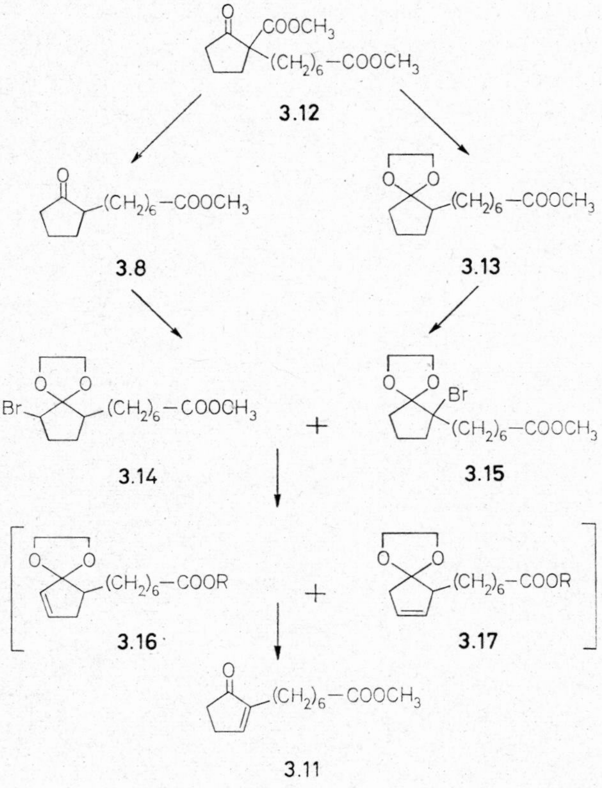

In this complex reaction, according to NMR analysis, the 5-bromo- and 2-bromocyclopentanone ketals (3.14 and 3.15) were formed in a ratio of 3 : 2. On treatment with potassium hydroxide in methanol, this mixture underwent both dehydrobromination and ester hydrolysis. The mixed product (3.16 and 3.17, R = Na) was subjected to acid-catalyzed deketalization and esterification, followed by transposition of the double bond to give 2-(6-methoxycarbonylhexyl)-2-cyclopentenone (3.11). There was no necessity to isolate the intermediates and the yield, from cyclopentanone (3.8), was 40%.

If elimination of hydrogen bromide was effected with alkoxide as a base in an aprotic solvent (e.g. sodium methoxide in dimethyl sulfoxide or dimethylformamide), hydrolysis and reesterification at a later stage could be avoided. Under these conditions elimination was fast, the mixture of ester ketals (**3.16** and **3.17**, $R = CH_3$) could be isolated in yields over 60%. On mild acid treatment and subsequent acid- or base-catalyzed double bond migration, these gave the cyclopentenone (**3.11**) in good yield.

The foregoing process required bromination in ethylene glycol the use of which, in excess, became unnecessary if instead of the ketone the corresponding ketal (**3.13**) was brominated in ether. The application of the ketal presented no disadvantage from the preparative point of view, since this could be obtained directly from the diester (**3.12**) by refluxing it in benzene for a couple of hours with one equivalent of ethylene glycol in the presence of p-toluenesulfonic acid as catalyst.

This sequence is also suitable for the synthesis of cyclopentenones of (Z)-geometry in the side chain [7, 8]. An intermediate for the synthesis of E-type prostaglandins may be prepared by alkylating the keto ester (**3.3**) with ethyl chloroacetate in dry acetone in the presence of potassium carbonate to give, after hydrolysis of the diester and decarboxylation, the cyclopentylacetic acid derivative (**3.18**). Bromination of the ester in ethylene glycol at 10°C gave the ketals of the isomeric bromoketones (**3.19** and **3.20**), which were dehydrobrominated with sodium methoxide in dry dimethyl sulphoxide.

While in the synthesis of enone (**3.11**) ketalization merely served to stabilize the bromo compound, in the esters (**3.21** and **3.22**) the ketal has also the function of masking the ring carbonyl group permitting thus the selective transformation of the ester carbonyl.

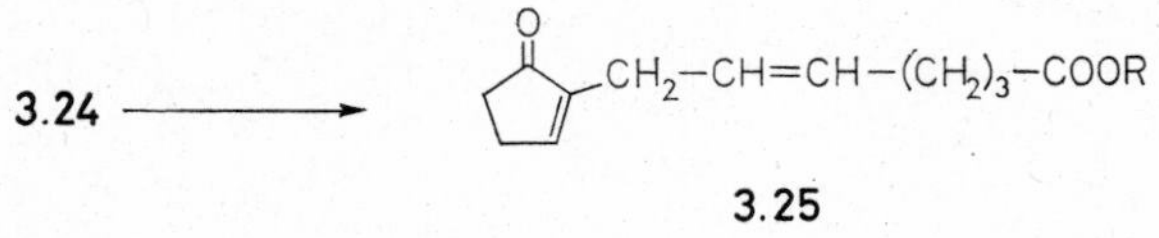

3.24 $\longrightarrow$ [structure: cyclopentenone] $-CH_2-CH=CH-(CH_2)_3-COOR$

3.25

Reduction of the mixture of ketal esters with diisobutylaluminium hy·dride at $-70°C$ gave rise to the corresponding aldehydes (only one isomer depicted, **3.23**), which on condensation with the phosphorane derived from triphenyl-4-carboxybutylphosphonium salt, followed by cleavage of the ketal group with dilute acid afforded the cyclopentenone (**3.24**). Base-catalyzed isomerization of the latter yielded 2-(6-carboxy-(2Z)-hexenyl)-2-cyclopentenone (**3.25**, R = H) and, after esterification with diazomethane, the methyl ester (**3.25**, R = CH_3).

Conversion of the cyclopentenone (**3.7**) to a 5-hydroxycyclopentenone derivative (**3.29**) has been solved both by chemical and biochemical methods. Van Dorp and his co-workers employed allylic bromination with N-bromosuccinimide and converted the bromo compound (**3.26**) successively with silver acetate to the 4-acetoxyketone (**3.27**, R = H), with diazomethane to the methyl ester (**3.27**, R = CH_3), and finally with ethylene glycol to the ketal (**3.28**), in order to prevent β-elimination. Alkaline hydrolysis of the acetoxy group and then the ketal moiety by acid gave the racemic 4-hydroxycyclopentenone (**3.29**) in poor yields [9].

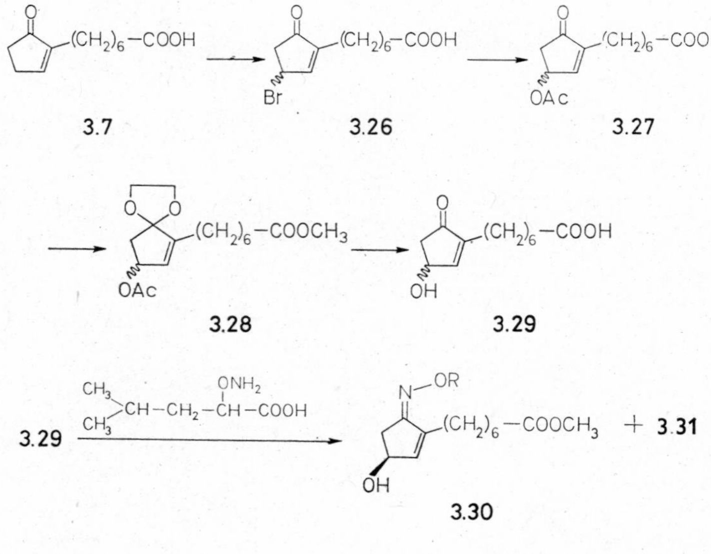

[structures 3.7, 3.26, 3.27]

3.7   **3.26**   **3.27**

[structures 3.28, 3.29]

3.28   **3.29**

3.29 $\xrightarrow{\text{(CH}_3\text{)}_2\text{CH-CH}_2\text{-CH(ONH}_2)\text{-COOH}}$ [structure 3.30] $\quad +\ \textbf{3.31}$

3.30

Resolution of the racemic alcohol in order to separate the (R)-enantiomer, i.e. the one having the same configuration as natural prostaglandins, was accomplished by Pappo et al. [10] by forming an oxime with (R)-2-amino-oxy-4-methylvaleric acid. Fractional crystallization failed, but the diastereomeric esters **3.30** and **3.31** could be separated by column chromatography on silicic acid (Mallinckrodt Silic AR CC-4; eluant: chloroform containing 1% ethanol). The ketones **3.32** and **3.33** were recovered from the oximes using titanium(III) chloride, and the dextrorotatory alcohol (**3.33**; $[\alpha]_D + 16.8°$) was used in the further transformations.

Japanese researchers [11] developed the microbiological hydroxylation of the enone (**3.7**) using a strain of *Aspergillus niger* (ATCC 9142) to give the partially resolved alcohol (**3.33**, $[\alpha]_D +8°$) in 67% yield.

3.1.2 Synthesis of Cyclopentenones from Cyclopentadiene

Several routes have been worked out in order to obtain cyclopentenone derivatives from inexpensive cyclopentadiene. Sih and co-workers alkylated lithium cyclopentadienate (**3.34**) with ethyl ω-bromoheptanoate in tetrahydrofuran at room temperature. As was pointed out before, under these conditions the 5-alkylcyclopentadiene formed in the primary process isomerized rapidly to the corresponding 1- and 2-alkyl compounds (**3.35**) [12–14]. Oxidation of the mixture in ethanol with sodium hypochlorite and hydrogen peroxide at −10°C furnished, in 1 : 1 ratio, racemic 4-hydroxy-2-alkyl- (**3.37**) and 4-hydroxy-3-alkylcyclopentenone (**3.38**), separable by chromatography.

The oxidative transformation of (**3.35**) is initiated by 1,4-cycloaddition of s.c. excited state singlet oxygen. In the second step the endoperoxide formed (**3.36**) rearranges to β-hydroxyketones (**3.37** and **3.38**).

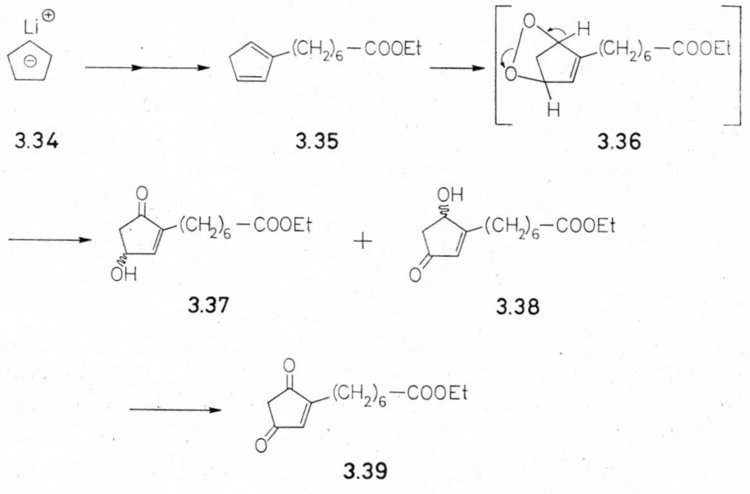

Excited state singlet oxygen generated in a chemical reaction is an efficient oxidant of olefins, especially 1,3-dienes and furans. It is usually generated *in situ* from hydrogen peroxide with sodium hypochlorite [15].

The above sequence provided the required 4-hydroxycylopentenone (**3.37**) only in poor yields. Oxidizing the mixture of the ketols (**3.37** and **3.38**) with Jones reagent (chromic acid in acetone) to the cyclopentenedione (**3.39**) and reducing it back with aluminium isopropoxide shifted the ratio of the parent ketols to 2 : 1 in favour of **3.37**.

Cyclopentadiene was also the starting material of a cyclopentenone synthesis reported by Grieco and Reap [16]. In an earlier synthesis of *cis*-jasmon [17], the addition of dichloroketene to cyclopentadiene (**3.40**) enabled Grieco to obtain a dichlorobicycloheptene (**3.41**); this was reduced with zinc in acetic acid to a bicycloheptenone (**3.42**). Baeyer–Villiger oxidation of (**3.42**) with hydrogen peroxide gave the lactone (**3.43**) and, after reduction with diisobutylaluminium hydride, the lactol (**3.44**).

Condensation of the lactol with the reactive phosphorane prepared from triphenyl-4-carboxybutylphosphonium salt furnished the cyclopentenol derivative (**3.45**) that was transformed by oxidation with chromium trioxide and esterification with diazomethane to the 3-cyclopentenone (**3.46**). Treatment with methanolic sodium hydroxide brought about the transposition of the double bond to give the key intermediate 2-(6-methoxy-carbonyl-(2Z)-hexenyl)-2-cyclopentenone (**3.25**).

According to Wiel and Rouessac [18], dicyclopentadiene can be carried through a similar sequence of reactions. Addition of dichloroketene to the

3.40   3.41   3.42   3.43

3.44 $\emptyset_3\overset{\oplus}{P}$=CH—(CH$_2$)$_3$—COO$^\ominus$ ───────→   3.45

3.46   3.25

diene (**3.47**), dehalogenation of the isomeric adducts (**3.48** and **3.49**, X = Cl), and Baeyer–Villiger oxidation (H$_2$O$_2$-AcOH) of the products (**3.48** and **3.49**, X = H) gave a mixture of lactones (**3.50**, only one isomer depicted). This was reduced with diisobutylaluminium hydride, then condensed with tri-phenyl-4-carboxybutylphosphorane followed by Jones oxidation of the resulting alcohols (**3.52**, R^1 = OH, R^2 = H) to the ketone (R^1 = O, R^2 = H). Formolysis of the corresponding methyl esters (**3.52**, R^1 = O. R^2 = CH$_3$) at 300 °C afforded a cyclopentenone (**3.53**), which was isomerized with a base to the intermediate (**3.25**) suitable for conversion to 11-deoxy-prostaglandin E$_2$.

Corey *et al.* investigated in detail the possibilities of a stereocontrolled conversion of the unsaturated lactone (**3.43**) to an α-epoxy lactone (**3.60**) [19, 20]. Direct epoxidation of the double bond led to a mixture of α- and β-epoxides (**3.57** and **3.58**). The stereoselectivity of oxidation with *m*-chloro-perbenzoic acid was solvent dependent; the α/β ratio in benzene was 0.89 : 1; in ether 0.93 : 1; in dichloromethane 2.3 : 1; in cyclohexane 2.7 : 1; and in hexane 4 : 1. Acetic acid containing 40% peracetic acid was optimal and gave 90% of the α-epoxide. The final solution to this problem was iodolac-tonization.

Ring opening of the lactone (**3.43**) with alkali gave the salt of the hydroxy acid (**3.54**) that was subjected to iodolactonization furnishing the hydroxy lactone (**3.55**). Ring opening of the latter with alkali was associated with the simultaneous formation of an α-epoxide moiety (**3.56**). One equivalent of acid effected relactonization to the α-epoxy lactone ((**3.57**).

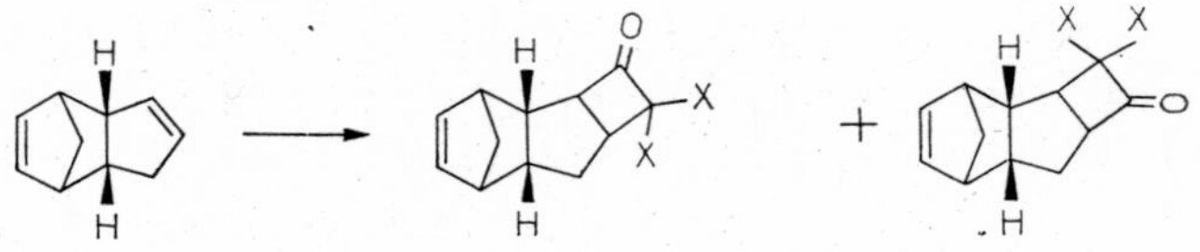

3.47   3.48   3.49

3.48

3.50   3.51

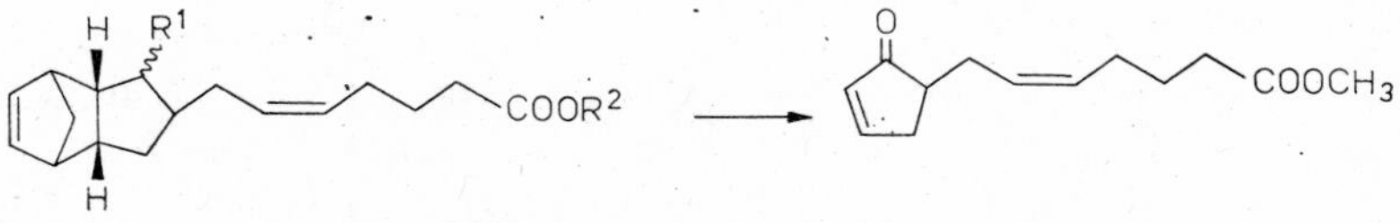

3.52   3.53

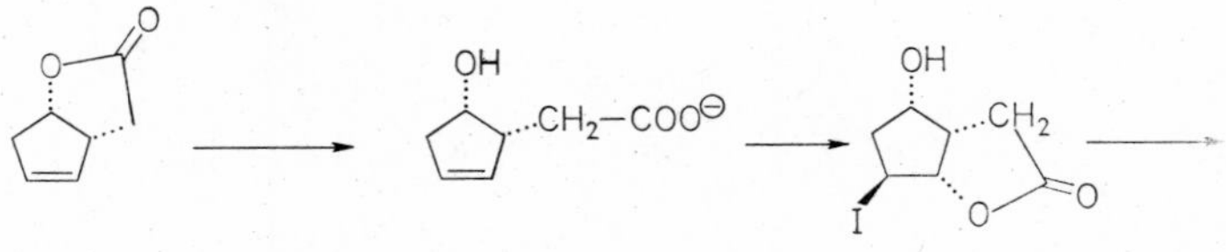

3.43   3.54   3.55

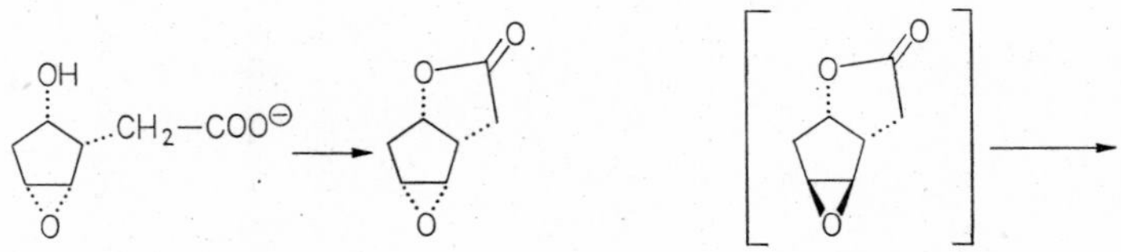

3.56   3.57   3.58

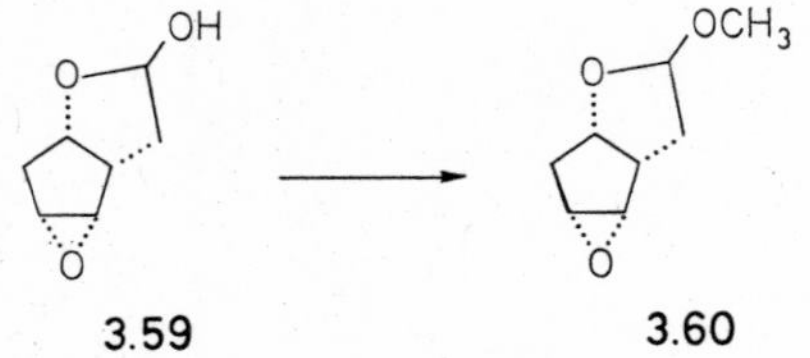

3.59   3.60

Diisobutylaluminium hydride reduced the epoxy lactone to the lactol (**3.59**) which, by treatment with methanol in the presence of boron trifluoride etherate catalyst, was converted into the methyl acetal (**3.60**) [21]. The transformation of (**3.60**) to prostaglandins will be discussed later.

Corey and Mann also accomplished the resolution of the unsaturated lactone (**3.43**) with α-methylbenzylamine [20] in the form of the hydroxy acid (**3.54**).

Tömösközi *et al.* developed a method which also allowed the utilization of the dextrorotatory enantiomer obtained in this resolution [22]. For this purpose the lactone (**3.61**) was hydroxylated by osmium(VIII) oxide catalyzed oxidation with sodium hypochlorite, the resulting *cis*-diol (**3.62**) was reduced, after conversion with 2,2-dimethoxypropane to the acetonide (**3.63**), with diisobutylaluminium hydride to the lactol (**3.64**) this being finally condensed with the sodium salt of triphenyl-4-carboxybutylidenephosphorane. After esterification of the product with diazomethane to (**3.65**) and oxidation with chromium(VI) oxide–pyridine complex to the cyclopentanone (**3.66**), the isopropylidene protecting group was removed by treatment with 20% sulfu-

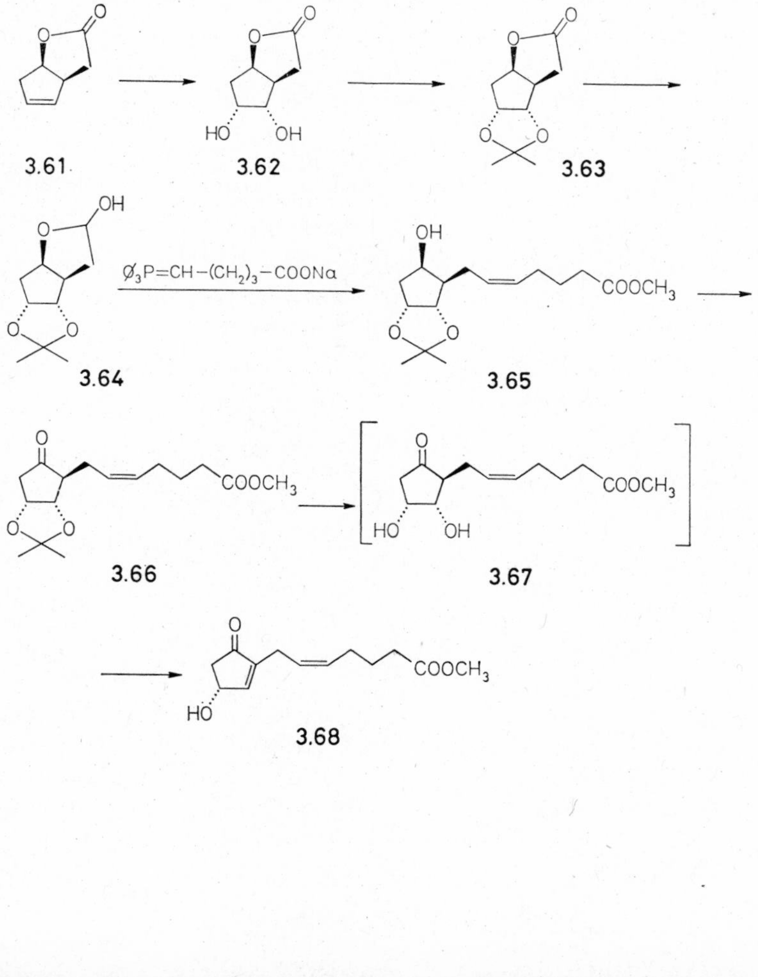

3.61   3.62   3.63

3.64 $\emptyset_3P=CH-(CH_2)_3-COONa$ 3.65

3.66   3.67

3.68

ric acid to yield the diol (**3.67**); this was then dehydrated with oxalic acid–sodium oxalate in chloroform to obtain the 4-hydroxycyclopentenone derivative (**3.68**).

Recently Stork and his co-workers devised a general method for the synthesis of hydroxycyclopentenone derivatives [23]. Here we quote the sequence leading to a racemic key intermediate (**3.68**) useful for the synthesis of prostaglandin E_2.

As starting material cyclopentadiene epoxide was employed; this could readily be prepared from cyclopentadiene by successive addition of hypobromic acid and base-catalyzed hydrogen bromide elimination. The epoxide was allowed to react at low temperature with the lithium salt of 1-propynyl-trimethylsilane. Addition was both regio- and stereospecific and afforded, after removal of the trimethylsilyl protecting group, a *trans*-cyclopentenol (**3.69**, R = H). After the blocking of the hydroxyl by the addition of ethyl vinyl ether (**3.69**, R = $CH(CH_3)OC_2H_5$) and converting with butyllithium to the lithium salt, the propynyl compound was made to react with the 1-ethoxyethyl ether of 4-bromobutanol. The product (**3.70**, R = $-CH(CH_3)OC_2H_5$) was stripped of the protecting groups, epoxidized with *m*-chloroperbenzoic acid (**3.71**) and subjected to Jones oxidation at both hydroxyl functions to give the keto-acid (**3.72**).

Two products — (**3.73**) and (**3.68**, R = H) — may be envisaged to arise from a base-catalyzed intramolecular elimination of the epoxide (**3.72**). The one containing a more highly substituted double bond (**3.68**) is more stable, but its isomer (**3.73**) is expected to form more rapidly. In fact the reaction,

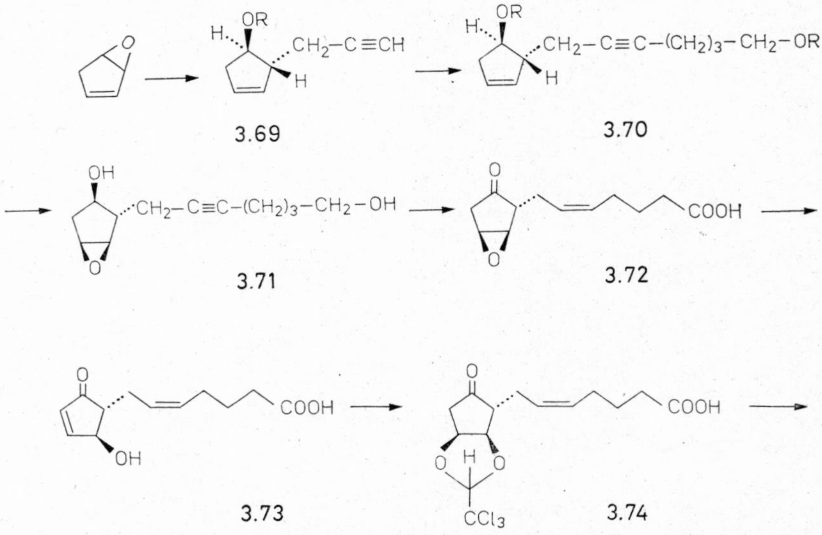

3.69

3.70

3.71

3.72

3.73

3.74

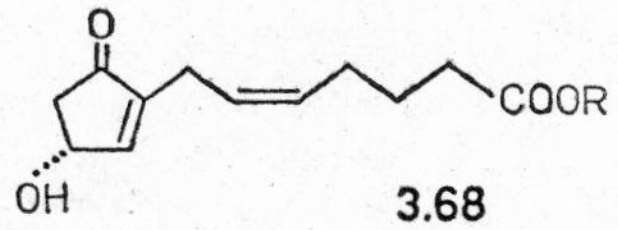

3.68

if triggered by triethylamine in ether, furnished exclusively the kinetically controlled product (**3.73**). However, this could be smoothly converted to the desired disubstituted enone (**3.68**) *via* the acetal (**3.74**) obtained by reaction with chloral.

3.1.3 *Ring Contraction of 1,3-Dioxocyclohexanes*

The alkylation of 1,3-cyclopentanediones with alkyl halides of enhanced reactivity gives predominantly O-alkylated products, but the C-alkylation of 1,3-dioxocyclohexanes is unexceptional. A method for the alkylation of cyclohexanediones and their subsequent ring contraction to cyclopentenones reported earlier by Büchi *et al.* [24] was successfully adapted by Bagli and Bogri for the synthesis of prostaglandin intermediates [25]. The method comprised the alkylation of an anion generated from 1,3-dioxocyclohexane (**3.76**) with methyl 7-bromo-2-heptynoate (**3.77**), chlorination with *t*-butyl hypochlorite and rearrangement of the chloro compound (**3.79**) with sodium carbonate in xylene to obtain the cyclopentene derivative (**3.80**).

The base-catalyzed ring contraction (**3.79** → **3.80**) is introduced by the abstraction of the proton adjacent to the carbonyl (**3.75**) followed by intramolecular nucleophilic substitution of chlorine giving a cyclopropanone

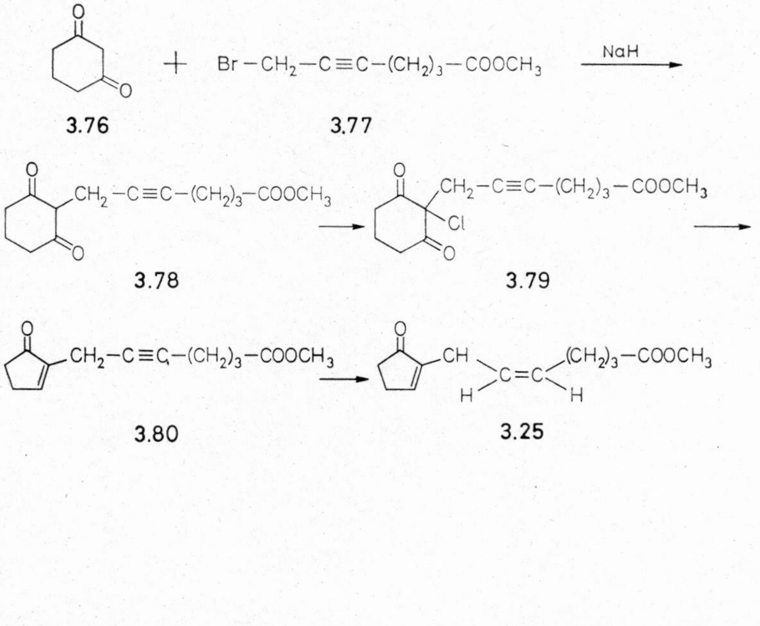

3.76

$Br-CH_2-C{\equiv}C-(CH_2)_3-COOCH_3$

3.77

$\xrightarrow{\text{NaH}}$

$CH_2-C{\equiv}C-(CH_2)_3-COOCH_3$

3.78

$CH_2-C{\equiv}C-(CH_2)_3-COOCH_3$

3.79

3.80

$CH_2-C{\equiv}C-(CH_2)_3-COOCH_3$

3.25

similar to the intermediate of the Favorsky rearrangement of α-halogeno-cyclohexanones. The cyclopropanone then eliminates carbon monoxide in a thermal reaction.

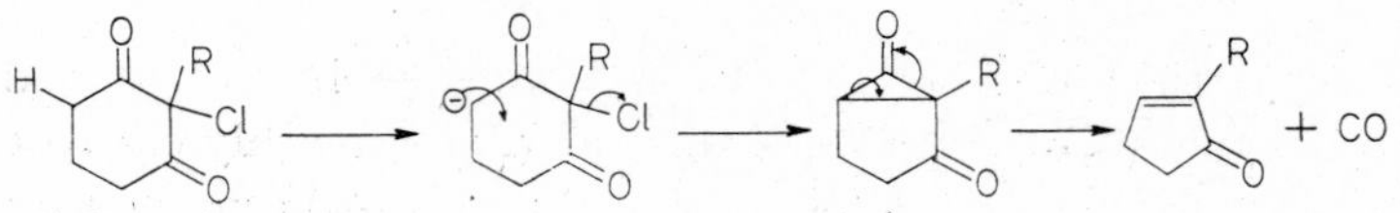

3.75

Cis-hydrogenation of the side chain triple bond in (**3.80**) in the presence of Lindlar catalyst gave the target intermediate (**3.25**).

A version of the foregoing sequence was realized by Kienzle *et al.* [26] starting from 3,5-dioxocyclohexanecarboxylic acid (**3.81**). Claisen-type [3,3] sigmatropic rearrangement [27] of the corresponding allyl enol ether (**3.82**) on heating in acetic anhydride gave, *via* (**3.83**), the acetate of the C-allyl ester (**3.84**).

Claisen rearrangement is a thermal reaction involving a cyclic intermediate. Acetic anhydride serves merely to prevent fast addition of the enol to the allylic double bond which would give a furan ring as the main product.

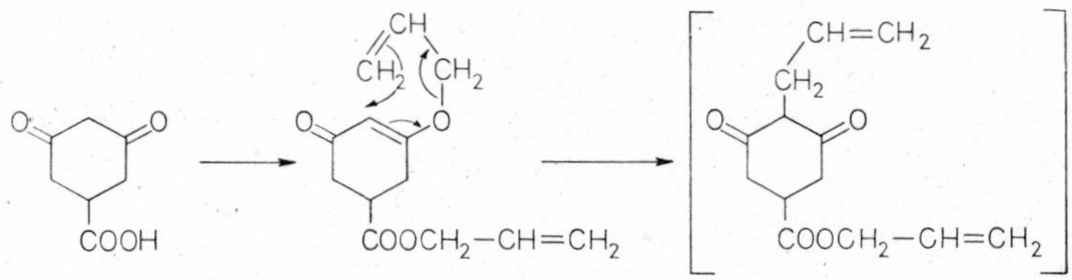

3.81	3.82	3.83

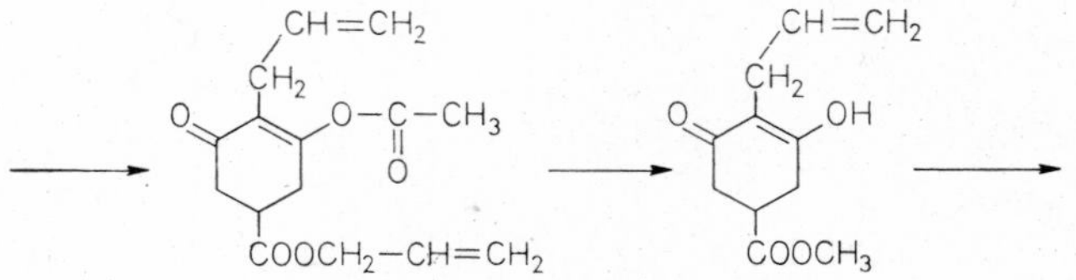

3.84	3.85

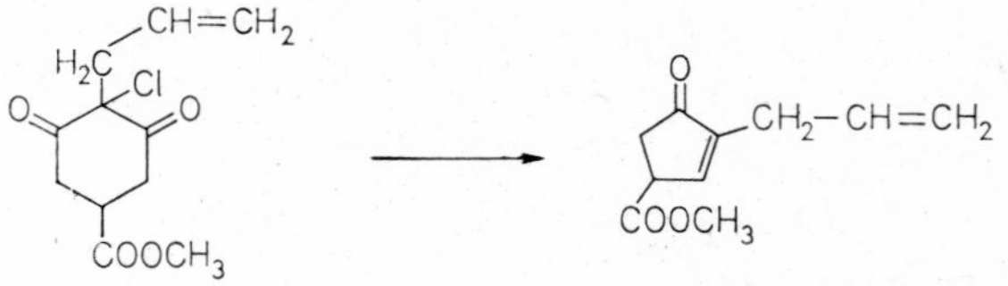

3.86	3.87

The rearrangement product was transesterified with lithium methoxide in methanol and then chlorinated with t-butyl hypochlorite. Ring contraction of the chloro ester (**3.86**) gave a cyclopentenone (**3.87**), whose transformation to prostaglandins will be discussed later.

3.1.4 *Routes Based on Trioxocyclopentanes*

1,2,4-Trioxocyclopentanes can be conveniently synthesized by condensation of methyl ketones and oxalic esters, providing 4-hydroxycyclopentenones in few steps.

The first synthesis of a trioxocyclopentane (Fig. 3.1, **3.91**) with the substitution pattern required for prostaglandin synthesis was reported by Katsube and Matsai [28]. They condensed diethyl ethoxymagnesium-malonate with methyl azelayl chloride (**3.38**) and converted the product (**3.89**) by hydrolysis and subsequent decarboxylation to methyl 9-oxodecanoate (**3.90**, R = CH$_3$). Sodium methoxide catalyzed condensation of the ketone with diethyl oxalate gave the trioxocyclopentane (**3.91**, R = H).

According to a version of Pappo *et al.* [29, 30] azelaic acid semi-ester (**3.92**) was activated by preparing the corresponding N-acylimidazol, and this was allowed to react with lithium methylmalonate. The end-product of this multistep reaction, the keto-diester (**3.93**) was hydrolyzed and decarboxylated to the keto acid (**3.90**, R = H) that was condensed with dimethyloxalate with the aid of potassium t-butoxide to obtain the triketone (**3.91** R = H).

Catalytic hydrogenation of the trione (**3.91**, R = H) on palladium catalyst was selective and gave a hydroxycyclopentanedione (**3.94**); this yielded on treatment with 2,2-dimethoxypropane the isomeric enolethers (**3.95** and **3.96**) of which the former could be isomerized by acid to the latter (**3.96**). Reduction of this α-ketol with sodium bis(methoxyethoxy)-aluminium hydride to the diol, followed by acid-catalyzed dehydration, furnished the racemic 4-hydroxycyclopentenone (**3.33**).

Recently Sih and associates reported an elegant method for the preparation of the optically active compound (**3.33**) based on the asymmetric

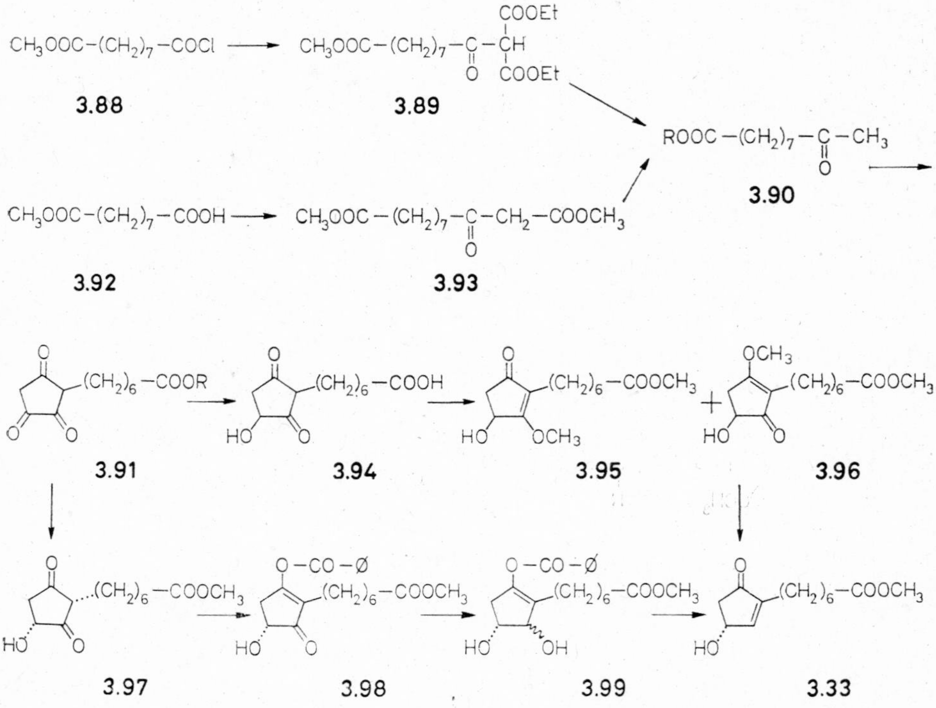

CH₃OOC—(CH₂)₇—COCl ⟶ CH₃OOC—(CH₂)₇—C—CH(COOEt)(COOEt), O

3.88   **3.89**

ROOC—(CH₂)₇—C—CH₃, O

3.90

CH₃OOC—(CH₂)₇—COOH ⟶ CH₃OOC—(CH₂)₇—C—CH₂—COOCH₃, O

3.92   **3.93**

3.91   **3.94**   **3.95**   +   **3.96**

3.97   **3.98**   **3.99**   **3.33**

Fig. 3.1. Synthesis of 4-hydroxycyclopentenone derivative

hydrogenation of the trione (**3.91**) in the presence of triethylamine and catalyzed by the chiral complex 1,5-cyclooctadiene-bis(*o*-anisyl-cyclohexyl-methylphosphine) rhodium(I) fluoroborate [31, 32]. The optical purity of the dextrorotatory hydroxydione (**3.97**) was 68% [12–14].

Microbiological reduction of the trione using *Dipodascus uninucleatus* was fully stereoselective and afforded the optically pure (4*R*)-hydroxyketone (**3.97**) in excellent yield. Treatment with benzoyl chloride gave the enol ester (**3.98**), from which the (4*R*)-hydroxycyclopentenone (**3.33**) was obtained by reduction with sodium bis(2-methoxyethoxy)aluminium hydride and acid-catalyzed dehydration of (**3.99**) [33, 34].

Sih and his group adapted their sequence to the synthesis of an optically active analogue of (**3.33**) containing in the side chain a double bond of (*Z*)-geometry (Fig. 3.2, **3.68**) [33, 34]. The side chain itself was elaborated starting from the pyrrolidine enamine (**3.101**) of ethyl acetoacetate (**3.100**), which was in succession alkylated with propargyl bromide, hydrolyzed, decarboxylated to the 1-hexyne-5-one (**3.103**), converted to the ethyleneketal, metallat-

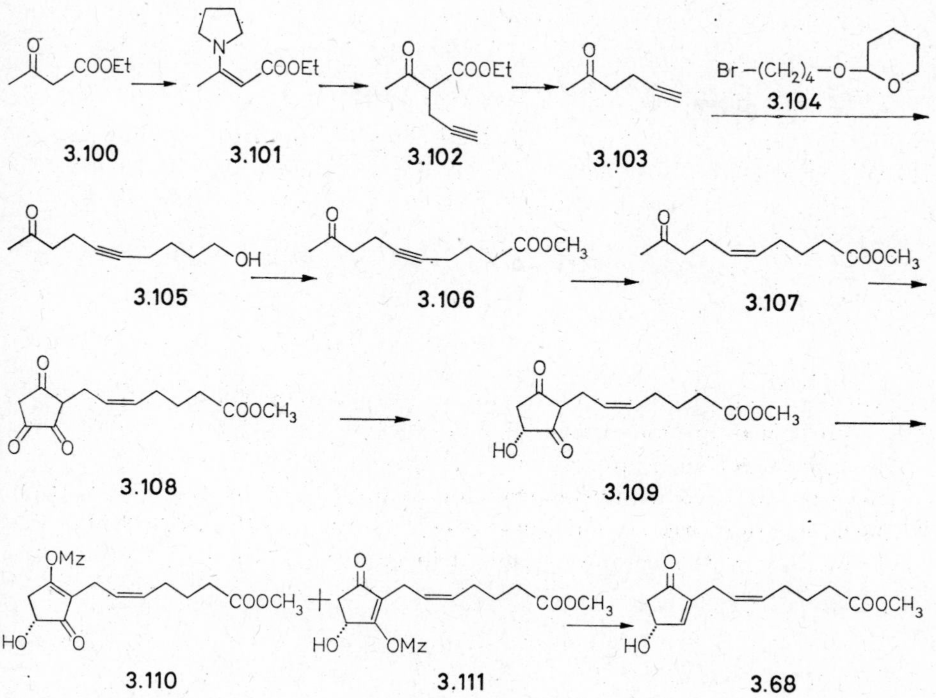

Fig. 3.2. Synthesis of optically active 4-hydroxycyclopentenone derivative

ed with lithium amide in liquid ammonia, and finally coupled with 1-bromo-
-4-tetrahydropyranyloxybutane (**3.104**). Jones oxidation of the free alcohol
(**3.105**) led to a carboxylic acid that was reduced as the methyl ester on
Lindlar catalyst (Pd/BaSO₄) to methyl 9-oxo-(5Z)-decenoate (**3.107**). Condensation with diethyl oxalate to obtain the trione (**3.108**) and microbiological reduction with *Dipodascus uninucleatus* gave 60% of the optically
pure (4R)-hydroxycyclopentenedione (**3.109**).

Mesyl chloride and triethylamine converted the dione (**3.109**) to a mixture
of enol mesylates (**3.101** and **3.111**) containing 90% of (**3.110**). Reduction
with sodium bis(2-methoxyethoxy) aluminium hydride and dehydration of
the diol obtained with a mixture of oxalic acid and sodium oxalate in chloroform yielded the (4R)-hydroxycyclopentenone (**3.68**).

3.2 NITRILE ADDITION TO CYCLOPENTENONE DERIVATIVES. SYNTHESIS OF 11-DEOXYPROSTAGLANDINS

In basic media, cyanide ions generated from acetone cyanohydrin attack conjugated enone systems in a Michael-type addition. On ketonization of the intermediate enolate, substituents take up the more stable *trans* arrangement.

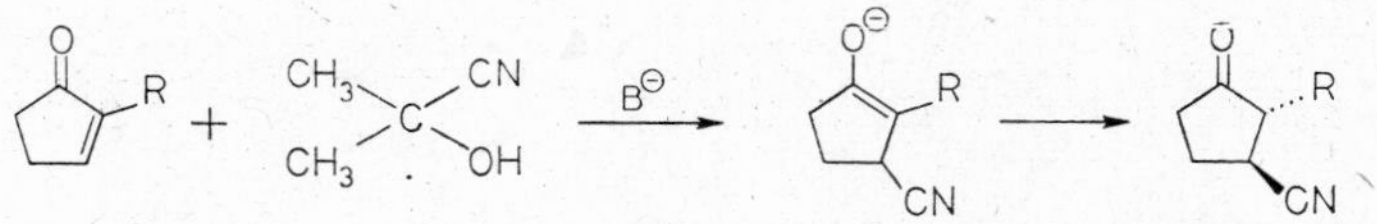

Syntheses of 11-deoxyprostaglandins can be based on this type of addition. These substances are noted for their hypotensive, smooth muscle controlling and gastric secretion inhibiting effects.

The first synthesis using this principle was reported by Bagli *et al.* [2, 3, 35, 36]. An appropriately substituted cyclopentenone (Fig. 3.3, **3.112**) was made to react with acetone cyanohydrin in methanol and the product, a

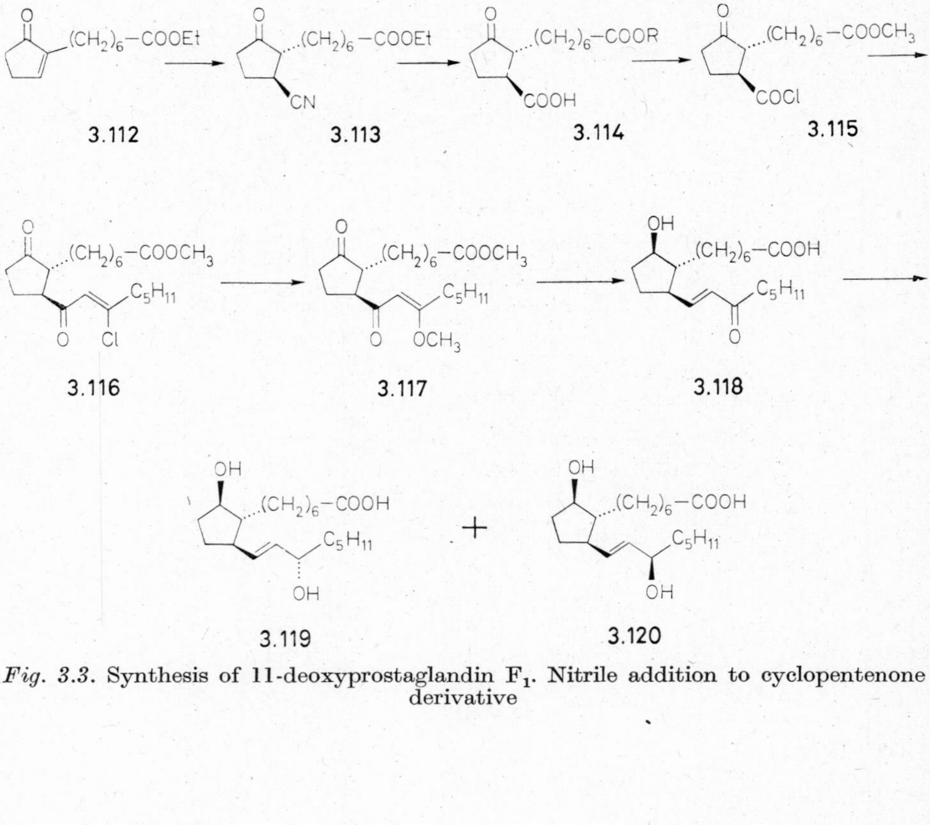

3.112 3.113 3.114 3.115 3.116 3.117 3.118 3.119 3.120

Fig. 3.3. Synthesis of 11-deoxyprostaglandin F_1. Nitrile addition to cyclopentenone derivative

β-cyanoketone (**3.113**) hydrolyzed with sodium hydroxide to the carboxylic acid (**3.114**, R = H). Partial esterification in the side chain (**3.114**, R = CH$_3$), conversion to the acid chloride (**3.115**) with oxalyl chloride and aluminium(III) chloride-catalyzed addition of the product to 1-heptyne gave the chlorodiketone (**3.116**). Chlor inewas substituted by methoxyl using methanolic sodium hydroxide and the resulting enol ether (**3.117**) reduced with sodium borohydride. Reduction was highly stereoselective and the reaction mixture, on acid treatment, gave only a single product containing a β-hydroxyl (**3.118**). Repeated reduction with sodium borohydride gave equal amounts of racemic 11-deoxyprostaglandin F$_{1\beta}$ (**3.119**) and its 15-*epi* stereoisomer (**3.120**).

Addition of cyanide ion was the key step of syntheses developed by Caton and his co-workers [37, 38]. The cyclopentenone intermediate (Fig. 3.4, **3.124**) was prepared by reaction of the morpholine enamine of cyclopenta-

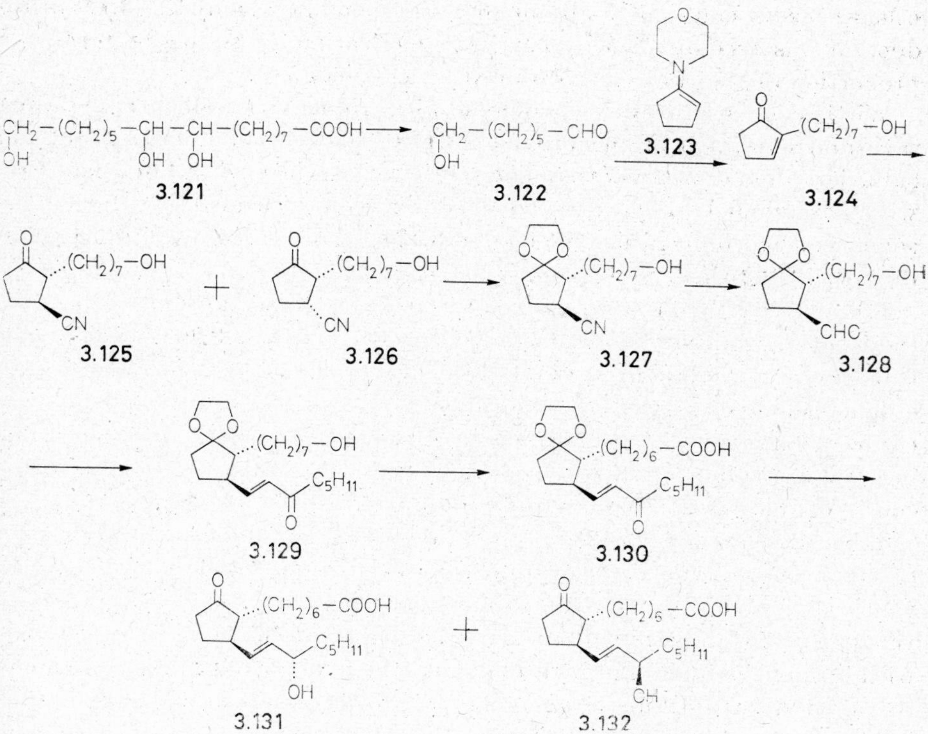

Fig. 3.4. Synthesis of 11-deoxyprostaglandin E$_1$. Nitrile addition to cyclopentenone derivative

none (**3.123**) with 7-hydroxyheptenal. This procedure has gained in importance since this aldehyde had become accessible by periodate oxidation of
the commercially available aleuritic acid (**3.121**).

Acetone cyanohydrin in methanol in the presence of potassium carbonate
converted the enone (**3.124**) to a mixture of *trans*- (**3.125**) and *cis*-3-cyano-
cyclopentenone derivatives (**3.126**) in a ratio of 2 : 1, as determined by gas–
liquid chromatography. Thus in this case, in spite of the basic medium, formation of the undesired *cis*-isomer could not be wholly suppressed.

Although earlier work demonstrated that in basic media *cis*-2,3-dialkylcyclopenta-
nones were rapidly and quantitatively isomerized to the *trans* compounds [39], the
above result was not quite unexpected considering that with the small cyanide group
the difference in thermodynamic stability between the *cis* and *trans* isomers became
less important [40, 41].

The cyano compounds were converted to ethylene ketals (**3.127**, only the
trans isomer depicted) and reduced with diisobutylaluminium hydride in
ether–benzene solution to obtain the corresponding aldehydes (**3.128**). Reduction was accompanied by partial isomerization; as shown by GLC, the
proportion of the *cis* isomer dropped to less than 7%.

Wittig condensation of the aldehyde with triphenyl-2-oxoheptyl phosphorane and oxidation of the product (**3.129**) with chromium(VI) oxide and
sulfuric acid in dimethylformamide to the carboxylic acid (**3.130**), reduction
with potassium borohydride and deketalization with acid concluded the
sequence, which furnished 11-deoxy-(**3.131**) and 11-deoxy-*epi*-prostaglan-
dins E$_1$ (**3.132**) in a 1 : 1 ratio.

Recently Bartmann *et al.* applied with success cyanoaddition for the synthesis of racemic 11-deoxyprostaglandin E$_2$ (Fig. 3.5, **3.144**) [42]. First,
from the known lactol (**3.44**) a dithioacetal (**3.133**) was made with 1,2-
ethanedithiol using boron trifluoride etherate as catalyst, and this was
oxidized subsequently with Moffatt's reagent (dicyclohexylcarbodiimide
in dimethyl sulfoxide) [43] to the ketone (**3.134**), which isomerized in the
course of the reaction largely to its conjugated isomer (**3.135**).

The cyclopentenone (**3.135**) gave, with acetone cyanohydrin in the presence
of sodium carbonate, a pair of stereoisomeric nitriles (**3.136** and **3.137**), from
which the *trans* isomer (**3.137**) crystallized from ether. The latter was converted with 2,2-dimethyl-1,3-propanediol to a ketal (**3.138**) that was reduced
with diisobutylaluminium hydride to the aldehyde (**3.139**). Condensation of
the aldehyde with dimethyl-2-oxoheptylphosphonate sodium salt followed
by reduction of the enone (**3.140**) with sodium borohydride gave the epimeric alcohols (**3.141**, R = H) which were protected by reaction with di-
hydropyran. The dithioacetal moiety of the product (**3.141**, R = THP) was

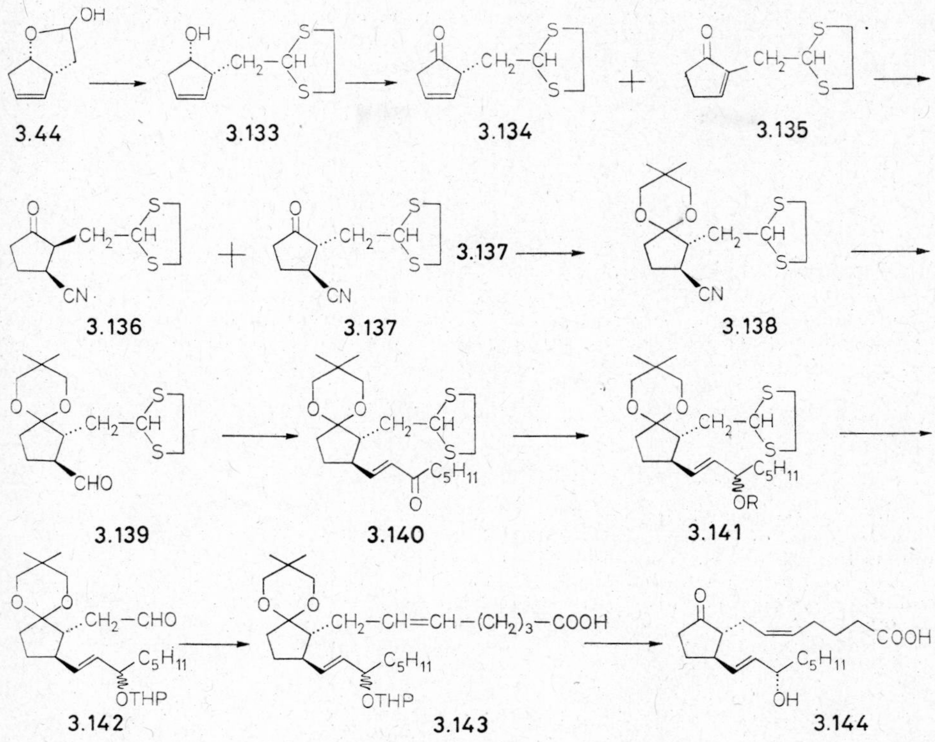

Fig. 3.5. Synthesis of 11-deoxyprostaglandin E$_2$. Nitrile addition to cyclopentenone derivative

cleaved with methyl iodide and potassium carbonate in dimethylformamide. The aldehyde thus obtained (**3.142**) was subjected to Wittig condensation with the phosphorane derived from triphenyl-4-carboxybutyl phosphonium salt, followed by removal of the protecting groups by successive treatment with oxalic acid and *p*-toluenesulfonic acid to furnish, after chromatographic separation, racemic 11-deoxyprostaglandin E$_2$ (**3.144**).

3.3 ADDITION OF NITROMETHANE TO CYCLOPENTENONE DERIVATIVES. SYNTHESIS OF PROSTAGLANDIN F$_{2\alpha}$

Owing to the strong electron attraction of the nitro group, a proton can easily be abstracted from nitromethane by bases and the resulting anion may serve as a nucleophile in Michael-type additions on α,β-unsaturated ketones, among them on cyclopentenones. The relative configuration of the

product is 2,3-*trans*, and the nitromethyl group can later be readily converted
to a formyl function.

The Nef reaction [44, 45] is a well established method for converting a nitro group
into an oxo function. With sodium hydroxide the sodium salt of the acinitro tautomer
is formed from primary or secondary nitro compounds which, when treated with
mineral acid at low temperature, give rise with concomitant nitrogen oxide evolution
to aldehydes or ketones. Good yields require the absence of acid sensitive functions
and a sterically unhindered nitro group.

Jacobson performed the Nef reaction in methanol instead of water, whereby the
dimethylacetal of the primarily formed aldehyde could be isolated [46]. This method
was useful also for water-insoluble substrates.

A method for the transformation of acid sensitive or sterically hindered nitro compounds to oxo compounds was developed by Shechter and Williams [47], based on
the oxidation with one mole of potassium permanganate of the potassium salt derived
from the corresponding nitronic acid in the presence of magnesium sulfate.

$$3\,R_2C=N\begin{smallmatrix}O\\ O\end{smallmatrix}^{\ominus}K^{\oplus} + 2\,KMnO_4 + H_2O \longrightarrow 3\,R_2C=O + 2\,MnO_2 + 3\,KNO_2 + 2\,KOH$$

Recently the transformation of a nitro to a carbonyl group without the aid of a base
has also been solved [48] applying reduction with titanium(III) chloride in aqueous
media to a nitroso compound; this in the form of the tautomeric oxime was reduced
further to an imine, which was ultimately hydrolyzed to furnish the carbonyl function.

The synthesis of 11-deoxyprostaglandin by Alvarez and Wren [49] was
based on the 1,4-addition of nitromethane. A suitable cyclopentenone (Fig.
3.6, **3.11**) was allowed to react with nitromethane in the presence of a weak
base followed by ketalization of the product (**3.145**) with ethylene glycol.
The ketal (**3.146**) was oxidized with potassium permanganate in the presence

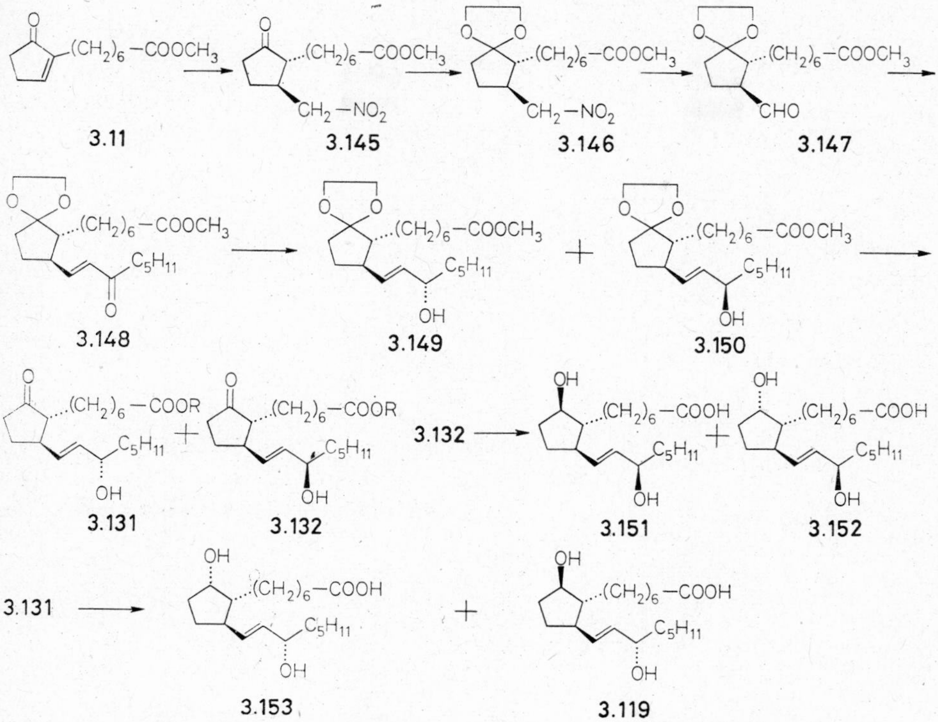

3.11   **3.145**   **3.146**   **3.147**

3.148   **3.149**   **3.150**

3.131   **3.132**   **3.132**   **3.151**   **3.152**

3.131   **3.153**   **3.119**

Fig. 3.6. Synthesis of 11-deoxyprostaglandin E_1 and F_1. Addition of nitromethane to cyclopentenone derivative

of magnesium sulfate to the aldehyde (**3.147**) that was subjected to a modified Wittig condensation with dimethyl 2-oxoheptylphosphonate, followed by reduction of the resulting ketone (**3.148**) with zinc borohydride. The epimeric alcohols (**3.149** and **3.150**), which were formed in about equal amounts, were separated (after deketalization) by column chromatography to give, on hydrolysis, ($\pm$)-11-deoxyprostaglandin E_1 (**3.131**, R = H) and its C_{15}-epimer (**3.132**, R = H).

Reduction with sodium borohydride of 11-deoxyprostaglandin E_1 methyl ester (**3.131**, R = CH_3) after separation by thin-layer chromatography gave ($\pm$)-11-deoxyprostaglandins $F_{1\alpha}$ (**3.153**) and $F_{1\beta}$ (**3.119**). Identical operations afforded the 15-*epi* analogues (**3.152**) and (**3.151**).

The relative configuration of the products at C_9 (α or β) has been assigned by the NMR chemical shift of C_9-H, known to be greater for $C_{9\alpha}$-alcohols than for the $C_{9\beta}$-epimers. For example, the carbinol protons (C_9-H and C_{15}-H) of 11-deoxyprostaglandin $F_{1\alpha}$ (**3.153**) exhibit a two-proton multiplet in the

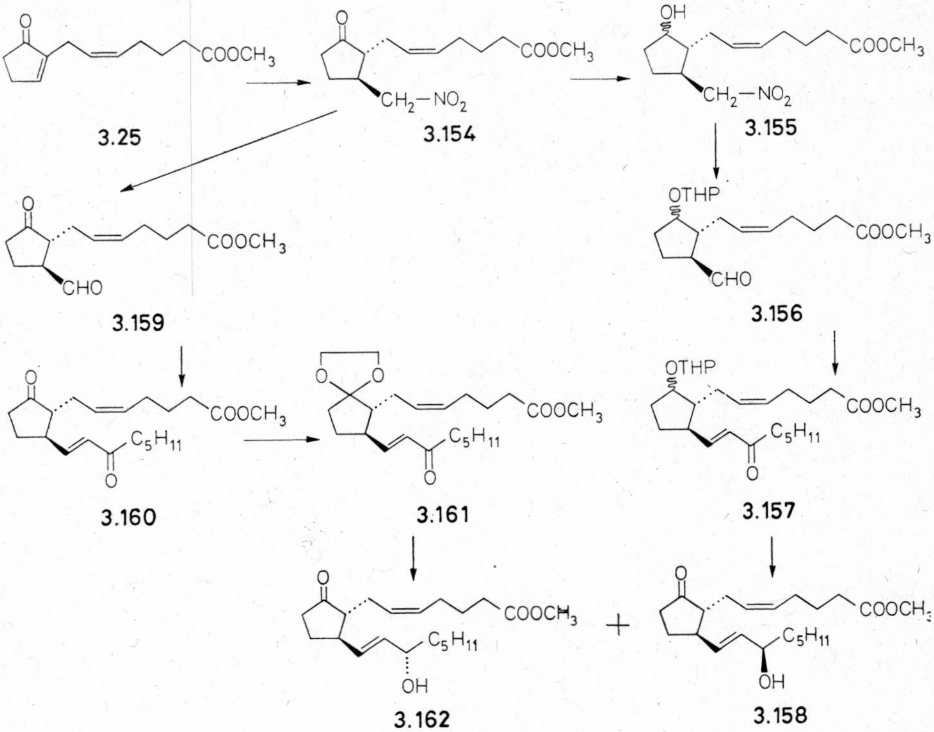

Fig. 3.7. Synthesis of 11-deoxyprostaglandin E_2. Addition of nitromethane to cyclopentenone derivative

range δ 4.0–4.3 whereas the corresponding signals of the $F_{1\beta}$-epimer appear between δ 3.78 and 4.1.

A synthesis of 11-deoxyprostaglandin E_2 (Fig. 3.7, **3.162**) reported by Bagli and Bogri [25] followed the preceding one in its important steps, but started necessarily with a cyclopentenone unsaturated in the side chain (**3.25**). Sodium methoxide-catalyzed nitromethane addition gave the key intermediate (**3.154**), which was then hydrolyzed *via* the sodium salt of the corresponding nitronic acid to an aldehyde (**3.159**). Reaction with sodium dimethyl 2-oxoheptylphosphonate to the diketone (**3.160**), ketalization (**3.161**), reduction with sodium borohydride, and acidic ketal hydrolysis afforded ($\pm$)-11-deoxyprostaglandin E_2 methyl ester (**3.162**) and its C_{15}-epimer (**3.158**).

The same authors described an alternative route leading to the same end products [25, 50] which comprised the reduction of the adduct (**3.154**), with sodium borohydride, prior to hydrolysis of the nitronic salt derived from the alcohol (**3.155**); protection of the aldehyde as the tetrahydropyranyl ether (**3.156**) and condensation with dimethyl 2-oxoheptylphosphonate gave the enone (**3.157**). This was then reduced with sodium borohydride and the product acetylated. After liberation of the C_9-hydroxyl the acetate was oxidized with Jones reagent to a ketone and finally hydrolyzed with alkali to ($\pm$)-11-deoxyprostaglandin E_2 (**3.162**) and its C_{15}-epimer (**3.158**).

Routes based on the 1,4-addition of nitromethane are in their original form inadequate for construction of the primary (i.e. C_{11}-hydroxylated) prostaglandins E and F since the required 4-hydroxycyclopentenone derivative — being a β-hydroxyketone — would suffer elimination in the basic media necessary for addition. 4-Hydroxycyclopentenones protected by groups stable to base (e.g. tetrahydropyranyl) would in turn lose their blocking groups and eliminate water in the acidic medium required for effecting the nitromethyl–formyl transformation.

This difficulty was circumvented recently by Kienzle *et al.* Preparation of natural prostaglandins became possible by starting with a 4-methoxycarbonylcyclopentenone (Fig. 3.8, **3.87**) and using the carboxy-inversion reaction which easily transformed this function at a later stage to a hydroxyl group [26].

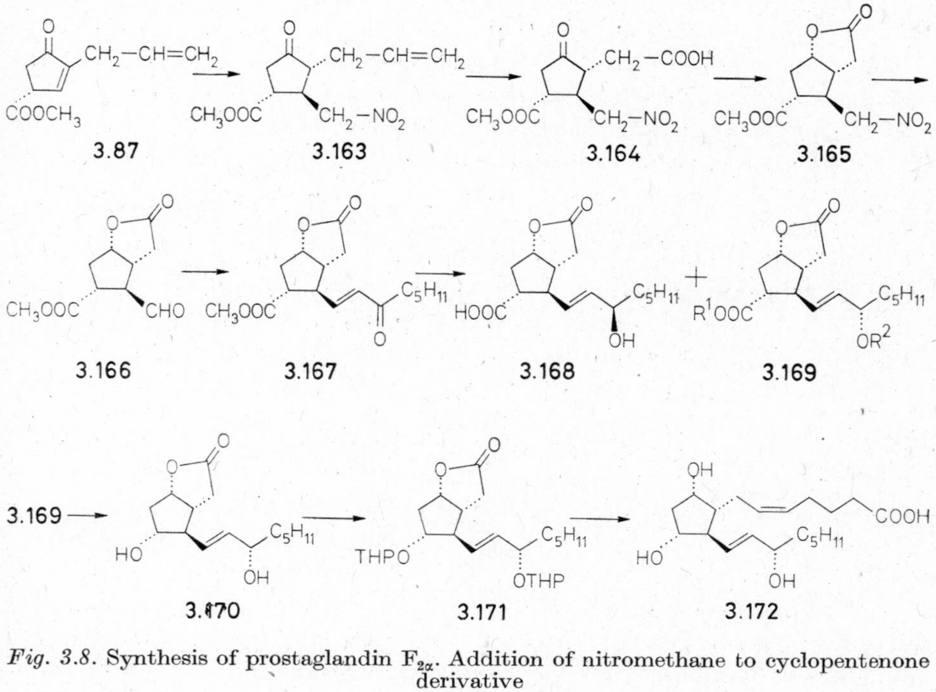

Fig. 3.8. Synthesis of prostaglandin $F_{2\alpha}$. Addition of nitromethane to cyclopentenone derivative

Carboxy-inversion is the thermal rearrangement of diacylperoxides to carbonic esters which, after hydrolysis, give alcohols [51]. The reaction is conveniently performed with diacylperoxides prepared with *m*-chloroperbenzoic acid; the hydrolysis of the carbonate to alcohol is, in turn, performed by some alkoxide base.

The rearrangement proceeds with retention of configuration at the centre bearing the carboxyl group [52].

Kienzle and his co-workers used "Triton B" (trimethylbenzylammonium hydroxide) to catalyze nitromethane addition to the base-sensitive cyclopentenone (**3.87**). The allyl side-chain of the adduct (**3.163**) was oxidized in acidic medium with sodium permanganate, and the oxo group of the product (**3.164**) was stereoselectively reduced to an α-hydroxyl using lithium perhydro-9b-boraphenalyl hydride [53]. The weakly basic medium effected spontaneous lactonization to (**3.165**).

The nitromethyl → formyl transformation of the lactone, either by the Nef reaction or by permanganate oxidation of the corresponding nitronic acid salt in the usual way, gave poor yields, but oxidation of a solution of the nitronic acid salt in saturated aqueous sodium tetraborate with one equivalent of sodium permanganate at 0° afforded the aldehyde (**3.166**) in 70% yield. Condensation with sodium dimethyl 2-oxoheptylphosphonate and zinc borohydride reduction of the resulting enone (**3.167**), separation of the alcohols (**3.168** and **3.169**, $R^1 = CH_3$, $R^2 = H$) by column chromatography and ester hydrolysis of the $C_{15\alpha}$-epimer (**3.169**, $R^1 = CH_3$ $R^2 = H$) with alkali gave the acid (**3.169**, $R^1 = R^2 = H$). After acetylation in pyridine with acetic anhydride (**3.169**, $R^1 = H$, $R^2 = Ac$) the mixed anhydride

(**3.169**, $R^1 = OOC-$, $R^2 = Ac$) was prepared with *m*-chloroperbenzoic acid and dicyclohexylcarbodiimide, and rearranged by boiling for 90 min. in acetonitrile to a carbonate which was hydrolyzed to the diol (**3.170**) with lithium methoxide.

Transformation of the diol to prostaglandin $F_{2\alpha}$ was accomplished according to Corey's scheme elaborated for the optically active series (*cf.* Chapter 2), i.e. by reduction of the bis-tetrahydropyranyl ether with diisobutylaluminium hydride to a lactol (**3.171**), condensation with the phosphorane derived from triphenyl-4-carboxybutylphosphonium salt and elimination of the blocking groups to furnish racemic prostaglandin $F_{2\alpha}$ (**3.172**).

The procedure was adaptable also for the synthesis of optically active prostaglandin $F_{2\alpha}$, as Kienzle *et al.* succeeded in resolving the carboxylic acid (**3.164**) with α-phenylethylamine and optical activity was not lost in the subsequent steps.

3.4 ADDITION OF ORGANOMAGNESIUM COMPOUNDS TO CYCLOPENTENONE DERIVATIVES. SYNTHESIS OF PROSTAGLANDIN B_1

Grignard-type compounds can combine with cyclopentenone systems either by 1,2- or 1,4-addition, depending on the reaction condition. 1,4-Additions furnish β-substituted cyclopentanones with the substituents in *trans* arrangement.

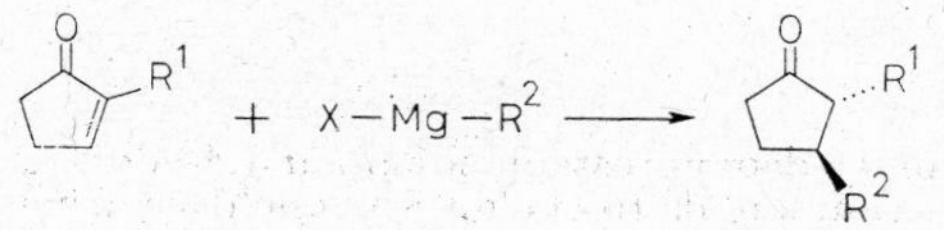

The product of a 1,2-addition is, in turn, an allyl alcohol, which can be induced to acid-catalyzed allylic rearrangement to result in a cyclopentenol. On simple oxidation the product can be converted to an α,β-disubstituted cyclopentenone — a structure characteristic of B-type prostaglandins.

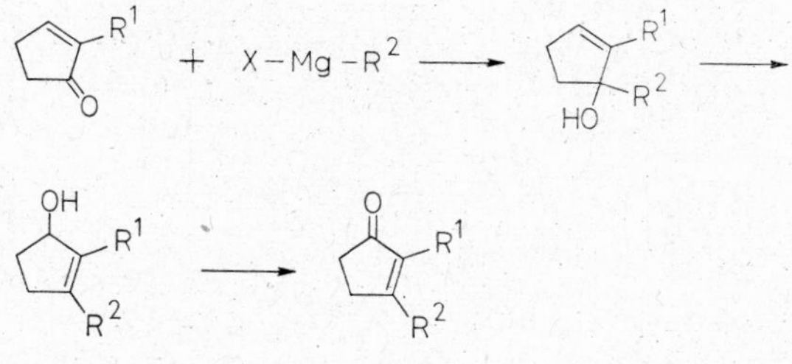

1,4-Addition of a Grignard compound has been utilized by Schaub *et al.* in the synthesis of 11-deoxy-13-dihydroprostaglandin E_1 (Fig. 3.9, **3.178**) [54, 55]. The biological effect of this compound is notable and more selective than that of natural prostaglandins. It lowers, similarly to prostaglandins, the blood pressure but has no influence on smooth muscle contraction [56,57].

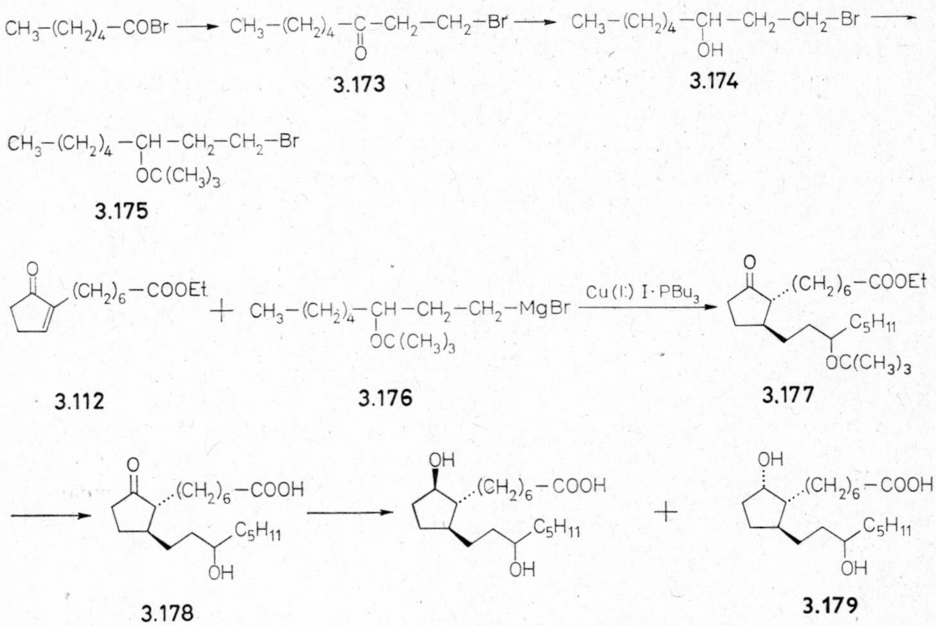

Fig. 3.9. Synthesis of 11-deoxyprostaglandins *via* 1,4-addition of organomagnesium compounds to cyclopentenone derivative

In order to elaborate the Grignard component (**3.176**), the product (**3.173**) of aluminium bromide-catalyzed addition of hexanoyl bromide to ethylene was reduced with sodium borohydride to ($\pm$)-3-hydroxyoctyl bromide (**3.174**). The alcohol was etherified in the presence of a catalytic amount of sulfuric acid with isobutylene, and the *t*-butyl ether (**3.175**) was converted with magnesium to the Grignard compound (**3.176**). Addition of the latter to the cyclopentenone (**3.112**), catalyzed by a complex of copper(I) iodide and tri-*n*-butylphosphine, was both regio- and stereospecific and gave, by 1,4-addition, exclusively the *trans*-dialkyl product (**3.177**). Ether cleavage with trifluoroacetic acid followed by alkaline ester hydrolysis gave a mixture of ($\pm$)-deoxy-13-dihydroprostaglandin E_1 (**3.178**) and its C_{15}-epimer. Reduction of the mixture with lithium perhydro-9b-borophenalyl hydride (*cf.* Chapter 1) gave predominantly (80%) the 9α-alcohol, *i.e.* ($\pm$)-11-deoxy-13-dihydroprostaglandin $F_{1\alpha}$ (**3.179**), and as the minor product, the corresponding $F_{1\beta}$ compound.

The first synthesis of prostaglandin B_1, reported by Hardegger *et al.* [58], exploited 1,2-addition of a Grignard compound to a cyclopentenone (Fig. 3.10, **3.112**). The Grignard component was 3-*t*-butoxy-1-octynyl magnesium

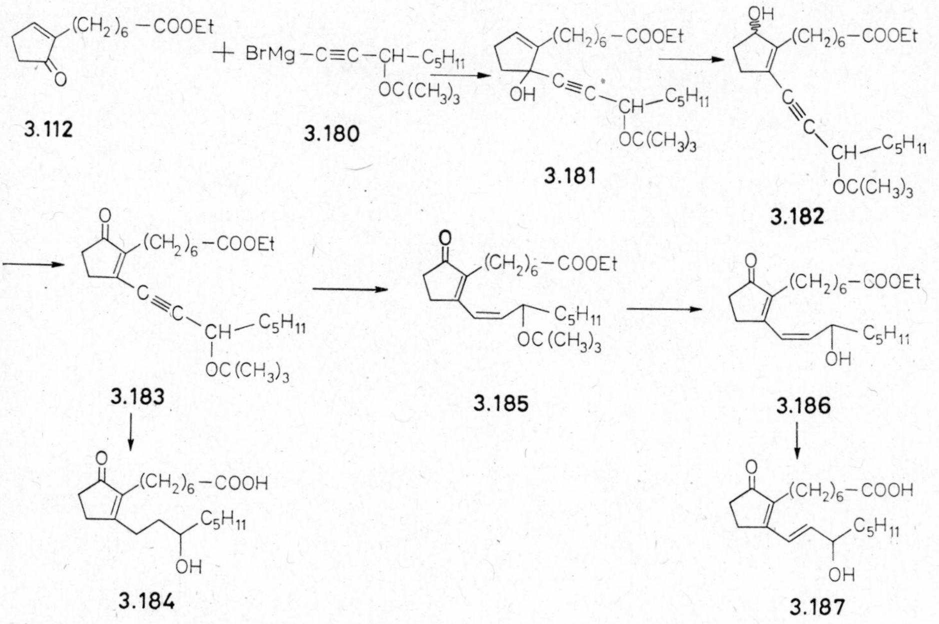

Fig. 3.10. Synthesis of prostaglandin B_1 via 1,2-addition of organomagnesium compounds to cyclopentenone derivative

bromide (3.180) and the allylic rearrangement of the carbinol obtained (3.181) was induced with dilute (0.01 N) hydrochloric acid. The product (3.182) was oxidized with the chromium trioxide–pyridine molecular complex to a cyclopentenone (3.183) that gave on hydrogenation over Lindlar catalyst a (13Z)-olefin (3.185). The blocking group was removed with trifluoroacetic acid and the hydroxy ester (3.186) hydrolyzed at room temperature with dilute (0.1 N) potassium hydroxide. Hydrolysis was accompanied by an unexpected $Z \to E$ isomerization in the side chain giving thus ($\pm$)-prostaglandin B_1 (3.187).

Isomerization of the side-chain double bond can also be effected by treating the ether (3.185) in cyclohexane with iodine, prior to ether cleavage; removal of the protecting group with trifluoroacetic acid and alkaline hydrolysis yielded racemic prostaglandin B_1 (3.187).

Hardegger et al. utilized the cyclopentenone intermediate (3.183) to prepare ($\pm$)-13-dihydroprostaglandin B_1 (3.184) by means of hydrogenation over palladium, followed by treatment with trifluoroacetic acid and hydrolysis.

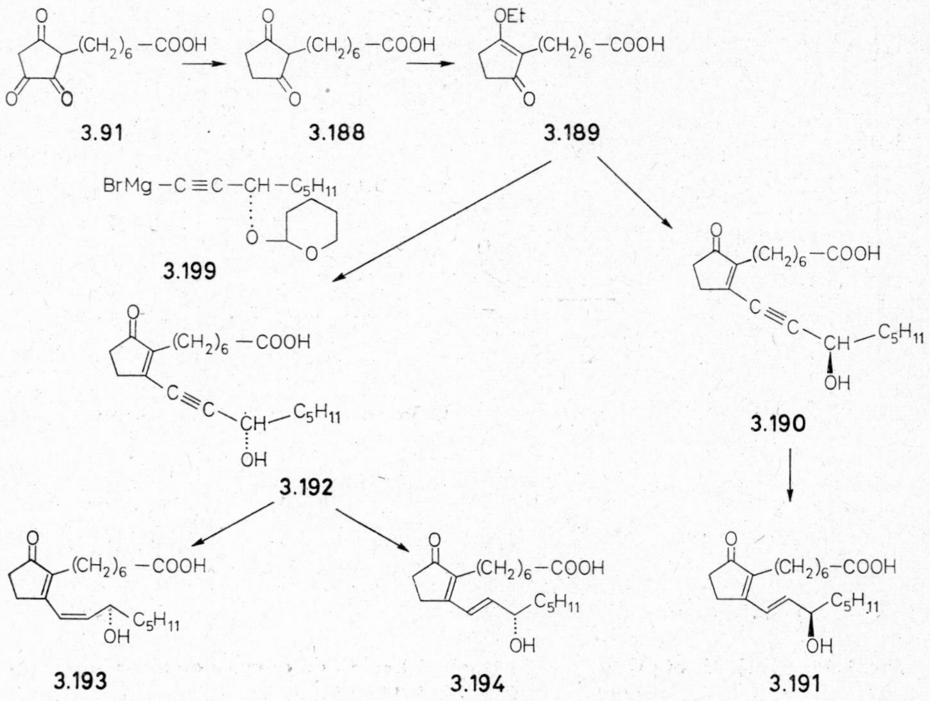

Fig. 3.11. Synthesis of prostaglandin B_1 *via* addition of organomagnesium compound to cyclopentanedione

Pappo *et al.* also devised a scheme suitable for the preparation of natural prostaglandin B_1 (Fig. 3.11, **3.91** → **3.194**) [29]. The key step was identical with that employed by Hardegger *et al.*, i.e. the elaboration of the lower chain by carbonyl addition of a suitable Grignard reagent. An important difference was, however, that an optically active Grignard reagent of (3*S*)-configuration was used.

Resolution could be performed at the stage of 3-hydroxyoctyne using the diastereomeric esters prepared by means of 3β-acetoxy-5,16-etiadienoyl chloride. Crystallization afforded the ester of the (3*S*)-alcohol (**3.195**), which was then hydrolyzed to (3*S*)-hydroxyoctyne (**3.196**). On esterification with 3β-acetoxy-5-etienoyl chloride it was the ester of the (3*R*)-alcohol (**3.197**) which crystallized more readily, affording after hydrolysis the (3*R*)-hydroxyoctyne (**3.198**).

Optical purity of the alcohols was checked by NMR in the form of their esters with (−)-α-methoxy-α-trifluoromethylphenylacetic acid. The rela-

tionship of the esters of this optically active acid with the enantiomeric alcohols (**3.197** and **3.198**) is diastereomeric and results in significant differences in the chemical shifts of certain signals of the esters.

Figure 3.12(a) shows the entire 60 MHz NMR spectrum of the mixture
of esters derived from racemic 3-hydroxyoctyne and (−)-α-methoxy-α-
trifluoromethyl-phenylacetic acid (MPTA). In the spectrum, two methoxy
signals can be identified as two close quartets due to H−F coupling separated by 5 Hz. Fig. 3.12(b) is an expansion of the methoxy region. The
quartets of the methoxy groups in the diastereomeric esters are well separated, their ratio can be determined from the integration curve. The same
detail of the spectrum for the ester of $(3R)$-hydroxyoctyne (**3.198**) is shown
in Fig. 3.12(c): a small contamination of the $(3S)$-ester is recognizable.

Pappo *et al.* reported a novel reaction for the synthesis of the necessary
cyclopentenone component as well. Hydrogenation of the cyclopentanetrione (**3.91**) over palladium catalyst in acidic solution yielded the cyclopentanedione (**3.188**), one of the oxo groups in which was masked by enol ether
formation (**3.189**). This ether was then made to react with the Grignard
reagent (**3.199**) derived from $(3S)$-hydroxyoctyne tetrahydropyranyl ether.
Subsequent acid treatment gave a propargyl alcohol (**3.192**); this was reduced
either with zinc–lead alloy in isopropanol to prostaglandin B$_1$ (**3.194**), or
with hydrogen over Lindlar catalyst to (13Z)-prostaglandin B$_1$ (**3.193**).

An identical sequence starting with the corresponding $(3R)$-Grignard reagent afforded (15R)-prostaglandin B$_1$ (**3.191**).

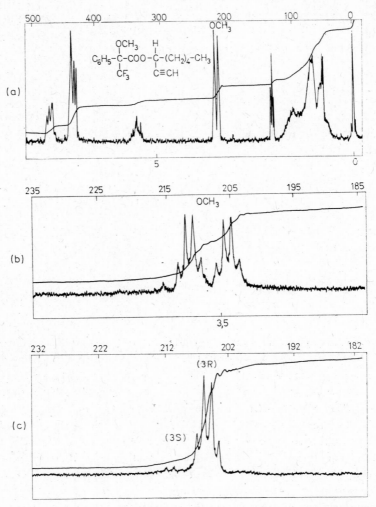

Fig. 3.12. 60 MHz NMR spectra of mixtures of esters formed from 3-hydroxyoctyne
enantiomers and (−)-α-methyl-α-trifluoromethylphenylacetic acid

3.5 CONJUGATE ADDITION OF ORGANOCUPRATE COMPOUNDS
TO CYCLOPENTENONE DERIVATIVES

Among organocopper compounds, lithium bis(alkyl)copper(I) compounds
— called homocuprates — have found widespread application in prostaglandin synthesis. Homocuprates can be prepared from copper(I) iodides
with two moles of alkyl lithium [59–61]

$$2 \text{ RLi} + \text{CuI} \longrightarrow \text{R}_2\text{CuLi} + \text{LiI}$$

It is convenient to use the tributylphosphine complex of copper(I) iodide which is readily soluble in ether-type solvents; moreover, the tributylphosphine complex of the resulting homocuprate ($\text{R}_2\text{CuLi}-\text{Bu}_3\text{P}$) is soluble and also comparatively stable in the same solvents.

Homocuprates readily enter 1,4-addition with α,β-unsaturated ketones yielding β-substituted carbonyl compounds in the enol form. The exact mechanism of the reaction is still unknown but it is assumed to be of radical character. The first step is a one-electron transfer from the copper compound to the β-carbon of the enone system; this is followed by transfer of the alkyl group from the reagent to the "anion radical" thus formed. The existence of a radical-type intermediate is supported by the observation that the reaction proceeded satisfactory only with α,β-unsaturated ketones having negative reduction potentials (between -1.1 and -2.4 V) even in aprotic solvents.

Alternatively, direct nucleophilic addition of the homocuprate to the enone system may be envisaged as the introductory step followed by intramolecular nucleophilic substitution by the alkyl group of the intermediate to give the enol.

The reaction is fast and highly stereoselective even at low temperatures. With cyclic enones the alkyl group enters from the less hindered face of the ring.

The synthesis of racemic prostaglandin E_1 worked out by Alvarez *et al.* [4] is based on the addition of a homocuprate (Fig. 3.13). The tetrahydropyranyl ether of a 4-hydroxycyclopentenone derivative (**3.200**) was allowed to react with the divinylcuprate reagent (**3.201**) generated from vinyllithium

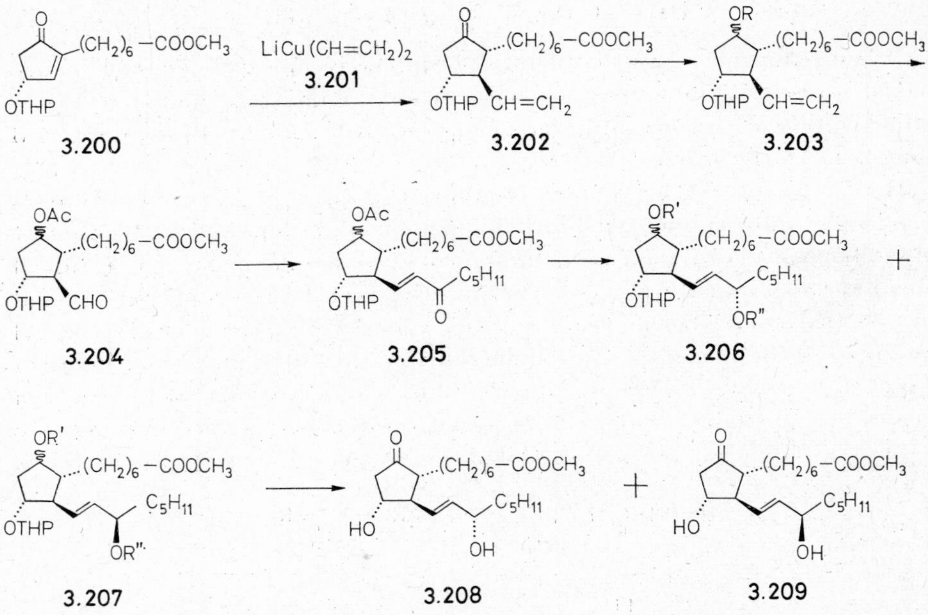

Fig. 3.13. Synthesis of prostaglandin E_1. Conjugate addition of organocuprate compound to cyclopentenone derivative

and bis(trimethylphosphine)copper(I) cyanide. In a stereospecific reaction the vinyl group entered from the less hindered face, i.e. opposite to the tetrahydropyranyloxy group. On acidification, the primary enol decomposed to the all-*trans*-β-vinylketone (**3.202**). Reduction with sodium borohydride gave a mixture of epimeric alcohols (**3.203**, R = H); this mixture was acetylated with acetic anhydride in pyridine. The vinyl group of the acetate (**3.203**, R = Ac) was ozonolyzed to provide an aldehyde function (**3.204**) that served for the introduction of the lower side-chain with sodium dimethyl 2-oxoheptylphosphonate. On reduction with zinc borohydride, the enone (**3.205**) yielded two racemic pairs (9α-15S, 9β-15S, 9α-15R and 9β-15R) of the epimeric C_{15}-alcohols (**3.206** and **3.207**, R' = Ac, R" = H). After successive conversion to the corresponding tetrahydropyranyl ethers (**3.206** and **3.207** R' = Ac, R" = THP), alkaline hydrolysis of the acetoxyl groups, Jones oxidation of the alcohols (**3.206** and **3.207**, R' = H, R" = THP) and acid hydrolysis of the ketones obtained provided, after chromatographic separation, ($\pm$)-prostaglandin E_1 (**3.208**) and ($\pm$)-15-*epi*-prostaglandin E_1 (**3.209**).

Sih and his co-workers utilized, in the synthesis of prostaglandin E_1, a homocuprate reagent containing the preformed C_{13}-C_{20} chain (Fig. 3.14) [62].

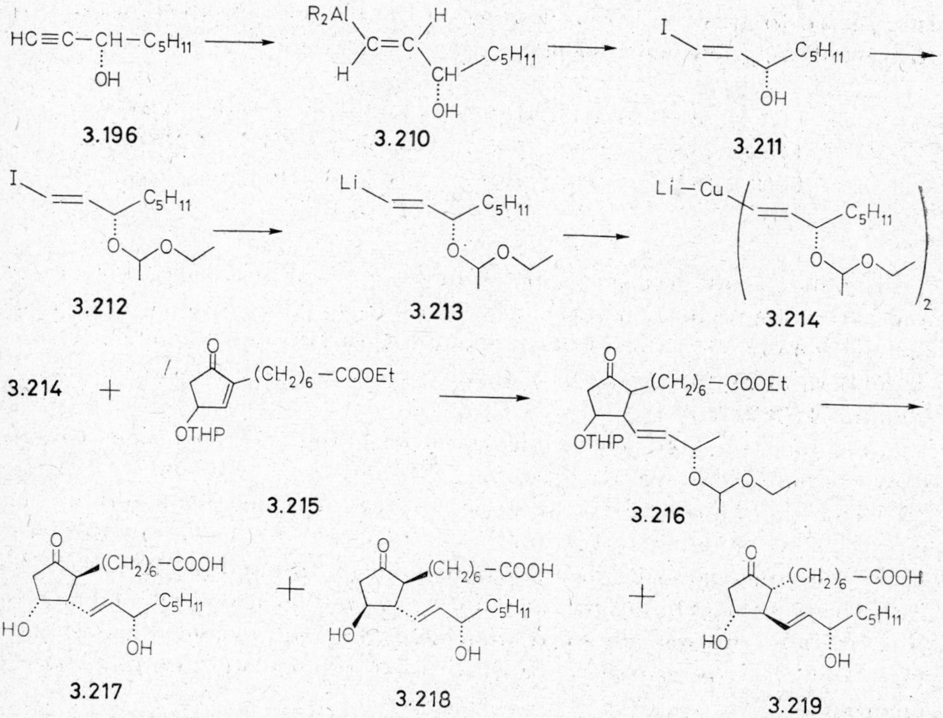

Fig. 3.14. Synthesis of prostaglandin E_1 *via* addition of homocuprate reagent to cyclopentenone derivative

This was prepared in a stereospecific manner from (3S)-hydroxyoctyne (**3.196**) using the hydroalumination method of Zweifel and Whitney [63, 64]. The acetylene derivative (**3.196**) reacted with dialkylaluminium hydride and the product, a dialkylvinylaluminium (**3.210**) was treated with iodine. Aluminium hydride addition took place through a cyclic transition state with *cis*-stereochemistry and gave an (E)-olefin; this furnished, on exchange with iodine, a vinyl iodide of the same (E)-geometry (**3.211**).

The hydroxyl group of the iodine compound was protected by forming the α-ethoxyethyl ether (**3.212**) by treatment with ethyl vinyl ether and metallation with lithium. Reaction of the lithium compounds (**3.213**) with the tributylphosphine–copper(I) iodide complex yielded the divinylcuprate reagent (**3.214**), which was made to react with the racemic 4-tetrahydropyranyloxycyclopentenone (**3.215**).

If it is assumed that addition resulted in a *trans* arrangement of the two side-chains, reaction of a racemic cyclopentenone with a (3′S)-homocuprate is expected to give rise [after cleavage of the blocking group from (**3.216**)] to the following four stereoisomers:

$$11R - (8S - 12S) - 15S \ldots 11,15\text{-}epi\text{-}ent\text{-}PGE_1 \; (\textbf{3.217})$$
$$11S - (8S - 12S) - 15S \ldots 15\text{-}epi\text{-}ent\text{-}PGE_1 \; (\textbf{3.218})$$
$$11R - (8R - 12R) - 15S \ldots PGE_1 \; (\textbf{3.219})$$
$$11S - (8R - 12R) - 15S \ldots 11\text{-}epi\text{-}PGE_1$$

In reality, acidic hydrolysis of the blocking group, cleavage of the ester and chromatographic separation afforded but three products: nearly equal amounts (46% and 43%) of prostaglandin E_1 (**3.219**) and 15-*epi-ent*-prostaglandin E_1 (**3.218**), together with smaller quantities of 11,15-*epi-ent*-prostaglandin E_1 (**3.217**, 11%).

Concerning the stereochemistry of the reaction, two conclusions can be drawn from these preparative results:

1) The reaction is highly stereoselective; the vinyl side chain adds to the enone system predominantly from the face opposite to the tetrahydropyranyloxy group, generating thereby compounds (**3.218**) and (**3.219**).

2) The fact that 11-*epi*-prostaglandin E_1 was not formed at all, and mainly prostaglandin E_1 was obtained, indicated that the cyclopentenone with $(4R)$-configuration reacted faster with the $(3'S)$-homocuprate than with its enantiomer.

From the results of the foregoing reaction (*trans* addition predominantly from the face opposite to the substituent at C_4) it could be predicted that with the use of an optically active 4-hydroxycyclopentenone, the configuration at C_4 would predetermine the configurations of the newly formed chiral centers at C_8, C_{11} and C_{12}. This principle has been applied by Sih and his group in their stereocontrolled synthesis of prostaglandins E_1 and E_2.

In order to prepare prostaglandin E_1 [33], the $(4R)$-hydroxycyclopentenone (Fig. 3.15, **3.220**), masked by the bulky dimethyl-*t*-butylsilyl group, was allowed to react with the divinylcuprate reagent (**3.221**) prepared from (3*S*)-hydroxyheptyne. Addition gave rise, as expected, to a single product (**3.222**, 70%), which furnished, after acidic ether cleavage and enzymic ester hydrolysis, optically active prostaglandin E_1 (**3.219**).

An analogous stereocontrolled sequence starting with a $(4R)$-cyclopentenone containing a double-bond in the side chain (Fig. 3.15, **3.223**) led *via* (**3.224**) to optically active prostaglandin E_2 (**3.225**) [34].

Conjugate addition of divinylcuprates is also the key step of prostaglandin syntheses developed by Fried and his co-workers [65, 66] but as opposed to Sih's method, instead of divinylcuprates containing olefinic bonds of (E)-

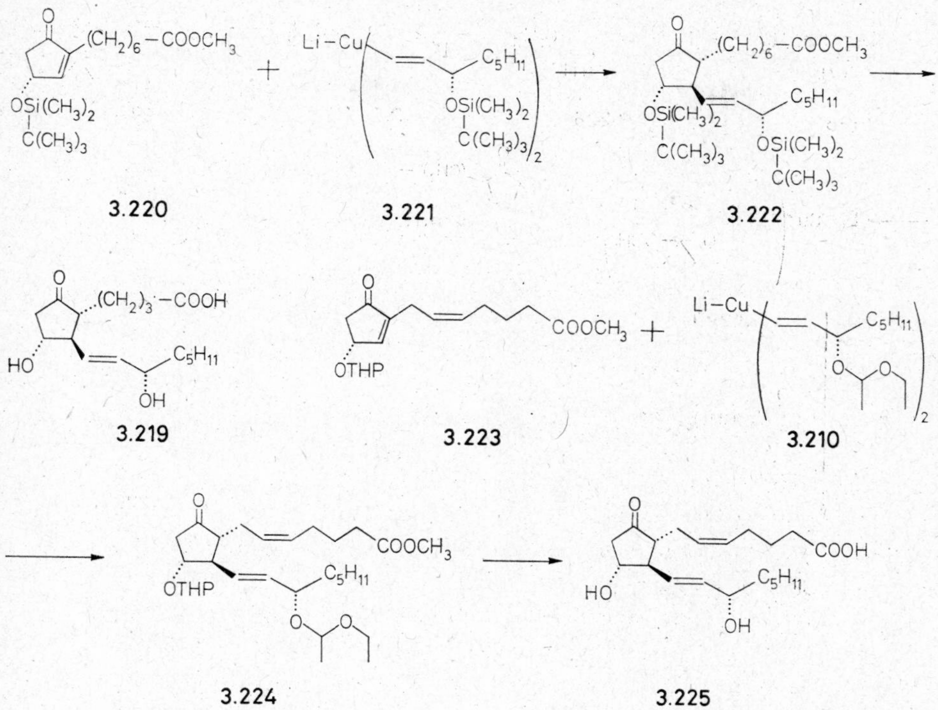

Fig. 3.15. Synthesis of prostaglandin E₂ *via* addition of organocuprate compound to cyclopentenone derivative

geometry, (Z)-diastereomers were employed. The latter are more reactive and of higher stereoselectivity in addition reactions.

The cuprate reagent was prepared from the tetrahydropyranyl ether of 3-hydroxyoctyne (Fig. 3.16, **3.196**); this was first metallated with butyllithium and then allowed to react with iodine. Reduction of the iodoacetylene (**3.226**) with diimide, generated in the system methanol–potassium azodicarboxylate–acetic acid, gave the (Z)-vinyliodide (**3.227**, R = THP). The protecting group was split off with dichloroacetic acid and the alcohol (**3.227**, R = H) re-etherified with isopropenyl methyl ether. Repeated metallation of the resulting ether [**3.227**, R = C(CH₃)OCH₃] with butyllithium to (**3.228**) and reaction with bis(trimethylphosphine)copper(I) iodide gave a homocuprate reagent containing (Z)-olefinic bonds (**3.229**).

The commencement of the sequence with racemic 3-hydroxyoctyne, and *trans* addition of the cuprate to the cyclopentenone (**3.11**) was expected to

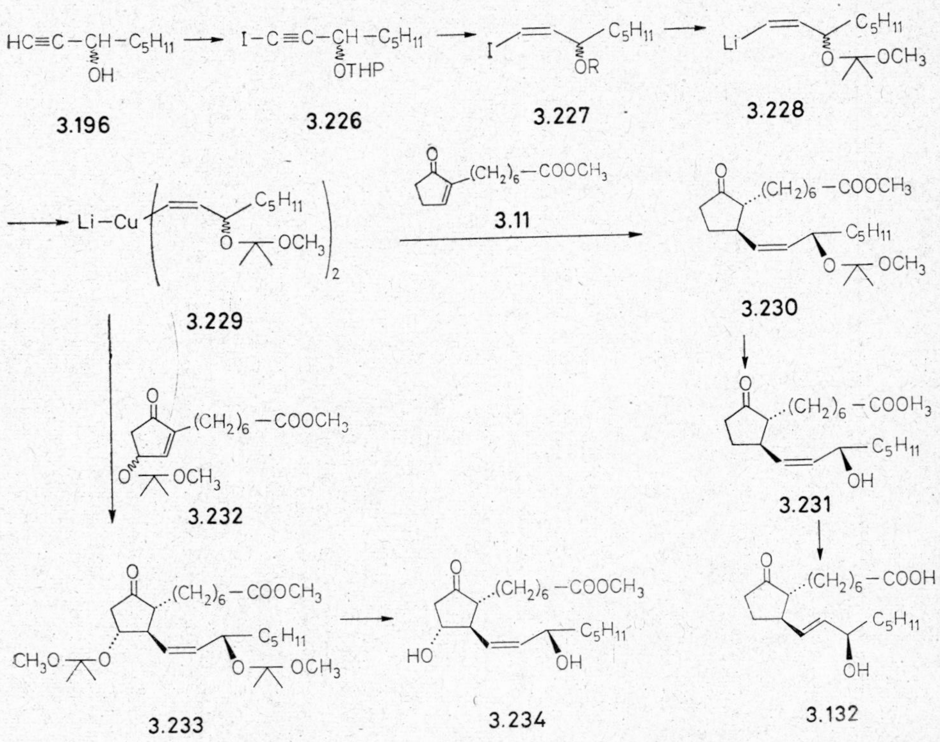

Fig. 3.16. Synthesis of prostaglandins *via* addition of homocuprate reagent containing (Z)-olefinic bond to cyclopentenone

give rise to the following two racemates:

$$(8R - 12R)\ 15S \brace (8S - 12S)\ 15R \ \ \ldots\ \text{11-deoxy-(13Z)-PGE}_1$$

$$(8R - 12R)\ 15R \brace (8S - 12S)\ 15S \ \ \ldots\ (\pm)\text{-11-deoxy-(13Z)-}epi\text{-PGE}_1.$$

Addition, however, gave rise to a single racemate (3.230). On hydrolysis and photochemical isomerization of the double-bond, this yielded 11-deoxy-15-*epi*-prostaglandin E$_1$ (3.132).

Accordingly, the addition of a racemic homocuprate reagent on a racemic 4-hydroxycyclopentenone derivative (3.232) may furnish (provided that *trans* addition involving the face opposite to the C$_4$-alkoxyl group takes place), stereoisomers of the following configuration:

$$\left.\begin{array}{l} 11R\ (8R - 12R)\ 15S \\ 11S\ (8S - 12S)\ 15R \end{array}\right\} \ldots (\pm)\text{-}(13Z)\text{-PGE}_1$$

$$\left.\begin{array}{l} 11R\ (8R - 12R)\ 15R \\ 11S\ (8S - 12S)\ 15S \end{array}\right\} \ldots (\pm)\text{-}(13Z)\text{-}epi\text{-PGE}_1.$$

Again the product consisted of a single racemate only with the relative configuration corresponding to that of (13*Z*)-15-*epi*-prostaglandin E_1 (**3.234**).

The exclusive formation of the racemates (**3.231**) and (**3.234**) in the above addition reactions can be rationalized assuming the stereoselective addition of the (*R*)-component of the racemic cuprate reagent to the *β*-face, and that of the (*S*)-component to the *α*-face of the enone system.

In the addition involving a cuprate of (*S*)-configuration (**3.235**) and a racemic 4-hydroxycyclopentenone (**3.232**), after the usual transformations, the end product was optically active (13*Z*)-15-*epi*-*ent*-prostaglandin E_1 (**3.236**). Conversely, the same sequence with the (*R*)-cuprate (**3.237**) afforded (13*Z*)-15-*epi*-prostaglandin E_1 (**3.238**).

3.232 3.235 3.236

3.237 3.238

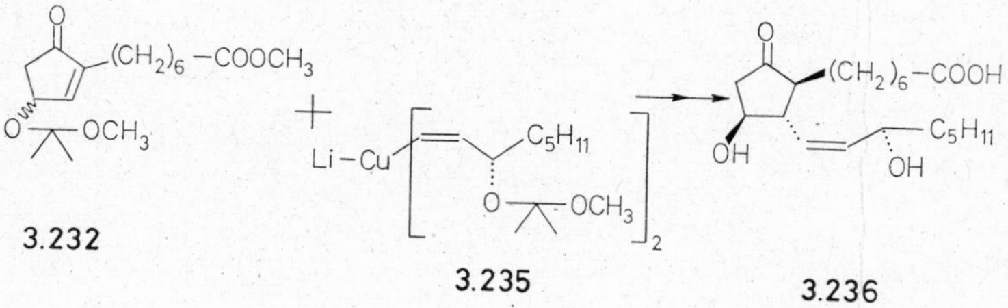

These two additions are among the rare examples of kinetic resolution combined with stereoselective addition, and deserve special interest since the chiral carbinolic centre of the homocuprate producing this effect, is relatively remote from the newly formed chiral centres at C_8 and C_{12}.

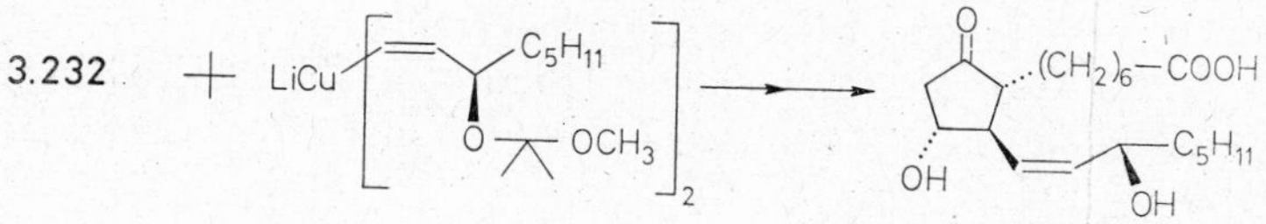

Subsequent to this Miller *et al*. found a method [67] which made possible the conversion of (13*Z*)-15-*epi*-prostaglandin E_1, prepared in the above procedure (**3.238**), by stereospecific reactions into natural prostaglandin E_1 methyl ester [67]. For this purpose a sulfenic ester (**3.240**) was synthesized from the alkoxide of the corresponding tetrahydropyranyl ether (**3.239**) prepared from the alcohol with butyllithium. This suffered [2,3]-sigmatropic shift to yield a sulfoxide (**3.241**) [68], and this underwent on treatment with trimethylphosphine a second [2, 3]-sigmatropic shift to give a sulfenic ester epimeric at C_{15} to the parent one, which, in turn, decomposed to the prostaglandin E_1 ether (**3.242**); ether cleavage resulted in prostaglandin E_1 methyl ester (**3.208**).

A novel route to 11-deoxyprostaglandins utilizing homocuprate addition was recently reported by Patterson and Fried (Fig. 3.17) [69]. This involved the introduction of the C_{1-7} side chain in the last step of the sequence by alkylation using a nonequilibrated enolate ion.

First cyclopentenone (**3.243**) was made to react with a racemic homocuprate reagent (**3.229**), and the resulting lithium enolate (**3.244**) was stabilized as the trimethylsilyl ether (**3.245**), prepared with trimethylsilyl chloride [70–72]. Reconversion with lithium amide in liquid ammonia gave the lithium enolate (**3.244**) which was then alkylated with the allyl bromide (**3.246**) in a regiospecific manner. Elimination of the blocking group gave a mixture of ($\pm$)-11-deoxyprostaglandin E_2 methyl ester (**3.162**) and its C_{15}-epimer (**3.158**). Starting with a cuprate of (S)-configuration (**3.235**), the same sequence provided the optically active analogues of (**3.162**) and (**3.158**).

5,6-Dehydro-11-deoxy derivatives were prepared in a similar way, but in this case the lithium enolate (**3.244**) was alkylated with a propargyl iodide derivative (**3.247**) to furnish, after the removal of the blocking group by

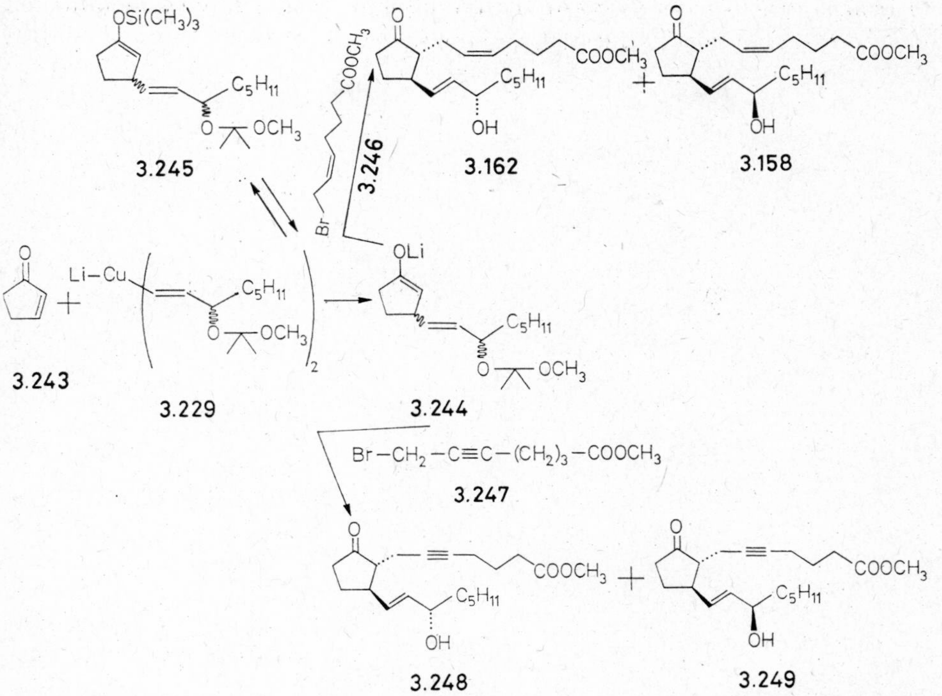

Fig. 3.17. Synthesis of 11-deoxyprostaglandin E_1 through nonequilibrated enolate ion

acid treatment, $(\pm)$-5,6-dehydro-11-deoxyprostaglandin E_2 methyl ester (**3.248**) and its C_{15}-epimer (**3.249**).

A new prostaglandin synthesis of Stork an Isobe [73] is, like the one just discussed, also based on the reaction of an enolate generated in a regiospecific way. The key intermediate was an α-bromocyclopentane (**3.250**) prepared in several steps from cyclopentene epoxide (**3.68**). On reduction with methyl diphenylphosphinite this directly gave an enol phosphinate (**3.251**) that was converted with *t*-butyllithium at $-78\,°C$ to a lithium enolate (**3.252**). In a trapping reaction with formaldehyde in the presence of zinc chloride the enolate gave the α-hydroxymethylcyclopentanone (**3.253**); the mesylate of this compound underwent elimination on treatment with *N*,*N*-diisopropylethylamine to give the α-methylenecyclopentenone (**3.254**). Reaction with the divinylhomocuprate (**3.255**) introduced the upper chain in a 1,4-addition process. Removal of the ethoxyethyl protecting groups from the product (**3.256**), followed by Jones oxidation of the primary alcohol function to carboxylic acid, the reduction with trialkylborohydride and finally cleavage of the benzyloxy group with sodium in ethanol and liquid ammonia gave prostaglandin $F_{2\alpha}$ and its C_{11}-epimer.

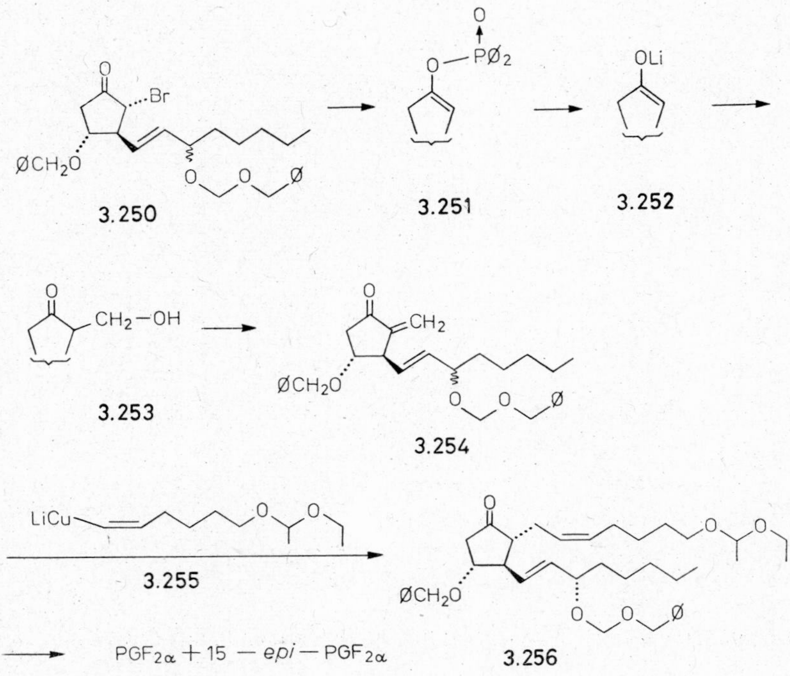

3.250   3.251   3.252

3.253

3.254

3.255

ØCH₂O

3.256

$$PGF_{2\alpha} + 15 - epi - PGF_{2\alpha}$$

In a later, improved version of this synthesis Stork and Isobe also employed as starting material the inexpensive cyclopentadiene (**3.40**) which was allowed to react in acetic acid containing copper(II) acetate with amyl hydroperoxide. The product was a mixture of *cis*- and *trans*-1,4-disubstituted 2-cyclopentenes (**3.257**, R = Ac) which gave on hydrolysis the corresponding epimeric alcohols (**3.257**, R = H); these were oxidized with Jones reagent (chromic acid–acetone) to the cyclopentenone (**3.258**) [93].

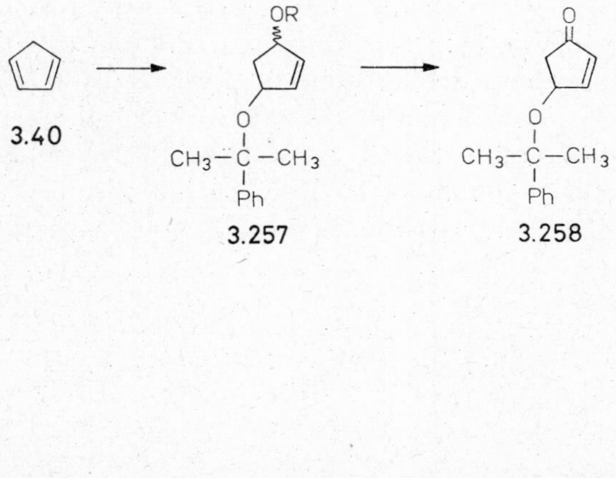

3.40

3.257   3.258

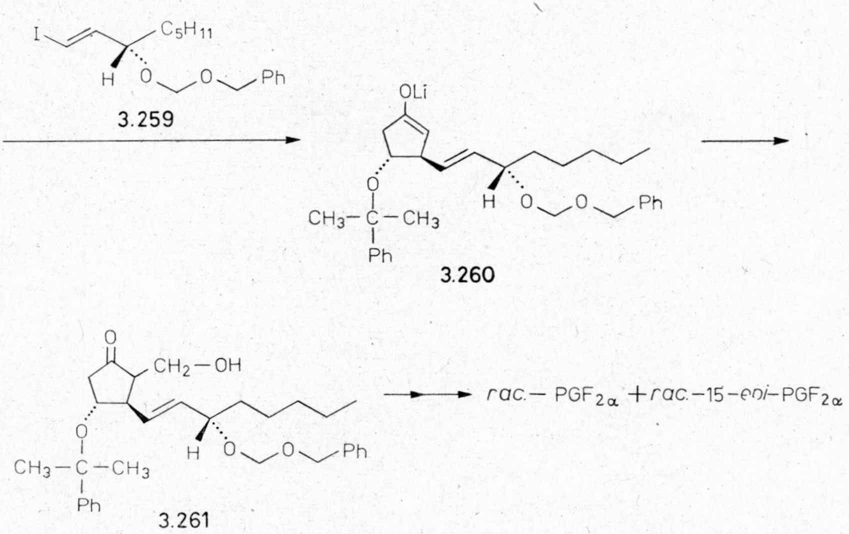

3.259

3.260

3.261

$rac. - PGF_{2\alpha} + rac. - 15 - epi - PGF_{2\alpha}$

This enone (**3.258**) gave on a reaction with the reagent prepared from the vinyl iodide (**3.259**) with t-butyllithium the enolate ion (**3.260**), which was treated, without isolation, with formaldehyde. Further transformation of the product (**3.261**) to racemic prostaglandin F$_{2\alpha}$ proceeded essentially as it had been reported by the same authors before.

Nucleophilic substitution with a homocuprate reagent was the key step of an interesting new version for the synthesis of prostaglandin A$_2$ (Fig. 3.18, **3.269**) worked out by Corey and Mann [20]. The divinylcuprate component was prepared from $(3S)$-hydroxyoctyne (**3.262**, R = H). The hydroxyl group was masked as the dimethyl-t-butylsilyl ether (**3.262**, R = Si(CH$_3$)$_2$ C(CH$_3$)$_3$) and the ether was made to react with 9-borabicyclo[3.3.1]nonane. Cis-addition furnished the trialkylborane (**3.263**), which was treated first with dimethylamine oxide and then with iodine to yield an (E)-vinyliodide (**3.264**) used for the preparation of the required homocuprate (**3.221**).

The optically active iodolactone (**3.55**), readily accessible from cyclopentadiene, was the other key intermediate of the synthesis. After blocking the hydroxyl with a dimethyl-t-butylsilyl group (**3.265**), hydrogen iodide was abstracted with the non-nucleophilic base 1,5-diazabicyclo[4.3.0]non-5-ene to arrive at an unsaturated lactone (**3.261**), that was allowed to react with the homocuprate (**3.221**) at low temperature.

Bimolecular nucleophilic substitution by homocuprates of compounds containing an allylic substructure, i.e. of "allyl electrophiles", had been

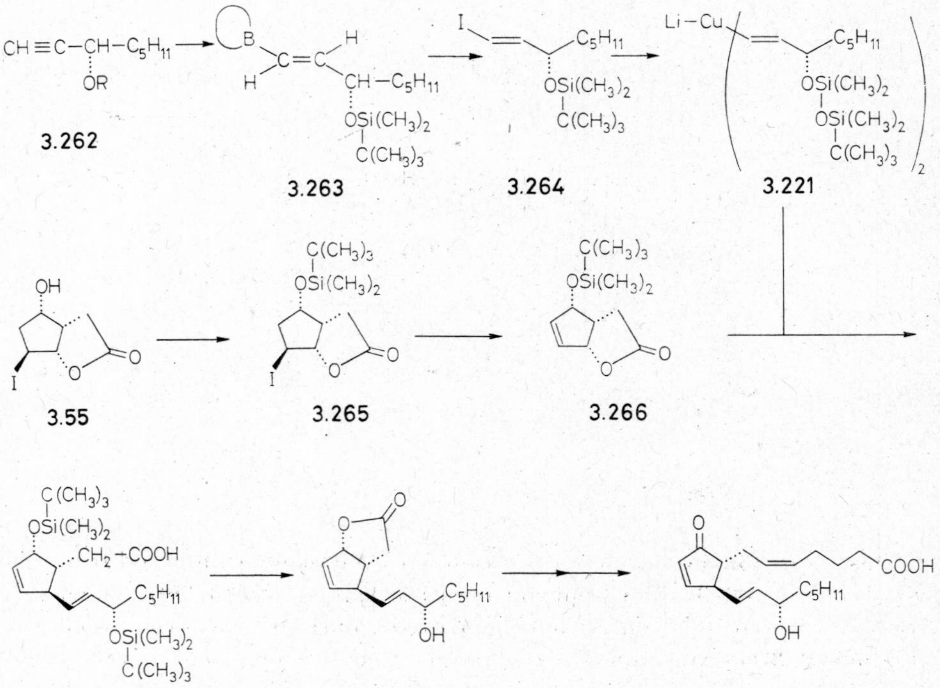

Fig. 3.18. Synthesis of prostaglandin A₂

known before. Although the substrate contained two allyl alcohol-type oxygens (at C_1 and C_4), attack only at C_4 could be anticipated in an S_N2-type reaction since, due to its resonance stabilization as the anion, the carboxyl is a much better leaving group than the ether oxygen.

The substitution product, a cyclopentylacetic acid (**3.267**) was freed from the blocking group and relactonized by heating with dilute hydrochloric acid to obtain an intermediate (**3.268**) the transformation of which to optically active prostaglandin A₂ (**3.269**) had been solved previously [74].

In all of the processes discussed so far only one of the vinyl groups of the divinylcuprate reagent was incorporated into the product; the other was lost for the purposes of the synthesis since the by-product, a vinyl-copper compound, could not be recovered in a pure state from the reaction mixture. For greater economy, Corey and Beames synthesized mixed cuprates with one of the ligands originating from some inexpensive starting material. These behaved in addition reactions as selective vinyl donors [75].

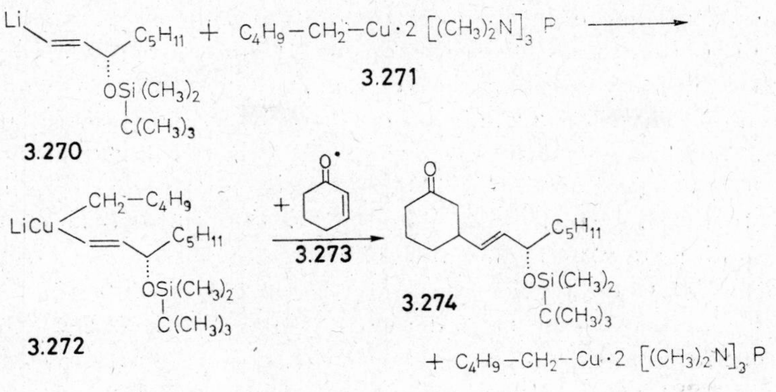

3.270 + **3.271**

3.272 + **3.273** → **3.274** + $C_4H_9-CH_2-Cu \cdot 2 \; [(CH_3)_2N]_3 P$

One of these mixed cuprates (**3.272**) was obtained from a vinyllithium derivative and an alkylcopper(I) compound complexed with hexamethylphosphoric triamide (**3.271**). Reaction of this reagent with cyclohexenone (**3.273**) was selective and led to (**3.274**).

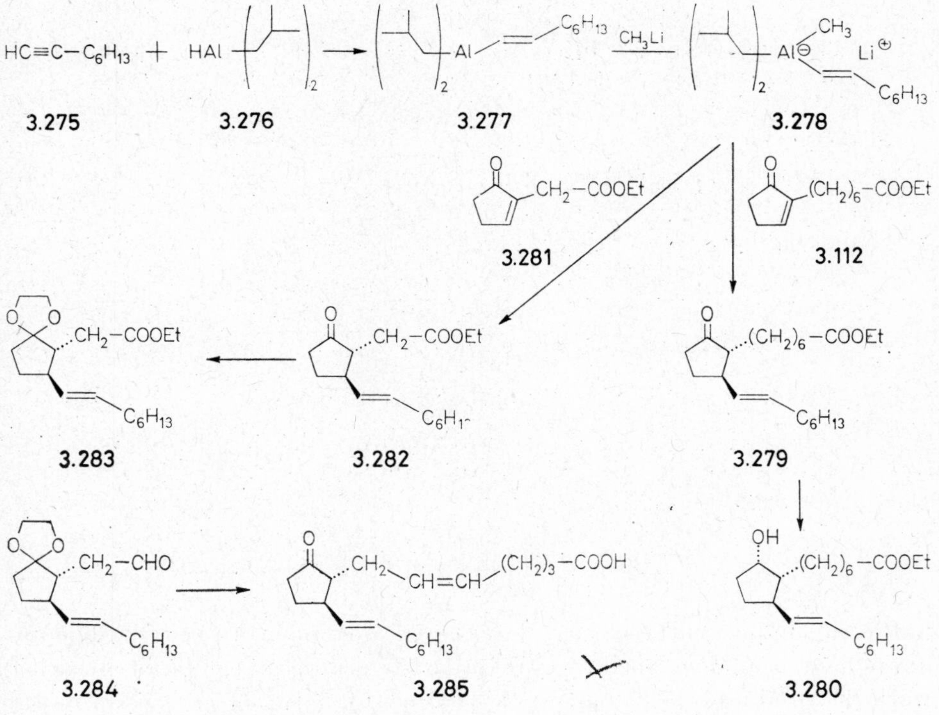

Fig. 3.19. Synthesis of 11,15-dideoxyprostaglandins

A reaction resembling the conjugate addition of homocuprates has been realized by Bernady and Weiss [76] using lithium tetraalkylalanate (Fig. 3.19, **3.278**). The latter was prepared from 1-octyne (**3.275**), to which diiso-butylaluminium hydride (**3.276**) was added to give a dialkylvinylalane deriv-ative (**3.277**); this was converted to the "ate"-complex (**3.278**) with methyl-lithium. The complex proved to be a selective vinyl donor towards enone systems. Reaction with the cyclopentenone (**3.112**) afforded 11,15-dideoxy-prostaglandin E_1 (**3.279**), from which, by reduction with a "Selectride"-type borohydride, 11,15-dideoxyprostaglandin $F_{1\alpha}$ (**3.280**) was obtained.

In order to synthesize 11,15-deoxyprostaglandin E_2 (**3.285**) the same alanate (**3.278**) was first made to react with the cyclopentenylacetic acid derivative (**3.281**); the carbonyl group of the product (**3.282**) was converted to the ethyleneketal, and the ester group of the ketal (**3.283**) reduced with diisobutylaluminium hydride to an aldehyde function (**3.284**); this was then condensed with the phosphorane generated from triphenyl-4-carboxybutyl-phosphonium salt to obtain, after ketal cleavage, 11,15-dideoxyprostaglan-din E_2 (**3.285**).

3.6 SYNTHESIS OF PROSTAGLANDINS *VIA* REGIOSPECIFIC RING OPENING OF EPOXYCYCLOPENTANE DERIVATIVES

α-Epoxycyclopentane derivatives are readily accessible from cyclopen-tenones and their oxirane ring can be smoothly opened with nucleophilic agents in stereospecific and highly regioselective reactions catalyzed either with acid or Lewis acid.

Prostaglandin syntheses based on the ring opening of epoxycyclopente-nones have been developed by Corey and Noyori. In the course of an earlier work, they reduced the racemic epoxylactone (Fig. 3.20, **3.57**) with diisobutyl aluminium hydride to the lactol (**3.286**, R = H), that was allowed to react

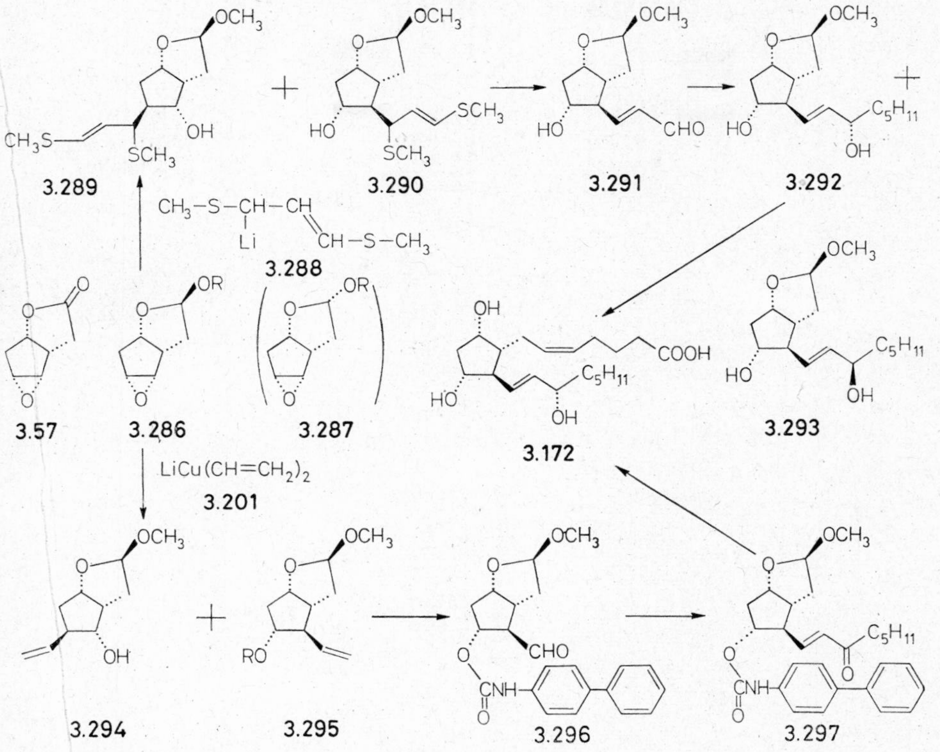

Fig. 3.20. Synthesis of prostaglandin $F_{2\alpha}$ *via* epoxycyclopentanone derivative

as the methyl acetal (**3.286**, R = CH_3) with 1,3-bis(methylthio)allyllithium (**3.288**) [19]. Ring opening gave rise to a mixture of two products (**3.289** and **3.290**) containing in a predominant part the unwanted isomer (**3.289**, 60%). This mixture was converted with mercury(II) chloride to the aldehydes, which could be then separated. Reaction of the desired component (**3.291**) with pentyllithium gave equal amounts of a product with prostaglandin F configuration (**3.292**) and its C_{15}-epimer (**3.293**). Transformation of the former to racemic prostaglandin $F_{2\alpha}$ (**3.172**) had been accomplished previously by the same authors.

Later Corey and Mann explored the utility of divinylcuprate reagent (**3.201**) in the epoxide ring opening [20]. In this case the synthesis started from the optically active epoxylactone (**3.57**), which was reduced to a mixture of the epimeric lactols (**3.286** and **3.287**), R = H). Boron trifluoride in methanol converted both of them quantitatively to the *exo*-acetal (**3.286**,

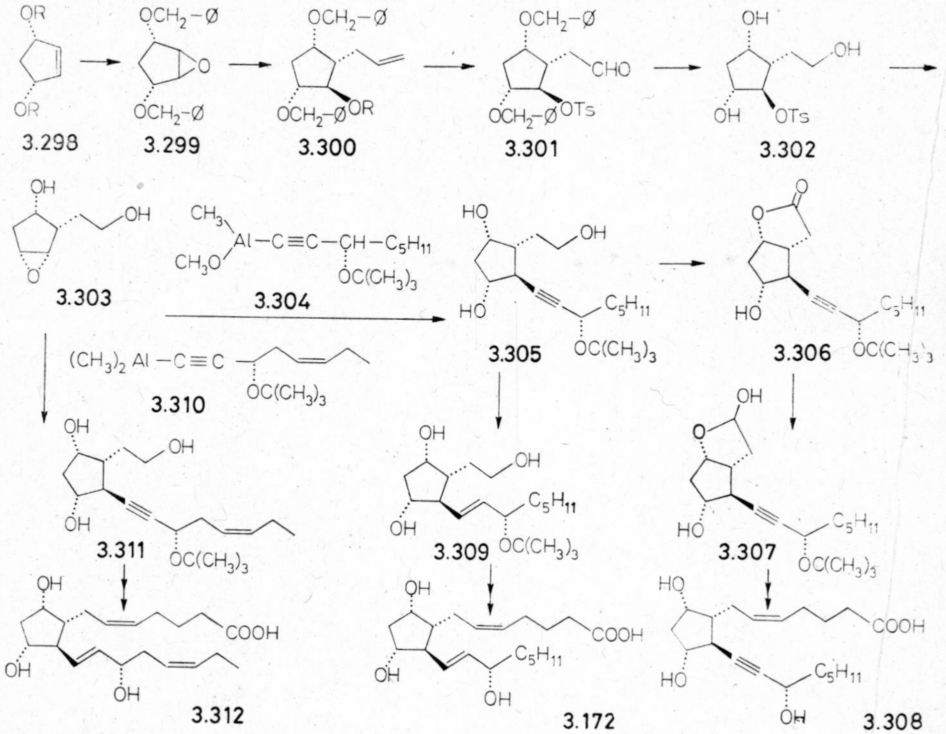

Fig. 3.21. Synthesis of prostaglandin $F_{2\alpha}$ *via* regioselective ring opening of epoxy-cyclopentane derivative

$R = CH_3$). On decreasing the reaction time, a mixture of the *exo*- and *endo*-acetals was formed (**2.286** and **3.287**, $R = CH_3$).

Configurational assignment of the acetals was based on NMR spectra recorded in the presence of a europium shift reagent. The upfield shift observed on addition of the shift reagent was higher for the *endo*- than for the *exo*-epimer in respect of the methoxyl and C_1 protons but lower for the *endo* C_7 proton.

Treatment of the *exo*-acetal (**3.286**) at low temperature ($-20°C$) with the divinylcuprate (**3.201**) led to a mixture of isomers containing predominantly the useful one (**3.295**, $R = H$, 80%). This was converted with *p*-phenylphenylurethane to the carbaminic ester (**3.295**, $R = p$-Ph-Ph-NH-CO); which was oxidized with sodium metaperiodate and catalytic amounts of osmium tetroxide to an aldehyde (**3.296**), followed by condensation with sodium dimethyl 2-oxoheptylphosphonate. The product, an enone (**3.297**), could be transformed to optically active prostaglandin $F_{2\alpha}$ (**3.172**) along established lines.

Regioselective ring opening of epoxycyclopentane derivatives and thereby the elaboration of the C_{12}-C_{20} side chain was solved by Fried and his co-workers using trialkylalanes (Fig. 3.21) [77–82]. The necessary epoxy-cyclopentanol (**3.303**) was prepared from 1,3-dihydroxy-2-cyclopentene (**3.298**, R = H), readily accessible from cyclopentadiene. After forming the benzyl ether (**3.298**, R = CH$_2$Ph) with benzyl chloride, the epoxide (**3.299**) was obtained by oxidation with m-chloroperbenzoic acid. With lithium diallylcuprate the epoxide gave an alcohol (**3.300**). Tosylation (**3.300**, R = Tos), cleavage of the double bond by ozonolysis to give the aldehyde (**3.301**), reduction of the aldehyde with sodium borohydride to an alcohol and finally debenzylation gave the trihydroxy compound (**3.302**); on heating with methanolic potassium hydroxide this furnished the required α-epoxide (**3.303**).

The other key intermediate, the alane component, was derived from the t-butyl ether (**3.313**) of 3(S)-hydroxyoctyne (**3.196**), which was made to react, in the form of its lithium salt, with dialkylaluminium chloride.

Later it turned out that the product, dimethyloctynylalane (**3.314**), was

largely contaminated with the methylmethoxyalane (**3.304**), since on contact with air during its manipulation, dimethylaluminium chloride became rapidly oxidized to methylmethoxyaluminium chloride. Since there was a marked difference in reactivity and regiospecificity between the two alanes, the pure methoxyalane (**3.304**) has also been prepared from methylmethoxyaluminium chloride obtained from dimethylaluminium chloride and methanol.

The reaction of the epoxycyclopentane (**3.303**) and the methoxyalane (**3.304**) was largely regioselective, and the desired 2-substituted cyclopentane-1,3-diol (**3.305**) could be isolated from the reaction mixture in 60% yield.

11 R.D.C.

The authors undertook a detailed examination of the reaction in order to increase its regioselectivity. The effect of variations in the substitution of the side chain of the epoxycyclopentane component (**3.315**) on the outcome of reaction with the dimethylalane (**3.314**) contaminated with methylmethoxy-alane (**3.304**) is shown in Table 3.1.

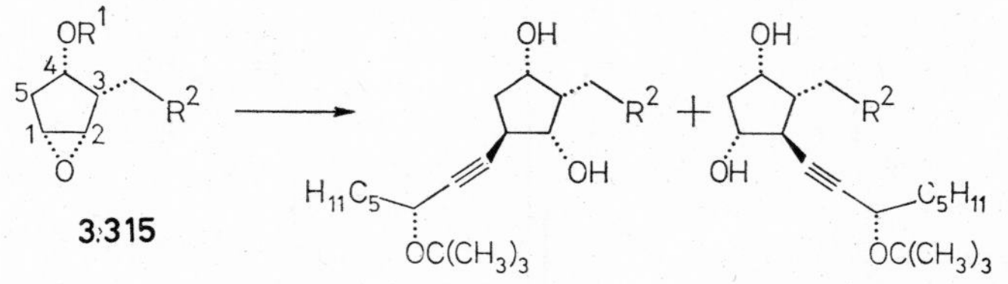

3.315   **3.316**   **3.317**

Table 3.1

(3.315)	R¹	R²	3.316 (%)	3.317 (%)	3.316/3.317
(a)	H	(CH₂)₆—OH	50	10	5
(b)	(CH₃)₃Si	CH=CH₂	51	19	2.7
(c)	H	CH⟨O-O⟩	26	21	1.2
(d)	(CH₃)₃Si	CH⟨O-O⟩	32	22	1.5
(e)	H	CH₂—OH	0	60	0
(f)	H	(CH₂)₂—OH	10	50	0.2

Table 3.1 demonstrates that regioselectivity in favour of the formation of the necessary isomer (**3.317**) requires the presence of a β- or γ-hydroxyl in the side chain (cases *e* and *f*). With the remaining models substitution takes place mainly in the C_1-position (C_{11} for prostaglandins).

These results can be rationalized by the formation of a covalent oxygen–aluminium bond prior to substitution. The epoxide bearing a β-hydroxy-ethyl side chain (**3.303**) may give rise to a complex in which substitution at C_2 is much preferred. The corresponding transition state (**3.318**) is un-strained, and the three-centre Al—C—Al bond is in accord with the known tendency of alanes to form dimers.

Dimethylalanes (**3.314**) are more reactive than their methylmethoxy ana-logues, therefore the latter are the reagents of choice if regioselectivity is attempted.

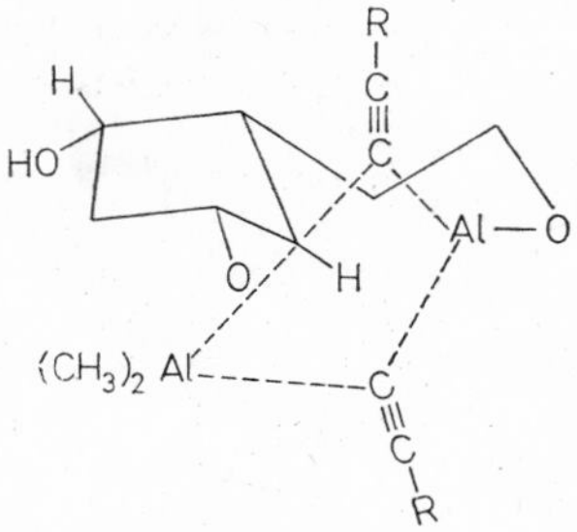

3.318

The product of the ring opening (Fig. 3.21, **3.305**) was selectively dehydrogenated (Pt/O$_2$) to a lactone (**3.306**) which was, in turn, reduced with diisobutylaluminium hydride to a lactol (**3.307**). Condensation of the lactol with the phosphorane generated from triphenyl-4-carboxybutylphosphonium salt led, after removal of the blocking groups, to optically active 13-dehydroprostaglandin F$_{2\alpha}$ (**3.308**).

13-Dehydroprostaglandins possess marked prostaglandin-like biological effects, which are of prolonged nature, since these analogues are not oxidized by prostaglandin dehydrogenase [78, 83, 84].

The intermediate obtained by ring opening (**3.305**) was suitable for the preparation of natural prostaglandin F$_{2\alpha}$ (**3.172**) as well. This was realized by reduction of the triple bond with lithium aluminium hydride in boiling tetrahydrofuran, tritylation of the primary hydroxyl followed by acetylation, and Collins oxidation after detritylation; the final steps were Wittig condensation and alkaline hydrolysis to (**3.172**).

The sequence outlined above was adapted by the same authors to the synthesis of prostaglandin F$_{3\alpha}$. (3Z)-Hexenal (**3.319**) served as the starting material for the alane component (**3.310**). Reaction of this with ethynylmagnesium bromide (**3.320**) gave the propargyl acohol (**3.321**). The latter was resolved with (−)-α-phenylethylamine in the form of its hemiphthalate, and the t-butyl ether of the (3S)-alcohol was made to react with dimethylaluminium chloride.

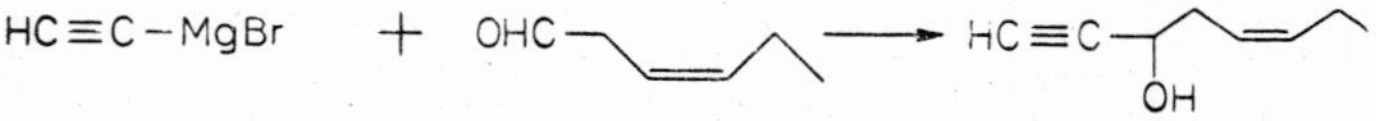

3.320   3.319   3.321

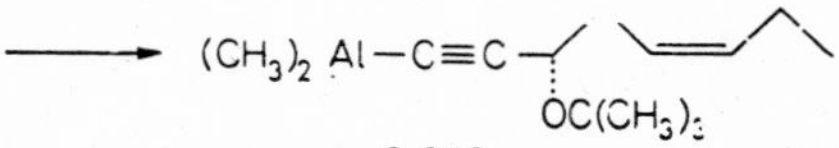

3.310

Ring opening of the epoxide (Fig. 3.21, **3.303**) with the alane (**3.310**) afforded a triol (**3.311**) which could be transformed to natural prostaglandin $F_{3\alpha}$
(**3.312**) using reactions already discussed.

Recently Evans and his co-workers reported a novel procedure suitable
for the synthesis of C_2-substituted *cis*-1,3-cyclopentenediols [85], which are
intermediates in Fried's synthesis discussed above. The underlying principle
was a thermal [2,3]-sigmatropic rearrangement of sulfoxides to sulfenic
esters.

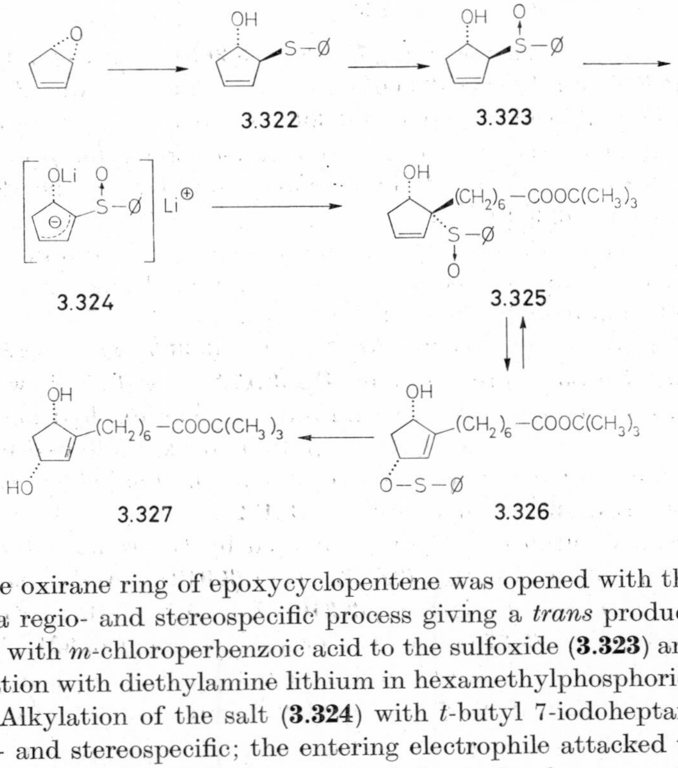

First the oxirane ring of epoxycyclopentene was opened with thiophenol.
This was a regio- and stereospecific process giving a *trans* product (**3.322**).
Oxidation with *m*-chloroperbenzoic acid to the sulfoxide (**3.323**) and lithium
salt formation with diethylamine lithium in hexamethylphosphoric triamide
followed. Alkylation of the salt (**3.324**) with *t*-butyl 7-iodoheptanoate was
also regio- and stereospecific; the entering electrophile attacked the centre
adjacent to the phenylsulfinyl group and from the face opposite to the
hydroxyl group. An equilibrium between the α-alkylsulfoxide (**3.325**) and
the sulfenate (**3.258**) was established by a [2,3]-sigmatropic shift. The sulfenate then hydrolyzed rapidly to the *cis*-1,2-cyclopentenediol (**3.327**).

3.7 SYSTEMATIC ANALYSIS AND COMPUTER-ASSISTED DESIGN OF PROSTAGLANDIN SYNTHESES

The use of computerized methods is gaining more and more importance in the design of organic syntheses. The efficiency of this approach has improved considerably since Wipke [86] elaborated programs enabling stereochemical features to be taken into consideration. Wipke's procedure is applicable, with certain restrictions, to the treatment of molecules of considerable complexity and containing several chiral centres such as prostaglandins, e.g. prostaglandin $F_{1\alpha}$.

Synthetic organic chemists are faced with a triple task, *viz.* selecting the target molecule, designing the synthetic sequence, and carrying it out at the bench. Of these, the theoretical design of synthesis has become recently the object of considerable efforts.

In view of the vast number of known organic compounds and reactions, further the poorly defined scope of the individual reactions, a systematic convergence to the optimal synthetic route leading to a certain compound seems to be an almost hopeless task. Nevertheless, in the last fifteen years several groups have been actively investigating this problem and have already achieved hopeful results.

The problems of chemical synthesis can be classified according to the relationship of what is known and what is sought:

$$\text{I. } S \rightarrow ?$$
$$\text{II. } S \rightarrow T$$
$$\text{III. } ? \rightarrow T$$

In the first group it is necessary to find out what sort of products can be prepared from a given starting material in a limited number of steps and with the aid of a limited number of reagents. This question is often posed in industry and the logical sequence is directed from starting material towards the end-product.

Group II includes the analysis of the synthesis of several drugs. In this case the complex target molecule (T) is given, and as starting material a similar, also rather complex but relatively easily accessible or easily prepared compound (S) is chosen. The task is to find the optimal synthetic route connecting S and T. In this search one may either proceed from the starting material towards the product or take the reverse course.

Group III comprises the majority of syntheses in which computer analysis may offer most possibilities. Here only the target molecule (T) is known and the task is to find an optimal combination of reactions, intermediates and starting materials leading to this target. This objective requires a gradual dissection of the target structure ending up at the starting materials.

The potentials of computer-assisted design of syntheses was first recognized by Sarret [87]. Programs serving this purpose fall into two categories. Some of them, information-oriented programs, apply algorithms working on existing knowledge and perform the required manipulations on these as input data. The other approach, the use of logic-oriented programs, is based, instead of empirical knowledge, on mathematical structures and formalism. A further aspect in classifying programs is the role of the chemist in the actual computational process. In the "conversational mode" (interactive program) the operator may take certain intermediate decisions in the knowledge of intermediary output data and may feed in further instructions. With the "batch programs" (noninteractive programs), the results are computed from a single initial input without any on-line intervention. The first type is generally more time-consuming and less efficient.

Corey and his group developed an information-oriented "conversational" program for the design of complex organic syntheses [88–91, 93]. The basic principle is the setting up of a "synthetic tree" with the target molecule at the point of origin, branching points representing intermediates, and connecting lines chemical transformations. The core of the program is a searching algorithm which evaluates already existing data concerning the molecule and the sets of reactions. Possible intermediates and reactions which may furnish the target molecules are established. The process is iterated for all of the eligible intermediates to provide several routes.

The program consists of the following main sub-units:

1. A data input sub-unit providing an interface between computer and user; the user is supposed as being a chemist without special mathematical training.

2. Transformation of data on the input molecules to a computer-oriented notation system.

3. A unit capable of recognizing and storing the structural features of the given target molecule.

4. A unit comparing the characteristics of the target molecule with the built-in set of chemical transformations.

5. A unit implementing the eligible transformations and producing thereby the next set of intermediates.

6. A unit evaluating intermediates and routes provided by preceding sub-units.

A prerequisite for the operation of the program is the storage of a sufficient number of reactions, which are then to be evaluated in respect of the target molecule. The program is empirical and utilizes known reactions only. The treatment of stereochemical features has not been solved in this program, and the availability of only 256 reactions stored restricts its use to hydrocarbons containing oxo and hydroxyl groups. Probability factors characterizing the usefulness of the individual reactions were assigned on an empirical and not on a theoretical basis [91].

Ugi and his co-workers created a basically different, logic-oriented program using a mathematical formalism [92], which at least in principle, did not require any empirical background; in practice it used some input based on existing knowledge, but considerably less than Corey's program.

Wipke extended the scope of Corey's program whereby it became suitable for the recognition and consideration of stereochemical features in the planning of syntheses [86]. This was a major improvement, because in the synthesis of complex molecules it is usually the elaboration of correct stereochemistry which is the most difficult problem.

Here we present one of the "optimal" routes leading to prostaglandin $F_{1\alpha}$ (**3.334**), computed with the aid of the Wipke program working on rather limited input information.

The synthesis starts with the epoxidation of cyclopentadiene (**3.40**). The epoxide is converted with a hydrogen halide in a regioselective reaction to *trans*-1-hydroxy-2-halogenocyclopentene (**3.328**). The upper chain of prostaglandin is introduced with a 1,7-dihalogenoheptane (**3.329**) involving inversion at C_2 in an S_N2 type reaction (**3.330**). The carboxyl group in the side chain is then elaborated, and the acid (**3.331**) converted to the α-epoxide (**3.332**). Regioselective ring opening of the oxirane ring with an organometallic compound and removal of the protecting group lead finally to racemic prostaglandin $F_{1\alpha}$ (**3.334**).

According to present knowledge the realization of this sequence is feasible, though the efficiency of stereochemical control in some of the steps in questionable. The key steps are stereospecific, but the regiospecificity of the oxirane ring opening may be problematic. However, the computed scheme is rather similar to Fried's prostaglandin synthesis discussed in Section 3.6.

REFERENCES

1. ELLISON, R. A., "Methods for the Synthesis of 3-Oxocyclopentenes." *Synthesis*, *1973*, 397.
2. BAGLI, J. F., BOGRI, T. DEGHENGHI, R., WIESNER, K., *Tetrahedron Lett.*, *1966*, 465.
3. BAGLI, J. F., BOGRI, T. (to Am. Home Prod. Co.), *U. S. Patent* 3 432 541 (1969).
4. ALVAREZ, F. S., WREN, D., PRINCE, A., *J. Am. Chem. Soc.*, **94**, 7823 (1972).
5. NOVÁK, L., SZÁNTAY, CS., *Synthesis*, *1974*, 353.
6. SZÁNTAY, CS., NOVÁK, L., KOVÁCS, G., INSTITORISZ, L. (to Pharmaceutical and Chemical Works Chinoin), "Procedure for the production of 1-(6-methoxycarbonyl-hexyl)-2-oxocyclopentene." *Hungarian Appl.* (Sept. 1973).
7. NOVÁK, L., GOMBOS, ZS., SZÁNTAY, CS., "Synthesis of cyclopentenones." Lecture held at the *Symposium on Prostaglandins*, Hungarian Academy of Sciences, Mátrafüred (Hungary), October, 1974.
8. NOVÁK, L., VISKY, Z., SZÁNTAY, CS., "Synthesis of cyclopentenone intermediates of prostaglandins." *International Conference on Prostaglandins*. Florence, May 1975. *Advances in Prostaglandin and Thromboxane Research*, Vol. 2, 874 (Ed. B. Samuelsson and R. Paoletti). Raven Press, New York, 1976. NOVÁK, L., SZÁNTAY, CS., VISKY, ZS., MAROSFALVI, J., *Synthesis* 1977, 575.
9. HESLINGA, L., VAN GORKOM, M., VAN DORP, D. A., *Rec. Trav. Chim.*, **87**, 1421 (1968).
10. PAPPO, R., COLLINS, P., JUNG, C., *Tetrahedron Lett.*, *1973*, 943.
11. KUROZUMI, S., TOM, T., ISHINOTO, S., *Tetrahedron Lett.*, *1973*, 4959.
12. SIH, C. H., SALOMON, R. G., PRICE, PH., PERUZZOTI, G., SOOD, R., *Chem. Commun.*, *1972*, 240.
13. SIH, CH. J., SALOMON, R. G., PRICE, PH., SOOD, R., PERUZZOTTI, G., *J. Am. Chem. Soc.*, **97**, 857 (1975).
14. SIH, CH. J., HEATHER, J. B., SOOD, R., PRICE, PH., PERUZZOTTI, G., HSU, L. F., LEE, S. S., *J. Am. Chem. Soc.*, **97**, 865 (1975).
15. FOOTE, CH. S., WEXLER, S., *J. Am. Chem. Soc.*, **86**, 3879 (1964).
16. GRIECO, P. A., REAP, J. J., *J. Org. Chem.*, **38**, 3413 (1973).
17. GRIECO, P. A., *J. Org. Chem.*, **37**, 2363 (1972).
18. WIEL, J.-B., ROUESSAC, F., *Chem. Commun.*, *1975*, 180.
19. COREY, E. J., NOYORI, R., *Tetrahedron Lett.*, *1970*, 311.
20. COREY, E. J., MANN, J., *J. Am. Chem. Soc.*, **95**, 6832 (1973).
21. COREY, E. J., NICOLAON, K. C., BEAMES, D. J., *Tetrahedron Lett.*, *1974*, 2439.

22. GRUBER, L., TÖMÖSKÖZI, I., MAJOR, E., KOVÁCS, G., *Tetrahedron Lett.*, *1974*, 3729.
23. STORK, G., KOWALSKI, C., GARCIA, G., *J. Am. Chem. Soc.*, *97*, 3258 (1975).
24. BÜCHI, G., EGGER, B., *J. Org. Chem.*, *36*, 2021 (1971); BÜCHI, G., HOCHSTRASSER, U., PAWLAK, W., *J. Org. Chem.*, *38*, 4348 (1973).
25. BAGLI, J., BOGRI, T., *Tetrahedron Lett.*, *1972*, 3815.
26. KIENZLE, F., HOLLAND, G. W., JERNOW, J. L., KWOH, S., ROSEN, P., *J. Org. Chem.*, *38*, 3440 (1973).
27. RHOADS, S. J., *Molecular Rearrangements*. Part I (11) 667 (Ed. P. DE MAYO). Interscience Publ., New York—London, 1963.
28. KATSUBE, J., MATSAI, M., *Agr. Biol. Chem.*, *33*, 1078 (1969).
29. PAPPO, R., COLLINS, P. W., JUNG, C., *Ann. N. Y. Acad. Sci.*, *180*, 38 (1971).
30. PAPPO, R., COLLINS, P. W., *Tetrahedron Lett.*, *1972*, 2627.
31. KNOWLES, W. S., SABACKY, M. J., VINEYARD, B. D., *Chem. Commun.*, *1972*, 10.
32. HARMON, R. E., GUPTA, S. K., BROWN, D. J., "Hydrogenation of Organic Compounds Using Homogeneous Catalysts." *Chem. Rev.*, *73*, 21 (1973).
33. SIH, CH. J., HEATHER, J. B., PERUZZOTTI, G., PRICE, PH., SOOD, R., HSU LEE, L.-F., *J. Am. Chem. Soc.*, *95*, 1676 (1973).
34. HEATHER, J. B., SOOD, R., PRICE, Ph., PERUZZOTTI, G., LEE, S. S., HSU LEE, L.-F., SIH, CH. J., *Tetrahedron Lett.*, *1973*, 2313.
35. BAGLI, J. F., BOGRI, T., *Tetrahedron Lett.*, *1967*, 5.
36. BOGRI, T., BAGLI, J. F., DEGHENGH, R., "An Improved Synthesis of the Prostanoic Acids." *Nobel Symposium 2, Prostaglandins* (Ed. BERGSTROM, S., and SAMUELSSON, B.,). Almquist and Wiksell, Stockholm, 1967.
37. CATON, M. P. L., COFFEE, E. C. J., WATKINS, G. L., *Tetrahedron Lett.*, *1972*, 773.
38. CATON, M. P. L., COFFEE, E. C. J., WATKINS, G. L., *Tetrahedron Lett.*, *1974*, 585.
39. VARECH, D., OOANNES, C., JACQUES, J., *Bull. Soc. Chim.*, *6*, 1662 (1965).
40. ELIEL, E. L., ALLINGER, N. L., ANGYAL, S. J., MORRISON, G. A., *Conformational Analysis*. Interscience Publ., New York, 1965.
41. TŐKE, L., HONTY, K., SZÁNTAY, Cs., *Chem. Ber.*, *102*, 3248 (1969).
42. BARTMANN, W., BECK, G., LERCH, U., *Tetrahedron Lett.*, *1974*, 2441.
43. FIESER, L., FIESER, M., *Reagents for Organic Synthesis*, 304. John Wiley and Sons, Inc., New York, 1967.
44. NEF, J. U., *Ann.*, *280*, 263 (1894).
45. NOLAND, W. E., *Chem. Rev.*, *55*, 137 (1955).
46. JACOBSON, R. M., *Tetrahedron Lett.*, *1974*, 3215.
47. SHECHTER, H., WILLIAMS, F. T., *J. Org. Chem.*, *27*, 3699 (1962).
48. MCMURRY, J. E., MELTON, J., *J. Org. Chem.*, *38*, 4367 (1973).
49. ALVAREZ, F. S., WREN, D., *Tetrahedron Lett.*, *1973*, 569.
50. BAGLI, J. F., BOGRI, T., *J. Org. Chem.*, *37*, 2132 (1972).
51. DENNEY, D. B., SHERMAN, N., *J. Org. Chem.*, *30*, 3760 (1965).
52. KASHIWAGI, T., KOZUKA, S., CAE, S., *Tetrahedron*, *26*, 3619 (1970).
53. BROWN, H. C., DICKASON, W. C., *J. Am. Chem. Soc.*, *92*, 709 (1970).
54. SCHAUB, R. E., WEISS, M. J., *Tetrahedron Lett.*, *1973*, 129.
55. BERNADY, K. F., WEISS, M. J., *Tetrahedron Lett.*, *1972*, 4083.
56. LIPMANN, W., *J. Pharm. Pharmacol.*, *22*, 65 (1970).
57. PIKE, J. E., *Nobel Symposium 2, Prostaglandins* (Ed. BERGSTROM, S. and SAMUELSSON, B.). Almquist and Wiksell, Stockholm, 1967.
58. HARDEGGER, E., SCHENK, H. P., BROGER, E., *Helv. Chim. Acta*, *50*, 2501 (1967).
59. NORMANT, J. F., "Organocopper(I) Compounds and Organocuprates in Synthesis." *Synthesis*, *1972*, 63.
60. HOUSE, H. O., UMEN, M. J., "The Chemistry of Carbanions. XXV. The Reaction of Various Organocopper Reagents with α,β-Unsaturated Carbonyl Compounds." *J. Org. Chem.*, *1973*, 3893.
61. CARROPHERS, W., "Lithium Organocuprates." *Chemistry and Industry*, *1973*, 932.
62. SIH, CH. J., PRICE, PH., SOOD, R., SALOMON, R. G., PERUZZOTTI, G., CASEY, M., *J. Am. Chem. Soc.*, *94*, 3643 (1972).
63. ZWEIFEL, G., WHITNEY, C. C., *J. Am. Chem. Soc.*, *89*, 2753 (1967).
64. REUCROFT, J., SAMMES, P. G., "Stereoselective and Stereospecific Olefin Synthesis." *Quart. Rev.*, *25*, 135 (1971).
65. KLUGE, A. F., UNTCH, K. G., FRIED, J. H., *J. Am. Chem. Soc.*, *94*, 9256 (1972)

66. KLUGE, A. F., UNTCH, K. G., FRIED, J. H., *J. Am. Chem. Soc.*, *94*, 7827 (1972).
67. MILLER, J. G., KURZ, W., UNTCH, K. G., STORK, G., *J. Am. Chem. Soc.*, *96*, 6774 (1974).
68. BICKART, P., CARSON, F. W., JACOBUS, J., MILLER, E. G., MISLOW, K., *J. Am. Chem. Soc.*, *90*, 4869 (1968); EVANS, D. A., ANDREWS, G. C., *Accounts Chem. Res.*, *7*, 147 (1974); EVANS, D. A., ANDREWS, G. C., SIMS, C. L., *J. Am. Chem. Soc.*, *94*, 3672 (1972).
69. PATTERSON, J. W., FRIED, J. H., *J. Org. Chem.*, *39*, 2506 (1974).
70. STORK, G., ROSEN, P., GOODMAN, N., COOMS, R. V., TSUJI, J., *J. Am. Chem. Soc.*, *87*, 275 (1965).
71. STOTTER, PH. L., HILL, K. A., *J. Org. Chem.*, *38*, 2576 (1973).
72. POSNER, G. H., WHITTEN, CH. E., STERLING, J. J., BRUNELLE, D. J., *Tetrahedron Lett.*, *1974*, 2591.
73. STORK, G., ISOBE, M., *J. Am. Chem. Soc.*, *97*, 4745, 6260 (1975).
74. COREY, E. J., MOINET, G., *J. Am. Chem. Soc.*, *95*, 6831 (1973).
75. COREY, E. J., BEAMES, D. J., *J. Am. Chem. Soc.*, *94*, 7210 (1972).
76. BERNADY, K. F., WEISS, M. J., *Tetrahedron Lett.*, *1972*, 4083.
77. FRIED, J., SIH, J. C., *Tetrahedron Lett.*, *1973*, 3899.
78. FRIED, J., LIN, C. H., *J. Med. Chem.*, *16*, 429 (1973).
79. FRIED, J., SIH, J. C., LIN, C. H., DALVEN, P., *J. Am. Chem. Soc.*, *94*, 4343 (1972).
80. FRIED, J., LIN, C. H., SIH, J. C., DALVEN, P., COOPER, G. F., *J. Am. Chem. Soc.*, *94*, 4342 (1972).
81. FRIED, J., LIN, C. H., FORD, S. H., *Tetrahedron Lett.*, *1969*, 1379.
82. FRIED, J., HEIM, S., ETHEREDGE, S. J., SUNDER-PLASSMANN, P., SANTHANA-KRISHNAN, T. S., HIMIZU, J., LIN, C. H., *Chem. Commun.*, *1968*, 634.
83. FRIED, J., "Chemical and biological studies on 13-dehydro-prostaglandins." Lecture held at the *International Conference on Prostaglandins*, Florence, May 1975.
84. GANDOLFI, C., PELLEGATA, R., CESERANI, R., AGRESTA, G., USARDI, M. M., "13-Dehydro-prostaglandins." Lecture held at the *International Conference on Prostaglandins*. Florence, May 1975.
85. EVANS, D. A., CRAWFORD, T. C., FUJIMOTO, T. T., THOMAS, R. C., *J. Org. Chem.*, *39*, 3176 (1974).
86. WIPKE, W. T., "Computer-assisted Three-dimensional Synthetic Analysis." *Computer Representation and Manipulation of Chemical Information*. Wiley and Sons, New York, 1974.
87. SARETT, L. H., "Synthetic Organic Chemistry, New Techniques and Targets." Lecture presented before Synthetic Manufacturers Association, June 9, 1964.
88. COREY, E. J., WIPKE, W. T., *Science*, *166*, 178 (1969).
89. COREY, E. J., WIPKE, W. T., CRAMER, R. D., HOWE, W. J., *J. Am. Chem. Soc.*, *94*, 421 (1972).
90. COREY, E. J., WIPKE, W. T., CRAMER, R. D., HOWE, W. J., *J. Am. Chem. Soc.*, *94*, 431 (1972).
91. COREY, E. J., HOWE, W., PENSAK, D. A., *J. Am. Chem. Soc.*, *96*, 7724 (1974).
92. BLAIR, J., GASTEIGER, J., GILLESPIE, C., GILLESPIE, P. D., UGI, J., *Tetrahedron*, *30*, 1845 (1974).
93. STORK, G., ISOBE, M., *J. Am. Chem. Soc.*, *97*, 6260 (1975).
94. BEHRSON, M., ESACK, A., "Computers and Organic Synthesis." *Chem. Rev.*, *76*, 269 (1976).

4. ASYMMETRIC SYNTHESIS OF PROSTAGLANDINS

4.1 BASIC PRINCIPLES
OF ASYMMETRIC ORGANIC SYNTHESIS

In the widest sense of the term, asymmetric synthesis covers reactions in which *prochiral* centres of molecules containing *enantiotopic* or *diastereotopic* groups or faces [1] are transformed to chiral centres in such a way that the ratio of the resulting stereo-isomers is *different from unity* [2]. Exceptionally the product, e.g. *meso*-tartaric acid, may be achiral as a whole. In discussing such phenomena the term reagent covers not only those in the usual sense, but also solvents, catalysts or a physical force field such as circularly polarized light.

The most thoroughly investigated aspect of asymmetric synthesis comprises the transformation of an achiral starting material with the aid of a chiral agent into a chiral product in such a way that the auxiliary molecule inducing chirality is removed later from the product leaving behind a new chiral molecule. The usual models in these studies were carbonyl compounds.

Most often, optically active molecules have been examined but sometimes valuable information has been gained from operations on racemic substrates as well.

According to Marckwald's more restricted definition, asymmetric syntheses are reactions in which optically active compounds are formed from symmetrically sub-stituted molecules with the temporary utilization of an optically active material, and without having recourse to any further analytical operations.

By the operational term "optical purity" the ratio of the actual rotation and that of the pure enantiomer is expressed:

$$\text{optical purity (in \%)} = \frac{[\alpha] \text{ measured}}{[\alpha] \text{ max.}} \cdot 100$$

Supposing a linear correlation, optical purity is identical with enantiomeric excess, i.e.

$$\text{enantiomeric excess (in \%)} = \frac{R - S}{R + S} \cdot 100 = R\% - S\%$$

The percentage of asymmetric synthesis and that of stereoselectivity are closely con-nected; the latter is of broader meaning also covering diastereomers. The above formula may also stand for stereoselectivity if R and S are replaced by molarities of the stereo-isomers.

The results of an asymmetric synthesis can be evaluated without the use of optically active reagents, too.

Marckwald's definition was the basis for the introduction of the concept of *asymmet-ric induction* for the interpretation of optical activity generated in reactions. It was postulated that asymmetry was "induced" in the course of the reaction by a stable centre of asymmetry of the molecule and this "induction" became manifest in the formation of diastereomers in unequal proportion.

Applying the modern theory of transition states, the postulation of an "inductive force" for the explanation of this phenomenon has become unnecessary, but the old terminology is still in use.

A study of asymmetric syntheses gives us, on the one hand, a deeper insight into organic reactions and is, on the other, of considerable practical significance for the preparation of optically active compounds. The ultimate objective in this field is to approximate the total stereoselectivity of enzyme systems.

Asymmetric syntheses are one kind of kinetically controlled asymmetric transformations. In these processes the reactants have, in the ground state, the same free energies ($\Delta G^0 = 0$), only the free energies of activation ($\Delta G^{\ddagger}$ associated with the different pathways are different. The degree of asymmetry of a transformation is dependent on this difference ($\Delta \Delta G^{\ddagger}$).

The condition $\Delta G^0 \neq 0$ can be fulfilled in two ways. Either a racemic substrate ((+)-A and (−)-A) reacts with a chiral reagent (R*) to form via two competing diastereomeric transition states two diastereomeric products of unequal ground state energy,

$$(-)\text{-A} + \text{R*} \rightarrow [(-)\text{-A} \cdot \text{R*}]^{\ddagger} \rightarrow \text{product}^1$$
$$(+)\text{-A} + \text{R*} \rightarrow [(+)\text{-A} \cdot \text{R*}]^{\ddagger} \rightarrow \text{product}^2,$$

or a single achiral compound (B) containing prochiral faces or groups, or a prochiral face or group within a chiral molecule, reacts with a chiral reagent (R*) to form diastereomeric transition states:

$$\text{B} + \text{R*} \begin{cases} [(-)\text{BR*}]^{\ddagger} \rightarrow \text{product}^1 \\ [(+)\text{BR*}]^{\ddagger} \rightarrow \text{product}^2 \end{cases}$$

The process in which one enantiomer of a racemate reacts preferentially in a reaction with a chiral reagent is denoted as *kinetic resolution*, whereas the reaction with a chiral reagent of an achiral (but prochiral) substance, or of a prochiral group or face in a chiral molecule, leading to a chiral product, is called *asymmetric synthesis*.

An example for kinetic resolution is the hydrolysis of racemic N-acetylamino acids with the enzyme acylase I, in which only the natural enantiomer is deacetylated. The ratio of the respective rates of hydrolysis is 1 : 10 000–40 000, i.e. the amino acids can be isolated in an optical purity of 99.9%.

In every asymmetric synthesis either (R)- or (S)-configuration dominates in respect of the newly formed chiral centre; it is, however, rather difficult to predict the direction and degree of preference.

4.2 ASYMMETRIC SYNTHESIS OF PROSTAGLANDIN $F_{2\alpha}$

Four of the five chiral centres of prostaglandin $F_{2\alpha}$ ($8R$, $9S$, $11R$, $12R$ and $15S$) are associated with the cyclopentane ring (Fig. 4.1, **4.10**). All of the schemes discussed before, including the stereoselective ones, produce racemates and the preparation of the optically active natural products requires the resolution of one of the intermediates, generally a cyclopentane having three chiral centres, and continuation of the sequence with the required enantiomer. Resolution necessarily involves the loss of at least fifty per cent of the intermediate in question, because racemization of the intermediates could not be realized so far.

Uskoković and his group earlier accomplished the asymmetric synthesis of loganin, a cyclopentane derivative containing five chiral centres [3]. Loganin is an important intermediate in the biosynthesis of indole alkaloids: the "non-tryptamine" part of their skeleton originates from this compound.

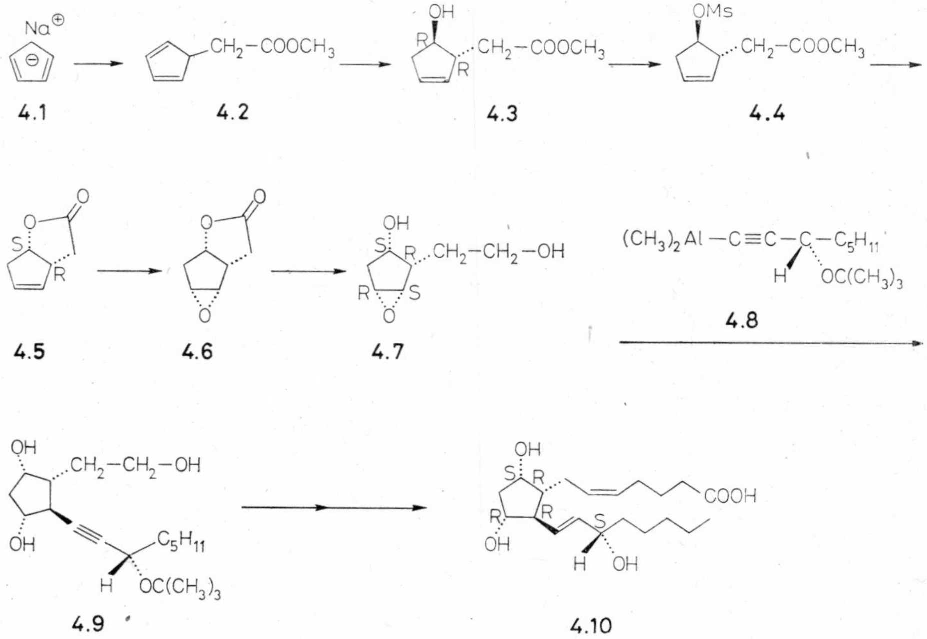

Fig. 4.1. Asymmetric synthesis of prostaglandin $F_{2\alpha}$

Experience gained in this work was put to use with the asymmetric synthesis of prostaglandin $F_{2\alpha}$ [4]. The concept of the authors was to convert a racemic cyclopentadiene by a reaction involving asymmetric induction to an optically active cyclopentene (A) containing two chiral centres, followed by the elaboration of two additional endocyclic chiral centres by a stereoselective reaction (B) and introducing the C_{12}-C_{20} side chain by another stereoselective step using a reactant which would ensure (S)-configuration at C_{15} of the prostaglandin.

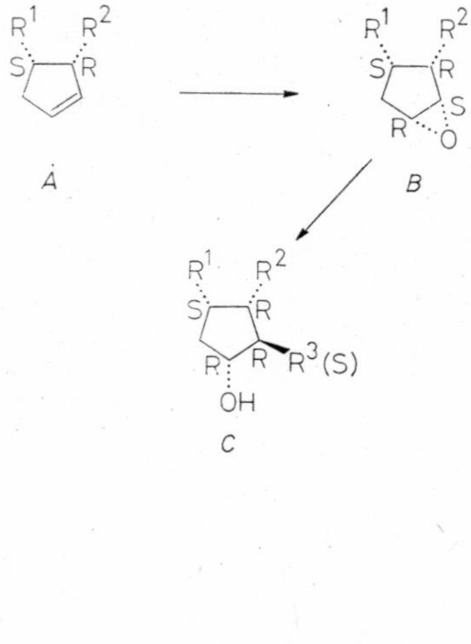

Cyclopentadienyl sodium (Fig. 4.1, **4.1**) served as the starting material, which was allowed to react at low temperature with methyl bromoacetate to give the ester (**4.2**). Hydroboration of the non-isolated ester with (+)-bis(3-pinanyl)borane, followed by oxidation with hydrogen peroxide afforded the hydroxy ester (**4.3**) in 45% chemical yield and with 96% optical purity.

The borane used in this reaction can readily be prepared from (+)-α-pinene and diborane or, according to a recent report [5], from sodium borohydride and aluminium chloride without the isolation of diborane. (+)-Bis(3-pinanyl)borane is one of the most stereoselective hydroborating reagents and is used extensively for asymmetric syntheses starting from olefins.

Optical purity of the hydroxy ester was determined by NMR-spectroscopy utilizing the separation of the methoxy-proton signals at 100 MHz of the corresponding diastereomeric esters formed with (R)-(+)-α-methoxy-α-trifluoromethylphenylacetic acid (cf. Chapter 3, p. 143) [6].

The sequence was continued by mesylation of the hydroxy ester (**4.3**) and by treating the product (**4.4**) with sodium hydroxide in aqueous tetrahydrofuran. This effected hydrolysis of the ester to form a carboxylate anion which, in a nucleophilic attack against the mesylated centre gave, by inversion from (R)- to (S)-configuration, the five-membered lactone (**4.5**). Oxidation of the crystalline lactone with peracetic acid furnished the cis-epoxylactone (**4.6**); this, on reduction with lithium aluminium hydride, gave the intermediate of Fried's prostaglandin synthesis (**4.7**).

Three of the four chiral centres conformed with those of prostaglandin $F_{2\alpha}$, only the one at C_{12} was unnatural. Therefore, the introduction of the lower chain by epoxide ring opening had to be both regio- and stereospecific.

Uskokovič et al. accomplished this objective using, similar to Fried's group, (3S)-t-butoxyoctynyldimethylalane (**3.8**) (cf. Chapter 3). Using a 4–9-fold excess of the reagent, ring opening was stereospecific and to a great extent also regioselective, giving the alkynylcyclopentane (**4.9**) in 60% yield. This was transformed to prostaglandin $F_{2\alpha}$ along the lines of Fried's scheme.

4.3 ASYMMETRIC PROSTAGLANDIN SYNTHESES BASED ON PSEUDOSYMMETRIC COMPOUNDS

Fischli and his co-workers used a different approach to solve the task of converting an achiral starting material without resolution into optically active prostaglandin $F_{2\alpha}$ or its enantiomer (ent-prostaglandin $F_{2\alpha}$) [7–9]. The principle of their scheme, the utilization of the pseudosymmetric properties of meso-compounds, is shown in Fig. 4.2.

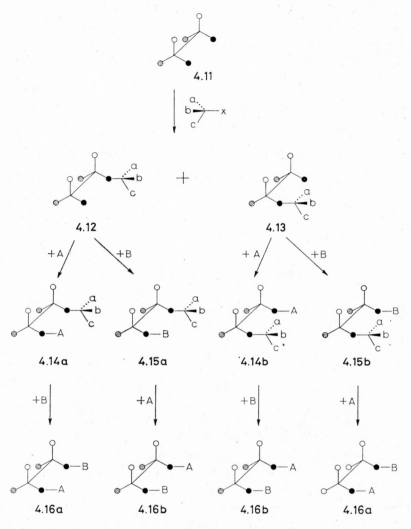

Fig. 4.2. Overall scheme for the utilization of *meso*-compounds in asymmetric synthesis

     Reaction of a pseudosymmetric *meso*-compound with a chiral partner produces a pair of diastereomers (**4.12** and **4.13**) which can be then separated by conventional physical methods. Combination of one of the diastereomers (e.g. **4.12**) with an achiral partner *A*, followed by replacement of the chiral group by another achiral group *B*, gives rise to an optically active molecule containing two chiral centres (**4.16a**). Accomplishing the same transformations in the reverse order, i.e. introducing first B and later A, leads to the enantiomer (**4.16b**) of the above compound.

Performing the same operations on the other diastereomer (**4.13**) gives identical results. This is of great advantage since both diastereomers can be converted by an appropriate sequencing of the same transformations to a common optically active intermediate. Alternatively, if only one of the diastereomers can be obtained in the pure state, the unwanted isomer can be reverted to the parent *meso*-compound, usually by hydrolysis.

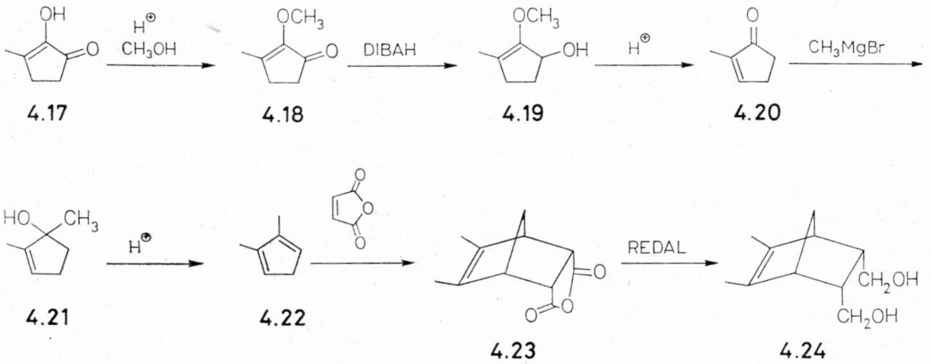

Fig. 4.3. Synthesis of the *meso*-intermediate of the asymmetric synthesis of $PGF_{2\alpha}$ and *ent*-$PGF_{2\alpha}$

The *meso*-compound actually used (Fig. 4.3, **4.24**) was prepared from the readily accessible corylone (**4.17**) by forming the enol ether (**4.18**) with methanol, reducing it with diisobutylaluminium hydride to the alcohol (**4.19**) and then carrying out acidic dehydration accompanied by isomerization to the more stable enone system of (**4.20**). Addition of methylmagnesium bromide on the enone and dehydration of the alcohol (**4.21**) gave 2,3-dimethyl-cyclopentadiene (**4.22**). Diels–Alder addition of maleic anhydride and reduction of the adduct with sodium bis(2-methoxyethoxy)aluminium hydride gave *endo*-2,3-dimethyl-5,6-dihydroxymethylnorbornene (**4.24**). Formation of a cyclic carbonate with phosgene completed the elaboration of the required *meso*-compound (Fig. 4.4, **4.25**).

Ring opening with levorotatory isonorbornylamine (**4.26**) generated a pair of diastereomeric urethanes (**4.27** and **4.28**,) which could be separated by crystallization from ethyl acetate. This gave 20–25% of the levorotatory compound (**4.27**); 75–80% of the *meso*-compound could be recovered from the mother liquor by evaporation and alkaline hydrolysis.

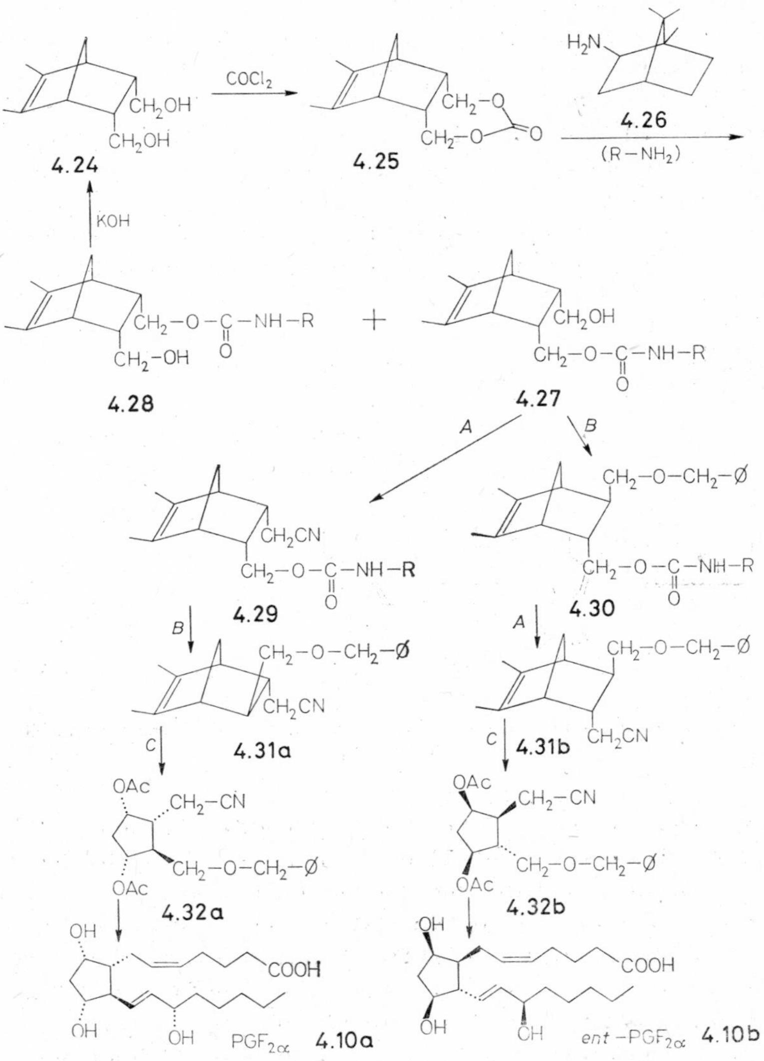

Fig. 4.4. Asymmetric synthesis of prostaglandin $F_{2\alpha}$ and ent-PGF$_{2\alpha}$

In the subsequent steps, the hydroxymethyl groups of the intermediate were used to construct the two side chains of the prostaglandin molecule. This required the homologation of one of the hydroxymethyl groups to provide the carbon atom between the ring and the double bond of the upper chain, and inversion of the configuration of one of the chiral centres, as required by the *trans* disposition of the side chains in the end-product.

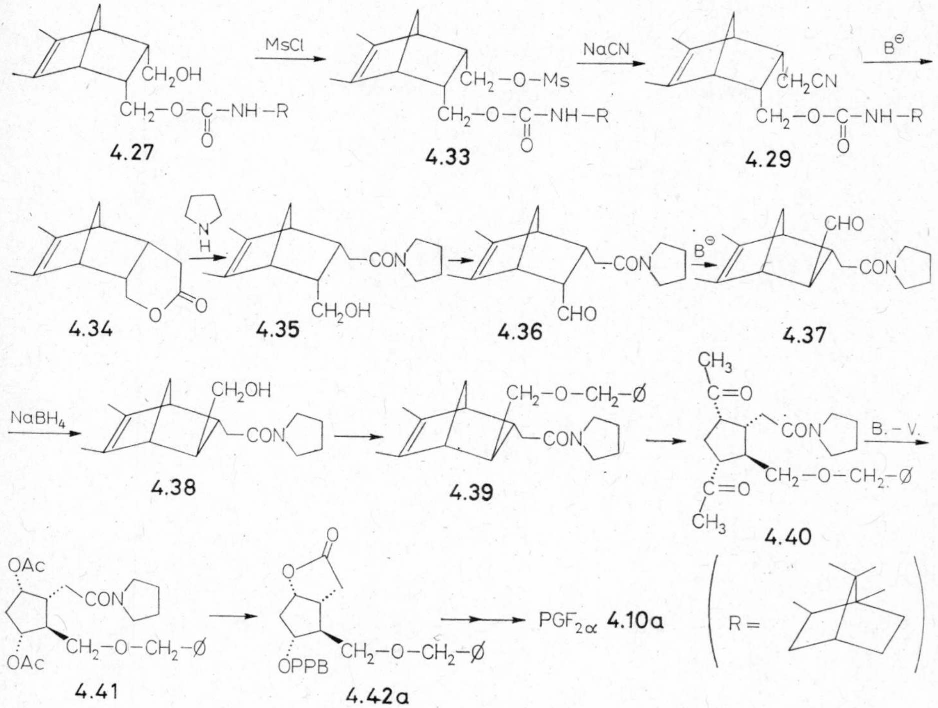

Fig. 4.5. Asymmetric synthesis of prostaglandin $F_{2\alpha}$

The foregoing requirements determined the nature of transformations A and B discussed above. The sequence leading to natural prostaglandins called for introducing first a cyano group (4.29), followed by inversion at C_5. The synthesis of *ent*-prostaglandins necessitated, in turn, epimerization at C_6 before the formation of the cyano group. The further transformations to be performed on the enantiomeric intermediates (4.31a and 4.31b) were identical.

Details of the synthesis of prostaglandin $F_{2\alpha}$ based on the above principles are shown in Fig. 4.5. The sequence started with mesylation of the free hydroxyl of the norbornene (4.26) in pyridine with mesyl chloride, and conversion of the mesylate (4.33) with sodium cyanide in dimethylsulfoxide to the cyanomethyl derivative (4.29). Alkaline treatment effected hydrolysis of both the cyano and urethane functions with concomitant lactonization. The opening of the lactone (4.34) with pyrrolidine yielded the amide (4.35). Oxidation of the carbinol group to the *endo*-aldehyde (4.36) with chromium

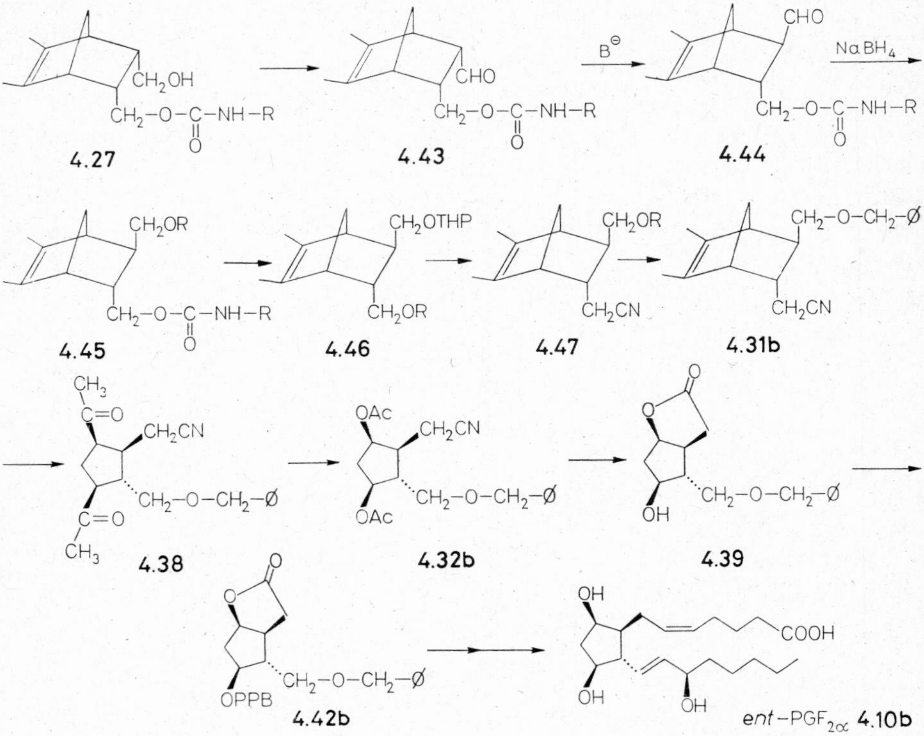

Fig. 4.6. Asymmetric synthesis of *ent*-PGF$_{2\alpha}$

trioxide–pyridine complex set the stage for base-catalyzed epimerization with piperidine acetate to the *exo*-epimer (**4.37**). This was again reduced with sodium borohydride to the alcohol (**4.38**); which was then benzylated (sodium hydride and benzyl chloride), the ether (**4.39**) ozonolyzed and transformed with dimethyl sulfide directly to the bis-methylketone derivative (**4.40**). Baeyer–Villiger oxidation with pertrifluoroacetic acid gave the diacetoxy compound (**4.41**) that was lactonized to a hydroxylactone. Conversion to prostaglandin F$_{2\alpha}$ *via* the *p*-phenylbenzoate (**4.42**) proceeded in the usual way (*cf.* Chapter 2).

The synthesis of *ent*-prostaglandin F$_{2\alpha}$ (**4.10b**) was accomplished by reversing the order of the transformation described above (Fig. 4.6). Accordingly, first Pfitzner–Moffatt oxidation (dimethyl sulfoxide–dicyclohexylcarbodiimide–trifluoroacetic acid–pyridine) converted the hydroxymethyl group to a formyl group of *endo* configuration (**4.43**). *Endo-exo* isomerization (to **4.44**), reduction to the alcohol (**4.45**, R = H), formation of the tetrahydropyranyl ether (**4.45**, R = THP) and alkaline hydrolysis of the urethane part afforded the alcohol (**4.46**, R = H). A sequence of mesylation (**4.46**, R = Ms), conversion with sodium cyanide to the cyanomethyl derivative (**4.47**, R = THP), acid hydrolysis, benzylation of the hydroxy-nitrile (**4.47**, R = H), ozonolysis of the ether (**4.31b**), and treatment with dimethyl sulfide furnished the bis-methylketone (**4.38**). Baeyer–Villiger oxidation, lactonization of the bis-acetoxynitrile (**4.32b**) and acylation with p-phenylbenzoyl chloride of the hydroxylactone (**4.39**) completed the synthesis of the enantiomer of Corey's lactone intermediate (**4.42b**), that was converted to ent-prostaglandin $F_{2\alpha}$ (**4.10b**) by established methods.

4.4 BIOCHEMICAL APPROACHES

Recently Sih and co-workers published a new total synthesis of prostaglandins E_1 and E_2, in which microbiological methods were exploited to lend

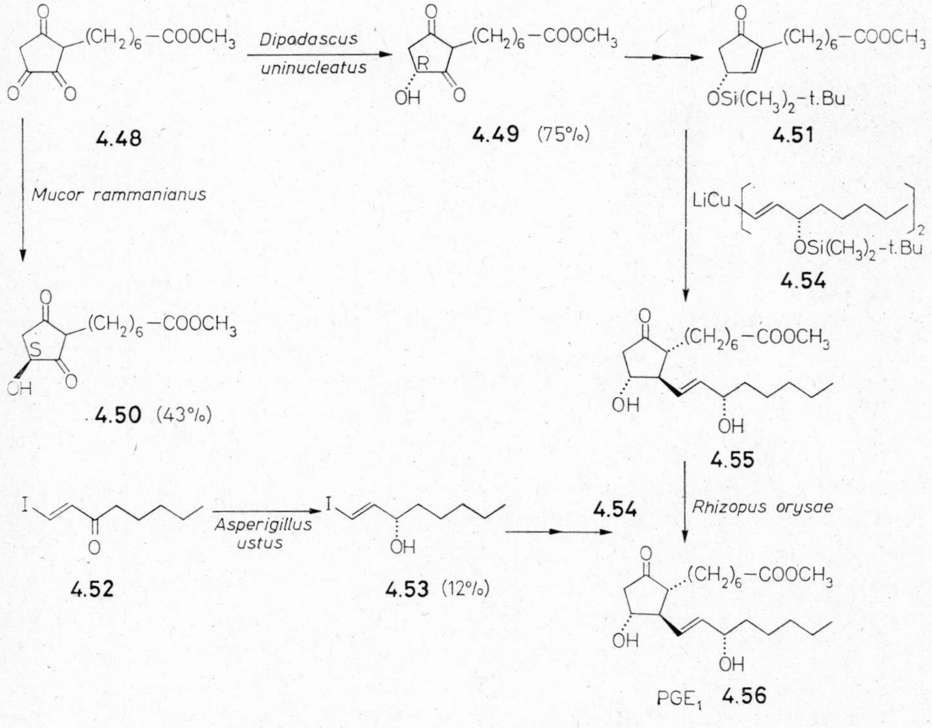

Fig. 4.7. Asymmetric synthesis of PGE$_1$

12*

optical activity to one of the intermediates [11, 12] (for some of the details, see Sections 3.14 and 3.5).

The crucial step of this asymmetric synthesis of prostaglandin E_2 was the reduction of the achiral cyclopentanetrione (**4.48**, Fig. 4.7) by incubation with the microorganism *Dipodascus uninucleatus* yielding the optically pure 4(*R*)-hydroxycyclopentanedione (**4.49**) in 75% yield. Interestingly, reduction with *Mucor rammanianus* gave the other enantiomer (**4.50**) in somewhat lower yields. Multistep transformation of the (4*R*)-alcohol to the cyclopentenone (**4.51**) (*cf.* Section 3.14) was followed by addition of a homocuprate of (3*S*)-configuration (**4.54**), obtained from the iodoenone (**4.52**) also by microbiological reduction (**4.52 → 4.53**).

Recently Japanese workers also accomplished the asymmetric reduction of the trione (**4.48**) by lithium aluminium hydride pretreated with 3 equivalents of (−)-N-methylephedrine. The product was the (*R*)-(−)-4-hydroxydione (**4.49**) [15].

As shown before (Section 3.5), homocuprate addition on cyclopentenones is highly stereoselective; the bulky reagent approaches the enone system

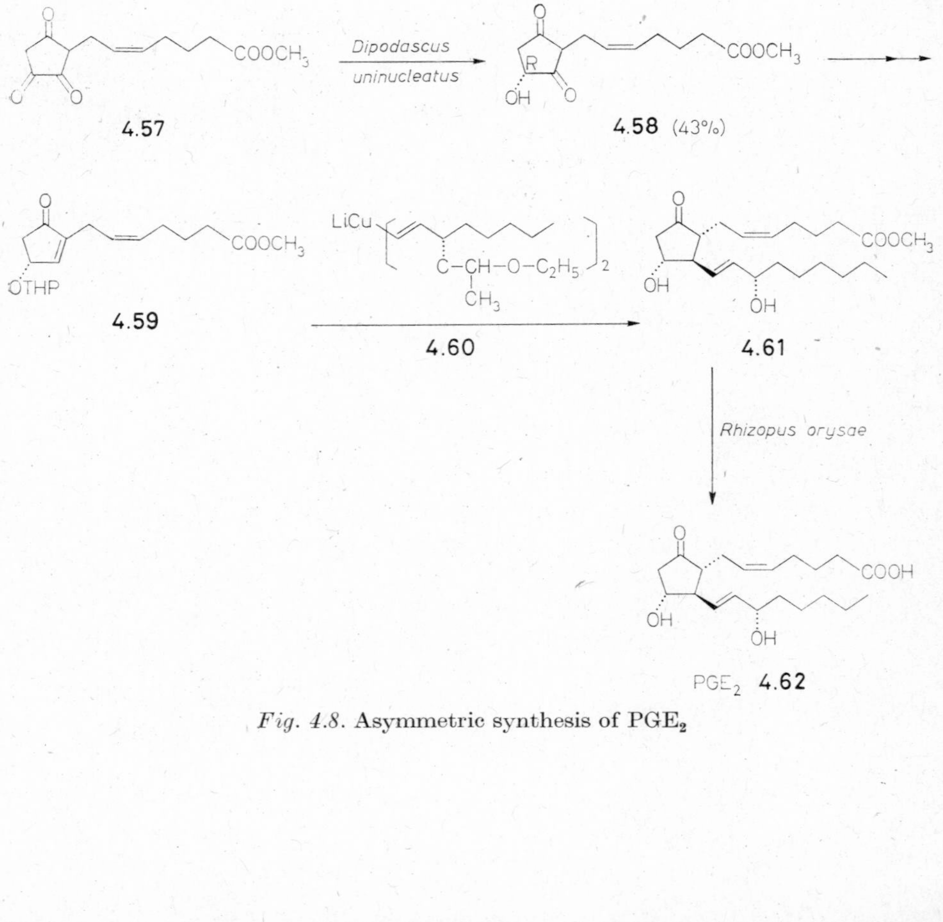

Fig. 4.8. Asymmetric synthesis of PGE$_2$

from the face opposite to the allylic ether group, securing thereby the required *trans-trans* substitution of the cyclopentane ring.

The above reaction afforded a single product giving, after ether hydrolysis,
prostaglandin E_1 methyl ester (**4.55**). The parent prostaglandin (**4.56**) was
obtained from the ester by hydrolysis with *Rhizopus orysae*.

Asymmetric synthesis of prostaglandin E_2 required as starting material
a cyclopentanetrione (**4.57**, Fig. 4.8) containing in the side chain a (Z)-
double bond. Microbiological reduction of the trione with *Dipodascus uninucleatus* gave the (4R)-hydroxydione (**4.58**) that was transformed to the
enone (**4.59**) (*cf.* Section 3.14), allowed to react with the optically active
homocuprate (**4.60**) to furnish prostaglandin E_2 methyl ester (**4.61**) and,
after microbiological hydrolysis (*Rhizopus orysae*), the acid (**4.62**).

4.5 ASYMMETRIC SYNTHESIS OF COREY'S IODOLACTONE INTERMEDIATE

Recently Corey and Ensley accomplished an asymmetric synthesis of the
key intermediate of Corey's stereocontrolled synthesis of prostaglandins,
namely of that of the iodolactone (*cf.* Chapter 2) (Fig. 4.9) [12]. Optical
activity was created by reacting 5-benzyloxymethylcyclopentadiene (**4.6**)
with the acrylic ester (**4.64**) of an optically active alcohol (**4.68**) in a Diels–
Alder reaction catalyzed by aluminium chloride. The levorotatory enantiomer of the *endo* adduct (**4.65**) isolated in 89% yield was converted to an
enolate salt with lithium diisopropylamide and oxidized with molecular
oxygen in tetrahydrofurane in the presence of triethylphosphite. This gave
a hydroxy ester (**4.66**, as a mixture of *endo* and *exo* isomers) that was first
reduced with lithium aluminium hydride to a diol (**4.67**) and then oxidized
with sodium metaperiodate to a ketone (**4.69**). Oxidation of the ketone with
alkaline hydrogen peroxide to a hydroxy acid and iodolactonization led to
the already known optically active iodolactone.

The alcohol component (**4.68**) was prepared from (S)-pulegone (**4.74**); the
chiral directing ability of this moiety proved to be much superior to that of
(−)-menthol. (S)-Pulegone itself was synthetized from (−)-citronellol (**4.72**)
by oxidation with pyridinium chlorochromate to isopulegone (**4.73**), and
subsequent isomerization by base to (S)-pulegone (**4.74**). 1,4-Addition of
phenylmagnesium bromide to the latter in the presence of copper(I) chloride
gave the ketone (**4.75**) which was reduced to the alcohol (**4.76**) and converted
to the acrylate ester (**4.64**) with acryloyl chloride in the presence of equivalent triethylamine.

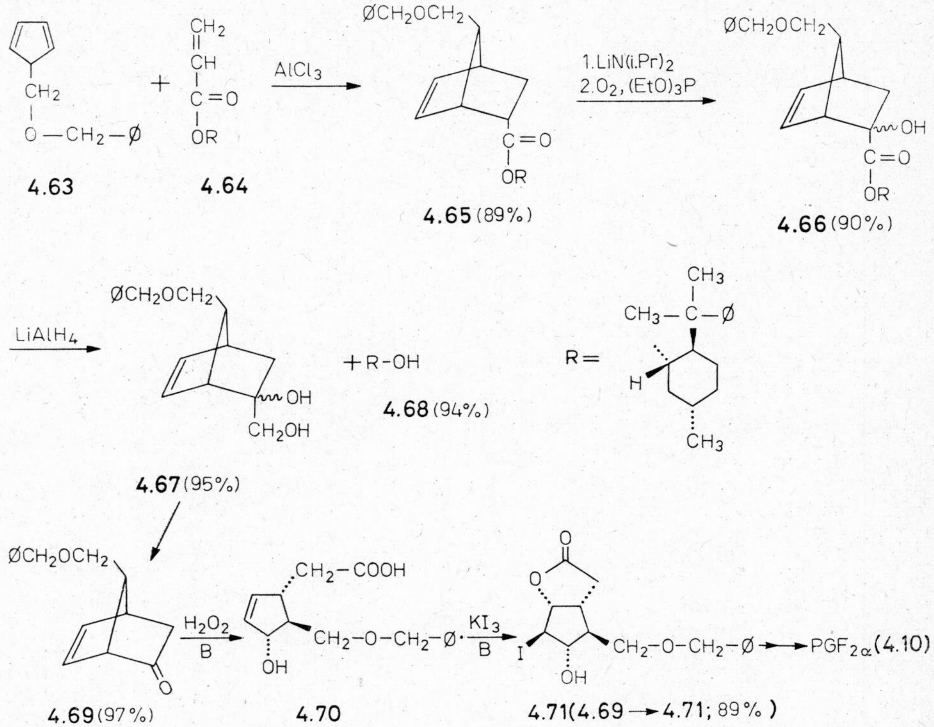

Fig. 4.9. Preparation of Corey's iodolactone intermediate *via* asymmetric induction

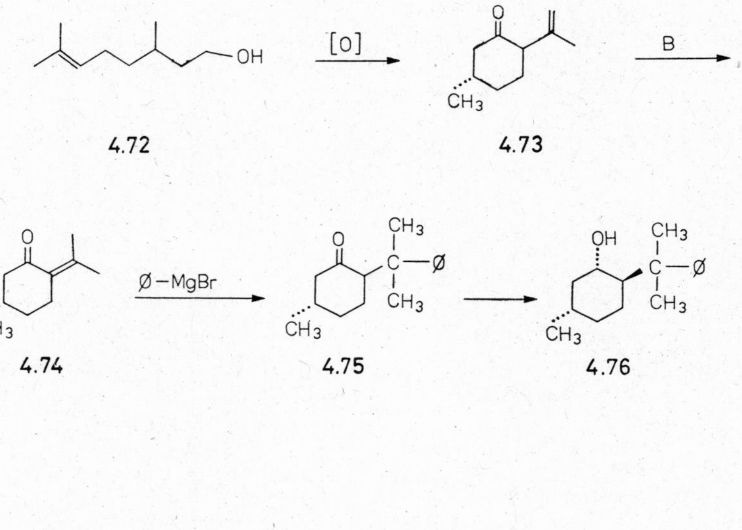

4.6 THE CHIRAL SYNTHESIS OF PROSTAGLANDIN A_2

Recently Stork and Raucher accomplished a chiral synthesis of prostaglandin A_2 starting from a simple sugar [13]. The idea was to utilize the two

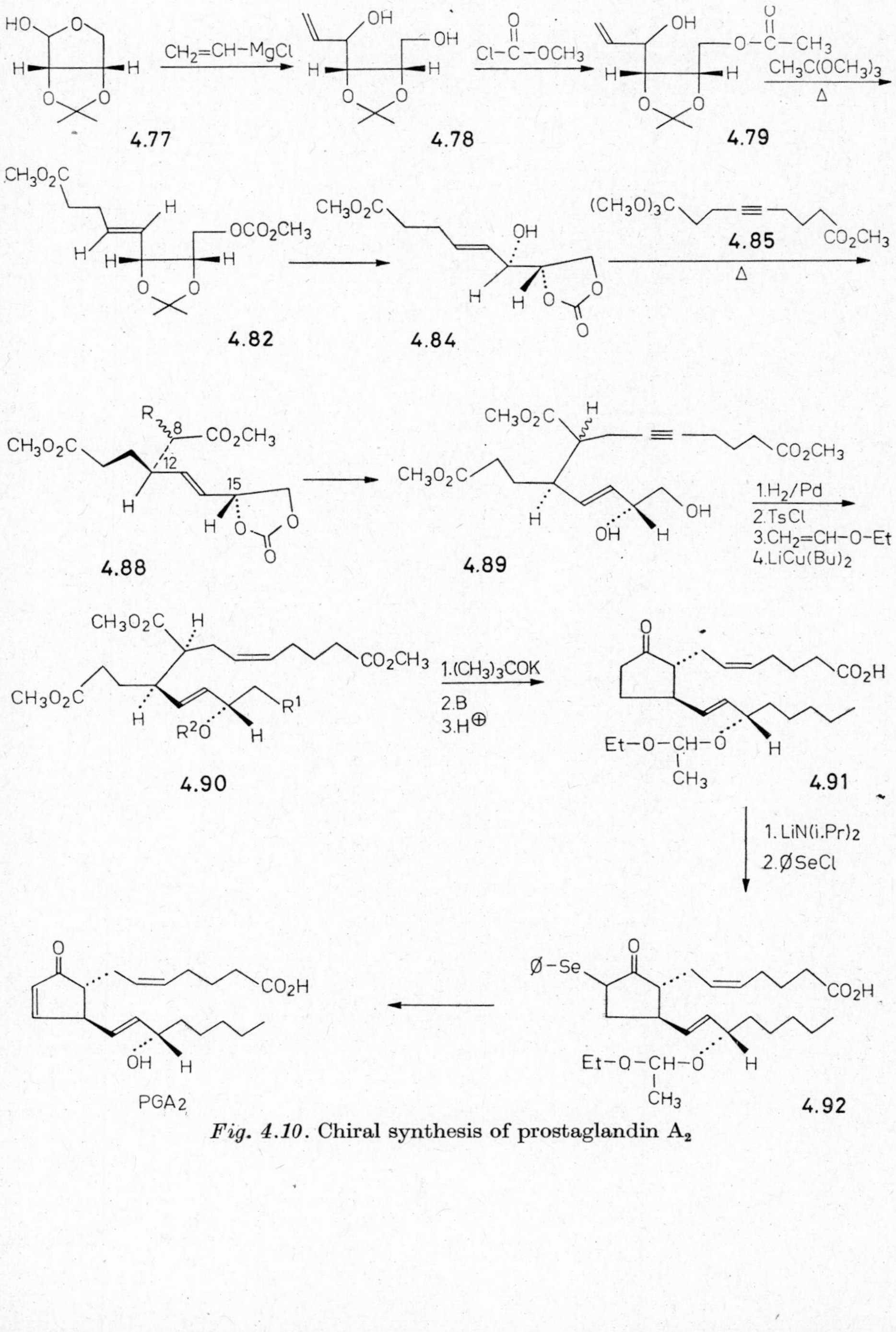

4.77 $CH_2=CH-MgCl$ 4.78 $Cl-C-OCH_3$ 4.79 $CH_3C(OCH_3)_3$ Δ

4.82   4.84   4.85 Δ

4.88   4.89   1.H_2/Pd   2.TsCl   3.$CH_2=CH-O-Et$ 4.LiCu(Bu)$_2$

4.90   1.$(CH_3)_3COK$ 2.B   3.$H^{\oplus}$ 4.91

1. LiN(i.Pr)$_2$ 2.$\emptyset$SeCl

PGA2   4.92

Fig. 4.10. Chiral synthesis of prostaglandin A_2

chiral centres of erythrose to elaborate chiral centres of prostaglandin, in particular to transform the C_3 atom of L-erythrose to C_{15} of the prostaglandin skeleton. Chirality at C_2 in turn was exploited to direct configuration at C_{12} in the end product. The latter transformation and the forming of a C_{13-14} double bond of (E) geometry was carried out using the Claisen rearrangement.

The known 2,3-isopropylidene-L-erythrose (Fig. 4.10, **4.77**) was made to react with vinyl magnesium chloride to give the allyl alcohol (**4.78**) the primary hydroxyl of which was masked by reaction with methyl chloroformate as a methyl carbonate. On heating the product (**4.79**) with trimethyl orthoacetate in the presence of propionic acid, a Claisen rearrangement occurred to yield an unsaturated diester with an (E) double bond (**4.82**). This result was predictable since assuming a chair-type transition state for the Claisen rearrangement of the allyl vinyl ether intermediate, the one (**4.80**) containing the bulky group R in the *equatorial* position is preferred to the other in which R is *axially* oriented (**4.81**) and *via* (**4.80**) an (E) double bond is produced.

The sequence was continued by acid hydrolysis of the isopropylidene moiety and blocking the non-allylic hydroxyls in the form of a cyclic carbonate by treatment with methyl chloroformate and triethylamine. The allyl alcohol (**4.84**) was now subjected to a similar sequence involving reaction with the orthoester (**4.85**) and Claisen rearrangement, which gave (**4.88**) as a mixture of epimers at C_8 (prostaglandin numbering). Configuration at C_{12} follows again from the geometry of the six-membered chair-like transition state of the thermal rearrangement: the preferred arrangements (**4.86** and **4.87**) are those in which both bulky substituents (R^1 and R^2) are *equatorially* oriented. On the other hand, in the absence of 1,3-*diaxial* interactions there is no such preference for the orientation of R^3, which explains the lack of stereoselectivity at C_8.

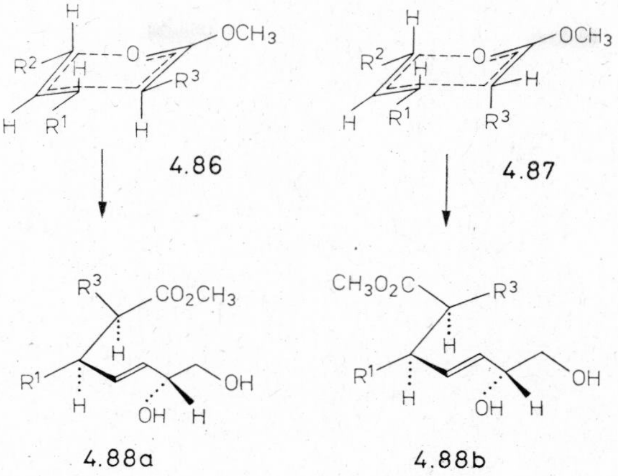

4.86   4.87

4.88a   4.88b

The product mixture was hydrolyzed with alkali and the resulting diol (Fig. 4.10, **4.89**) hydrogenated on palladium-barium sulfate catalyst, tosylated at the primary hydroxyl, blocked at the secondary hydroxyl with ethyl vinyl ether and finally the product (**4.90**; $R^1 = $ Ts, $R^2 = CH_3-CH-OEt$) was made to react with lithium dibutyl cuprate. This gave a key intermediate in which all the carbon atoms have been assembled (**4.90**, $R^1 = n$-butyl, $R^2 = CH_3CH-OEt$). Ring closure with potassium t-butoxide gave the

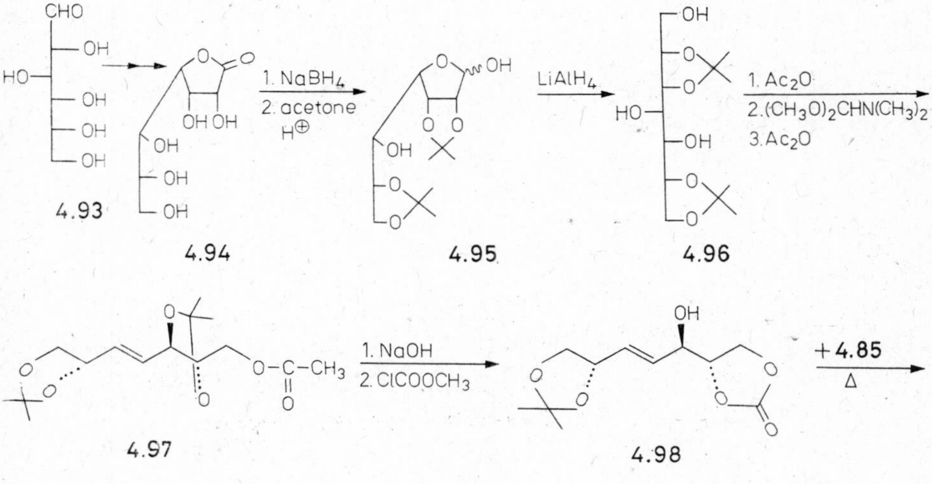

4.93   4.94   4.95   4.96

4.97   4.98   + 4.85

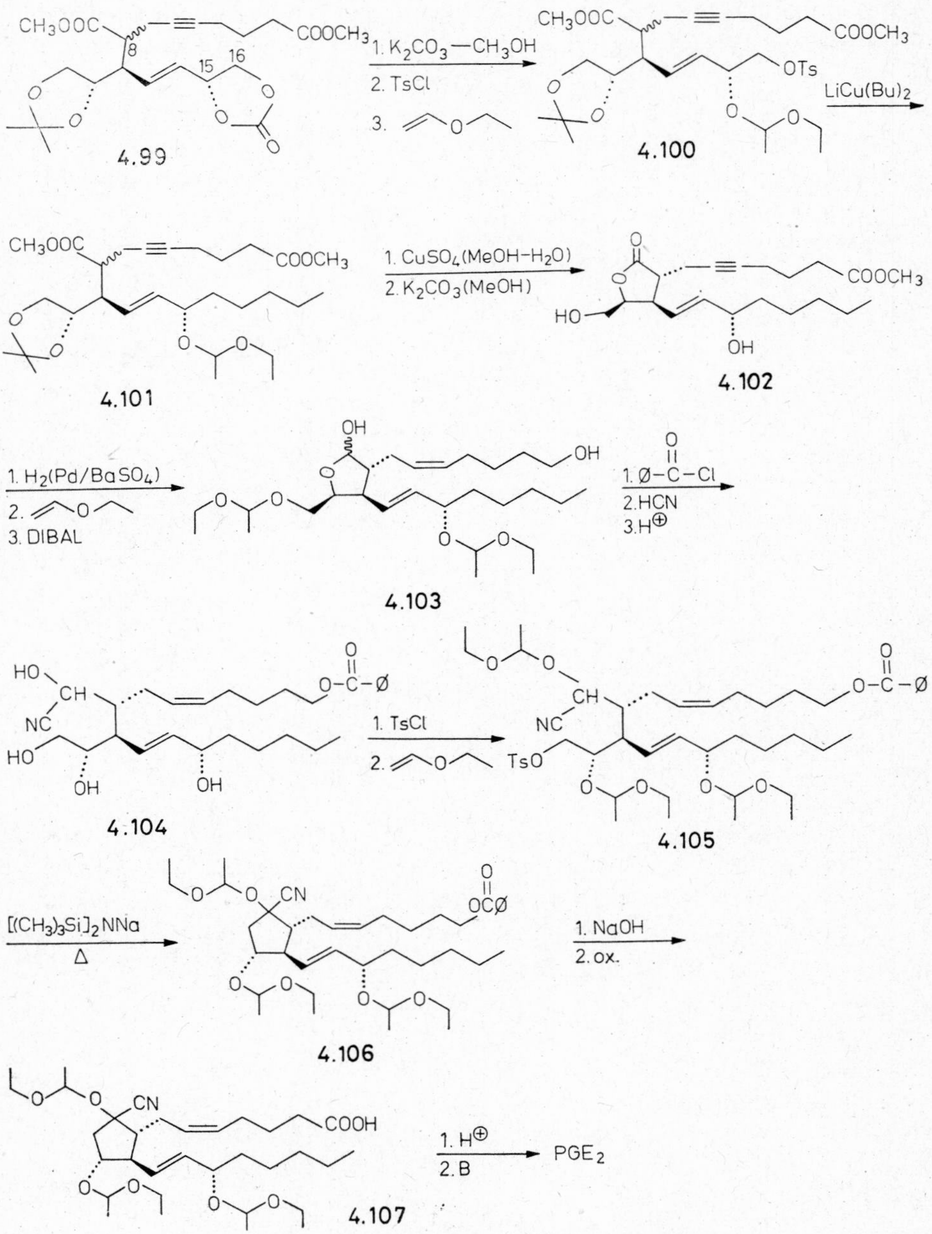

Fig. 4.11. Chiral synthesis of prostaglandin E_2

more stable *trans*-disubstituted cyclopentanone (**4.91**) from both epimers.
From this, an anion was generated with lithium diisopropylamide; reaction
of the product with phenylselenyl chloride gave (**4.92**). Oxidation with
sodium periodate and removal of the blocking groups afforded optically
active prostaglandin A_2, identical with the natural product.

Stork and Takashi also solved the chiral synthesis of prostaglandin E_2
using the seven-carbon aldonic-γ-lactone (**4.94**), which had been prepared
from D-glucose (**4.93**) earlier (Fig. 4.11). The C_2 atom of D-glucose appears
as C_{15} in the prostaglandin skeleton, whereas C_5 becomes C_{11}. Finally, as in
the chiral synthesis of prostaglandin A_2, the chirality of C_3 was exploited
to direct the configuration at C_{12}. The latter transformation was here also
accomplished by Claisen rearrangement [16].

As the first step the lactone (**4.94**) was reduced with sodium borohydride
to a lactol and protected as the diacetonide (**4.95**). Further reduction with
lithium aluminium hydride gave a heptite (**4.96**). After acetylation a double
bond of E geometry was generated using dimethylformamide dimethyl acetal. Saponification of the product (**4.97**) liberated the primary hydroxyl,
and this was reacylated with chloroformate ester. This was accompanied by
a cleavage of the adjacent dioxolane ring by the intermediate methyl carbonate to afford finally the allyl alcohol (**4.98**). Subjecting the latter after
reaction with the orthoester (**4.85**) to Claisen rearrangement yielded a pair
of products epimeric at C_8 (**4.99**) (prostaglandin numbering). The carbonate
ester function at $C_{15, 16}$ was removed with potassium carbonate in methanol
followed by tosylation of the primary hydroxyl and protection of the secondary one by ethyl vinyl ether. Coupling of the tosylate (**4.100**) with lithium
dibutyl cuprate gave (**4.101**) which was deprotected by heating with copper
sulfate in aqueous methanol and lactonized to (**4.102**) with potassium carbonate. Notable is the *trans* disposition of the two side chains in this lactone,
corresponding to natural prostaglandins. After partial reduction of the
triple bond and protection of the hydroxyl groups with ethyl vinyl ether,
the lactone moiety was reduced with diisobutylaluminium hydride to a

lactol (**4.103**). This also involved the reduction of the ester group to an alcohol. After selectively benzoylating the latter, the lactol was opened with hydrogen cyanide, followed by removal of the protective groupings by acid (**4.104**). The primary hydroxyls were then tosylated, and the secondary ones acetalyzed with ethyl vinyl ether.

Cyclization of the product to a cyclopentanone (**4.106**) was carried out with trimethylsilylamine sodium. Alkaline hydrolysis followed by oxidation gave the cyanohydrin of prostaglandin E_2 (**4.107**), which afforded the optically active natural product on successive treatment with acid and base.

A similar transformation of (R)-glyceraldehyde (**5.108**) to prostaglandin E_1 has also been reported by Stork and his co-workers [16].

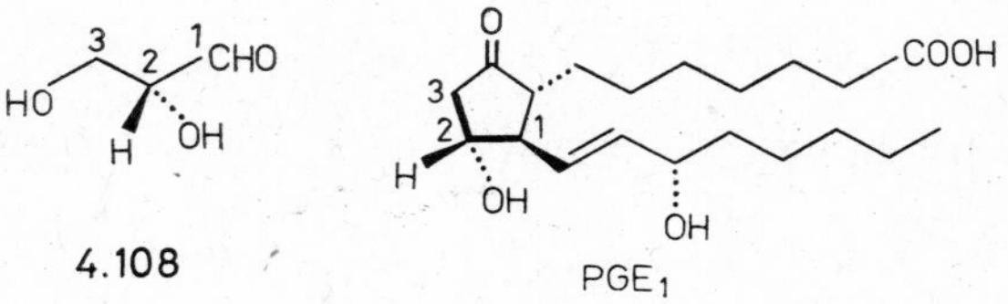

4.108   PGE$_1$

4.7 AN ASYMMETRIC SYNTHESIS OF COREY'S LACTONE INTERMEDIATE

Tömösközi *et al.* [14] used the bicyclic lactone prepared by asymmetric synthesis by Uskokovič *et al.* (Section 4.2; **4.5**) for a simple procedure to obtain Corey's lactone intermediate without resolution. Prins reaction of this lactone (paraformaldehyde in acetic acid) was regio- and stereospecific and gave, after chromatography, the diacetate of the hydroxylactone (**4.110**, $R^1 = R^2 = Ac$) in good yield, together with some of the monoacetate isomers. Methanolysis of the diacetate yielded the corresponding diol (**4.110**, $R^1 = R^2 = H$) which was selectively oxidized with thioanisol–chlorine complex, or Pfitzner–Moffatt reagent, to yield Corey's hydroxylactone intermediate (**4.111**) in the optically active form. The transformation of the latter to prostaglandin $F_{2\alpha}$ was solved earlier by Woodward *et al.* (*cf.* Chapter 2).

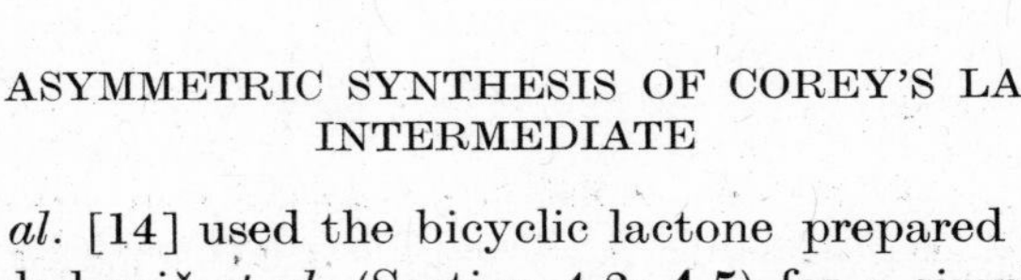

4.5   4.109

-4.110   4.111

4.8 THE CHIRAL SYNTHESIS
OF COREY'S LACTONE INTERMEDIATE

Paul *et al.* [17] devised a route based on natural (S)-$(-)$-malic acid for
the preparation of Corey's lactone (**4.111**) in the optically active form, a
key intermediate for the synthesis of natural prostaglandins. In their
scheme malic acid provided carbons 8, 9, 10 and 11 of prostaglandins.

4.112   4.111

Treatment with acetyl chloride first transformed (S)-$(-)$-malic acid
(**4.112**, Fig. 4.12) to (S)-$(-)$-2-acetoxysuccinic anhydride (**4.113**), which gave
the acid chloride (**4.114**) when treated with dichloromethylmethyl ether in
the presence of zinc chloride. This was allowed to react with the dianion
generated from methylhydrogen malonate and isopropylmagnesium bromide
to obtain the diester (**4.115**). Cyclization of the latter by triethanolamine
as a base afforded two cyclopentenones (**4.116** and **4.117**) which were separated. The useful product (**4.116**) predominated (**85%**) and was reduced
catalytically at the carbon-carbon double bond to yield the thermodynamically more stable *trans* product (**4.118**).

The preference for (**4.116**) can be rationalized by the difference in stability
of the enolate anions (**4.115a** and **4.115b**) formed in the first steps of the
reaction. Of the two anions, (**4.115a**) is the preferred one since in (**4.115b**)
two groups of similar polarization (acetoxy and enolate ion) come into
promixity.

The *trans* disposition of the side chains in (**4.118**) may be the result of
either a spontaneous epimerization of the primary product formed by a *cis*

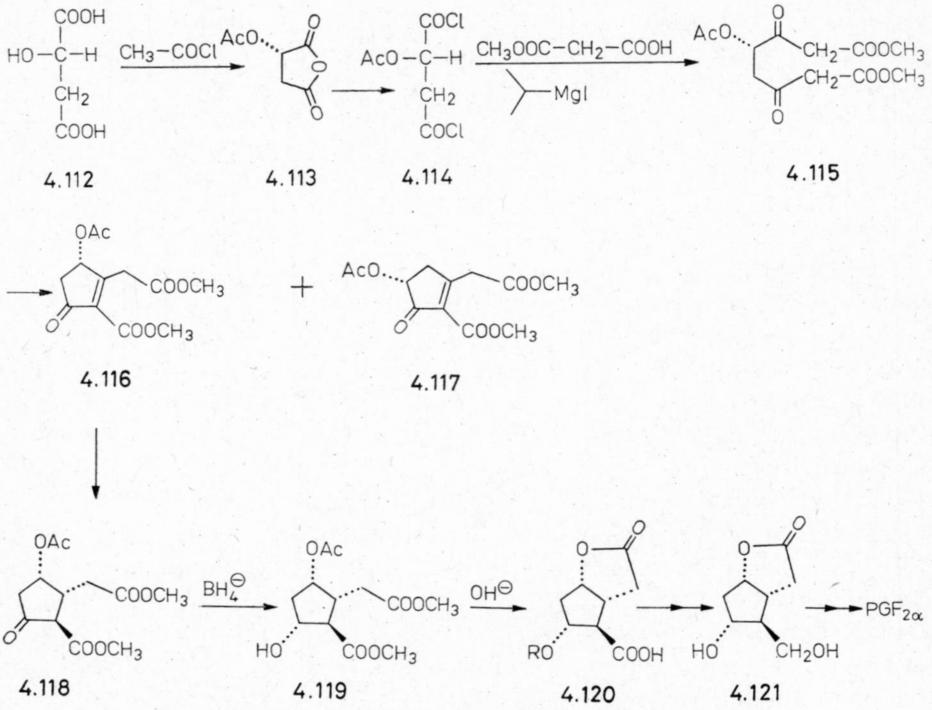

Fig. 4.12. **Chiral synthesis of Corey's lactone intermediate**

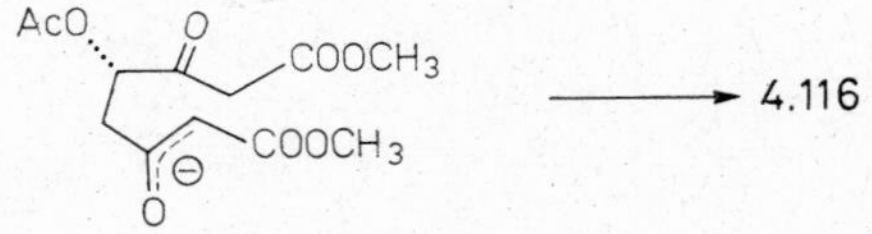

4.115a

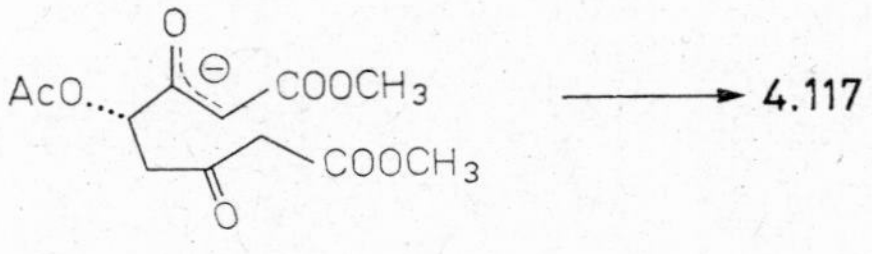

4.115b

addition of hydrogen, or by a 1,4-hydrogen addition to the enone system followed by ketonization.

Reduction of the cyclopentanone (**4.118**) with sodium borohydride, hydrolysis of the product (**4.119**) with potassium hydroxide and acidification gave the lactone (**4.120**, R = H). After protection of the free hydroxyl as the acetate (**4.120**, R = Ac), the carboxyl was converted to the acid chloride by dichloromethylmethyl ether and zinc chloride and reduced with sodium borohydride to Corey's lactone alcohol (**4.121**).

4.9 SYNTHESIS OF (R)-4-HYDROXY-2-CYCLOPENTENONE

Stork's synthesis of prostaglandins from racemic 4-cumyloxy-2-cyclopentenone (*cf.* Chapter 3) stimulated several research groups to elaborate processes for obtaining (*R*)-4-hydroxy-2-cyclopentenone, an intermediate suitable for the preparation of optically active prostaglandins without resolution. A chemical approach to achieve this aim based on a chiral synthesis starting from (2*R*,3*R*)-tartaric acid has been proposed by Ogura *et al.* [18], and a microbiological method consisting of the kinetic resolution of a dihydroxycyclopentene derivative by Tanaka and co-workers.

Ogura *et al.* transformed (2*R*,3*R*)-tartaric acid (**4.122**) in a known way to the acetonide (**4.123**), which was reduced with lithium aluminium hydride to the alcohol (**4.124**, R = OH). This was tosylated (**4.124**, R = OTos) and the tosyl groups were exchanged for iodine. Reaction of the iodo compound (**4.124**, R = I) with methylthiomethyl-sulfoxide-lithium (**4.125**), acid-catalyzed hydrolysis and subsequent acid-catalyzed dehydration gave (*R*)-4-hydroxy-2-cyclopentenone (**4.127**).

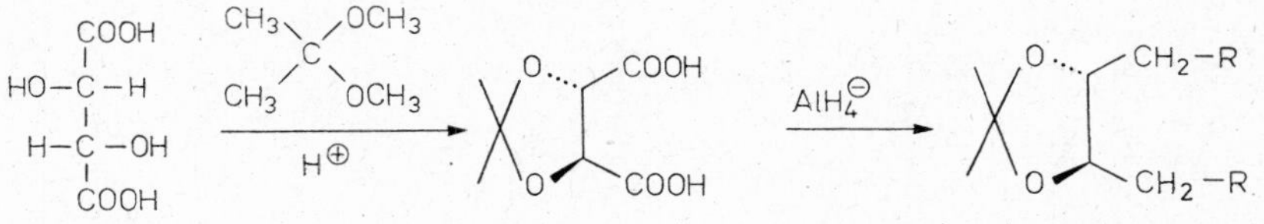

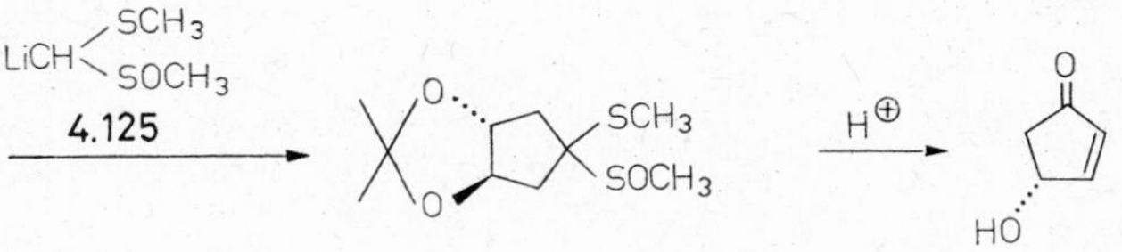

An identical sequence performed on (2*S*,3*S*)-tartaric acid gave the enantiomer, (*S*)-4-hydroxycyclopentenone.

The optical purity of the products was checked by taking NMR spectra of their acetates in the presence of an optically active europium shift reagent.

Acetyl-methyl singlets of the enantiomers were resolved under such conditions and optical purity could be inferred from the integral ratio (Fig. 4.13).

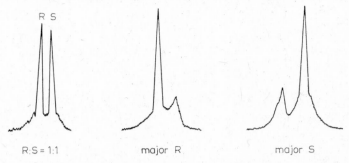

R   S

R:S = 1:1   major R   major S

Fig. 4.13. Methyl signals in the NMR spectra of the acetates of **4.127** in the presence of an europium shift reagent

Tanaka and his co-workers incubated a racemic 1 : 1 mixture of *cis-* and *trans-*3,5-diacetoxycyclopent-1-ene (**4.128**) with baker's yeast and obtained the following three products:

(3*R*,5*R*)-diacetoxycyclopent-1-ene (**4.129**),
(3*R*,5*R*)-3-acetoxy-5-hdyroxycyclopent-1-ene (**4.130**) and
3,5-dihydroxycyclopent-1-ene of predominantly (3*S*,5*S*)
    configuration (**4.131**).

The monoacetate (**4.130**) was silylated with *t*-butyldimethylchlorosilane, the silyl ether (**4.132**, R = Ac) reduced with lithium aluminium hydride and the product (**4.132**, R = H) was oxidized with active manganese dioxide to obtain (*R*)-4-hydroxy-2-cyclopentenone in silylated form (**4.133**) [19, 20].

OAc   OAc   OAc   OH

OAc   OAc   +   OH   +   OH

4.128   4.129   4.130   4.131

OR

$OSi(CH_3)_2$ t.Bu $OSi(CH_3)_2$ t.Bu

4.132   4.133

REFERENCES

1. MISLOW, K., RABAN, M., *Topics in Stereochemistry*, Vol. 1, p. 1 (Ed. E. L. ELIEL, N. L. ALLINGER), Interscience, New York, 1966.
2. MORRISON, J. D., MOSHER, H. S., *Asymmetric Organic Reactions*. Prentice-Hall, Englewood Cliffs, New Jersey, 1971.
3. PARTRIDGE, J. J., CHADHA, N. K., USKOKOVIČ, M. R., *J. Am. Chem. Soc.*, 95, 532 (1973).
4. PARTRIDGE, J. J., CHADHA, N. K., USKOKOVIČ, M. R., *J. Am. Chem. Soc.*, 95, 7171 (1973).
5. HULSHOF, L. A., McKERVEY, M. A., WYNBERG, H., *J. Am. Chem. Soc.*, 96, 3906 (1974).
6. DALE, J. A., DULL, D. L., MOSHER, H. S., *J. Org. Chem.*, 34, 2543 (1969).
7. FISCHLI, A., KLAUS, M., MAYER, H., WICK, A., "Synthetische Arbeiten auf dem Prostaglandin-Gebiet." Lecture held at the XXIVth IUPAC Congress, Hamburg, September 1973.
8. WICK, A., FISCHLI, A., KLAUS, M., MAYER, H., ííSynthetische Arbeiten auf dem Prostaglandin-Gebiet." Lecture held at the XXIVth IUPAC Congress, Hamburg, September 1973.
9. FISCHLI, A., KLAUS, M., MAYER, H., SCHÖNHOLZER, P., RÜEGG, R., *Helv. Chim. Acta*, 58, 564 (1975).
10. SIH, C. J., SALOMON, R. G., PRICE, P., SOOD, R., PERUZZOTTI, G., *J. Am. Chem. Soc.*, 97, 857 (1975).
11. SIH, C. J., HEATHER, J. B., SOOD, R., PRICE, P., PERUZZOTTI, G., HSU LEE, L. F., LEE, S. S., *J. Am. Chem. Soc.*, 97, 865 (1975).
12. COREY, E. J., ENSLEY, H. E., *J. Am. Chem. Soc.*, 97, 6909 (1975).
13. STORK, G., RAUCHER, G., *J. Am. Chem. Soc.*, 98, 1583 (1976)
14. TÖMÖSKÖZI, I., GRUBER, L., KOVÁCS, G., SZÉKELY, I., SIMONIDESZ, V., *Tetrahedron Lett.*, 1976, 4639.
15. YAMADA, SHUN-ICHI, KITAMOTO, MUTSOYOSHI, TERUSHIMA, SHIRO, *Tetrahedron Lett.*, 1976, 3165.
16. STORK, G., *Centennial A. C. S. Meeting, New York, April 1976, Abstract of Papers, Division of Organic Chemistry*, No. 17.; STORK, G., TAKAKASHI, T., *J. Am. Chem. Soc.*, 99. 1275 (1977).
17. PAUL, K. G., JOHNSON, F., FARARA, D., *J. Am. Chem. Soc.*, 98, 1285 (1976).
18. OGURA, K., YAMASHITA, M., TSUCHIHASHI, G., *Tetrahedron Lett.*, 1976, 759.
19. MIURA, S., KUROZUMI, S., TOM, T., TANAKA, T., KOBAYASHI, M., MATSUBARA, S., ISHIMOTO, S., *Tetrahedron*, 32, 1893 (1976).
20. TANAKA, T., KUROZUMI, S., TOM, T., MIURA, S., KOBAYASHI, M., ISHIMOTO, S., *Tetrahedron*, 32, 1713 (1976).

5. SYNTHETIC ROUTES TO PROSTAGLANDIN ANALOGUES

Natural prostaglandins are characterized by a broad spectrum of activity and owing to fast metabolism a short duration of their action. The half-life of intravenously administered prostaglandin $F_{2\alpha}$ is, e.g. about 30 minutes, and the metabolites are eliminated within five hours. From the pharmaceutical point of view, fast metabolism has its advantages since there is no danger of overdosage or of accumulation of metabolites. Sometimes, however, when a prolonged prostaglandin effect is required, as e.g. in labour induction, multiple dosage or the application of large doses may often become necessary.

For the rapid metabolism of prostaglandins the enzyme prostaglandin 15-hydroxy dehydrogenase is mainly responsible. This can be found in every organism producing prostaglandins and can be regarded as the principal factor controlling the cellular level of prostaglandins. This enzyme system oxidizes prostaglandins at C_{15} and, as the biological activity of 15-oxoprostaglandins (**5.2**) is by one order of magnitude lower than that of the parent molecule, activity drops rapidly. Oxidation is followed by saturation of the conjugated C_{13}–C_{14} double bond (**5.3**), cleavage of the upper chain by β-oxidation, and finally ω-oxidation involving the lower chain to furnish a dicarboxylic acid (**5.4**) that is then eliminated from the organism. The scheme delineated for prostaglandin E_2 (**5.1**) applies to other natural prostaglandins as well [1–3].

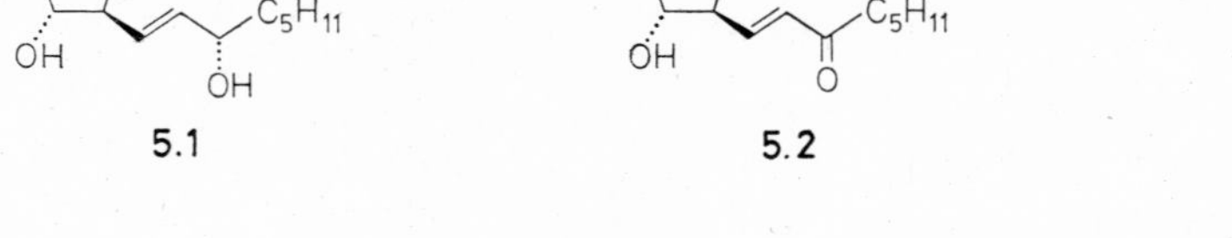

5.1   5.2

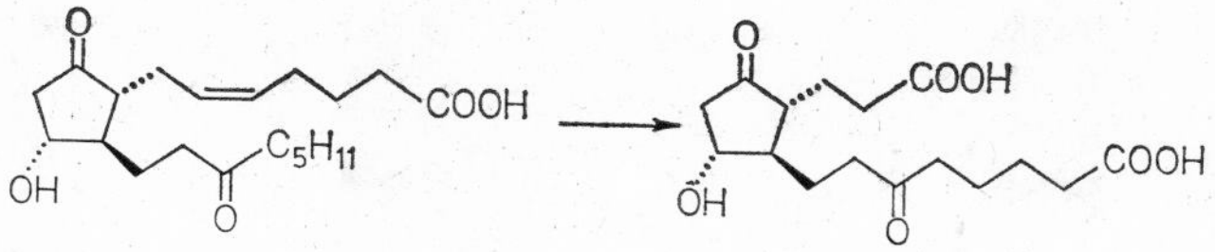

5.3   5.4

Modification of prostaglandins may serve two objectives, namely to produce analogues possessing more specific biological effects, and/or prolonged biological effects.

In recent years several hundreds of analogues have been prepared and tested for their biological activity. From all these in this book methyl-, oxa-, thia- and azaprostaglandins will be discussed.

5.1 METHYLPROSTAGLANDINS

The enzyme system triggering the metabolism of prostaglandins is specific to (15S)-hydroxyprostaglandins and, except for type B, is capable of oxidizing all the natural representatives and its action is practically independent of the substituents in the ring [4–6].

Therefore, it could be anticipated that modification at the centre of attack, i.e. at C_{15} or in its proximity, would inhibit enzymic dehydrogenation without destroying biological activity. The most plausible modification was to substitute the C_{15} hydrogen atom for a methyl group.

In fact, 15-methylprostaglandins proved to possess prolonged activity and a relatively narrow spectrum of effects. Compared with the native compounds, 15-methylprostaglandins E_2 and $F_{2\alpha}$ are considerably weaker hypotensives, whereas they induce labour more effectively [7–10].

The first synthesis of 15-methylprostaglandins E and F was described by Bundy et al. [7, 10, 11] who prepared, starting from natural prostaglandins, each of the representatives in groups E and F. For illustration we quote here the synthesis of 15-methylprostaglandin $F_{2\alpha}$ (5.7).

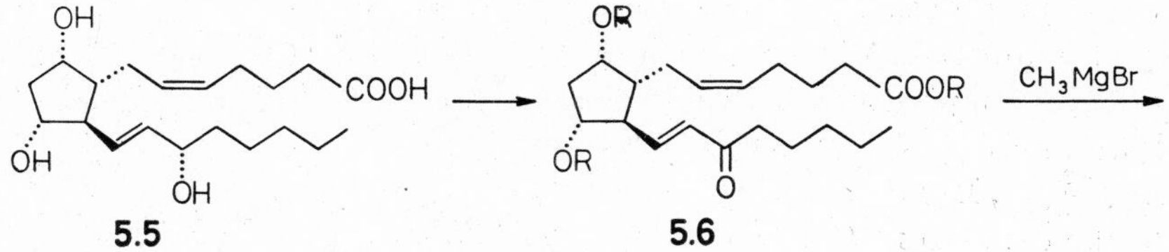

5.5   5.6

Prostaglandin $F_{2\alpha}$ (**5.5**) was first oxidized selectively with 2,3-dichloro-5,6-dicyano-1,4-benzoquinone to the 15-oxo derivative (**5.6**, R = H) and then the remaining hydroxyls were trimethylsilylated. Addition of methylmagnesium bromide to this ether (**5.6**, R = $Si(CH_3)_3$) gave, after removal of the blocking groups, a mixture of 15-methylprostaglandins $F_{2\alpha}$ epimeric at C_{15} (**5.7** and **5.8**) and separable by chromatography in the form of their methyl esters.

Configuration at C_{15} was originally assigned to these products using the empirical observation that chromatographic mobility of the more polar natural (15S)-epimers on thin-layer plates is lower than that of the (15R)-epimer. Later this assumption could be confirmed by X-ray analysis of the p-iodophenacyl esters [12].

The same authors converted 15-methylprostaglandin $F_{2\alpha}$ (**5.7**) to 15-methylprostaglandin E_2 methyl ester (**5.9**) by preparing with trimethylsilyl-diethylamine the 11-trimethylsilyloxy derivative of the methyl ester of (**5.7**) and oxidizing this with Collin's reagent. Removal of the protecting group furnished the E_2-type ester (**5.9**) [13–15].

Transformation of 15-methylprostaglandin E_2 methyl ester to the A-type analogue (**5.10**) proved to be problematic. While acid-catalyzed dehydration is an efficient method with the parent prostaglandins, the same fails with the 15-methyl analogues owing to the known sensitivity of the tertiary C_{15}-hydroxyl group. Elimination of the C_{11}-hydroxyl could be realized eventually under neutral conditions by treating 15-methylprostaglandin E_2 at room temperature with dicyclohexylcarbodiimide in the presence of catalytic amounts of copper(II) chloride.

Before long, Bundy and associates worked out the synthesis of 15-methyl-prostaglandins from Corey's iodolactone (**5.11**, Fig. 5.1) [16]. Following

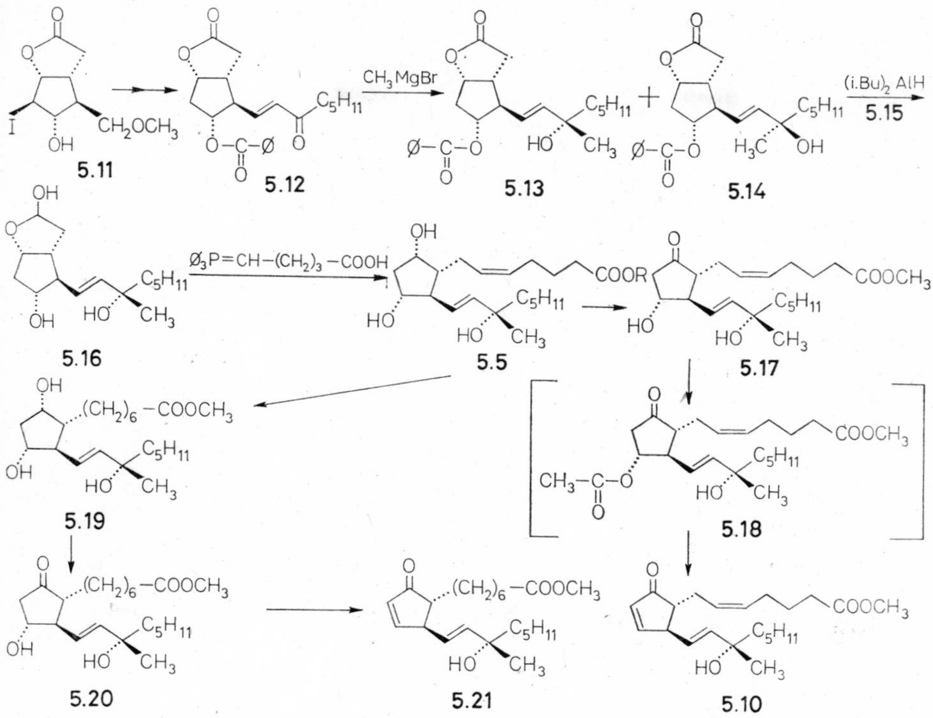

Fig. 5.1. Synthesis of 15-methylprostaglandins starting from iodolactone

Corey's scheme, the benzoylated enone (**5.12**) was prepared; this was made to react with methylmagnesium bromide at —70°C to furnish a 1 : 1 mixture of the epimeric C_{15}-alcohols (**5.13** and **5.14**), inseparable by chromatography.

The methyl singlets of the epimers coincided in the ^{1}H-NMR-spectrum at 60 MHz (δ 1.3), but separated on the addition of a lanthanide shift reagent, or could be distinguished in the ^{13}C-NMR spectrum (δ 28.0 and 28.4).

The synthesis was continued with the mixture and involved reduction with diisobutylaluminium hydride (**5.15**) to the lactol (**5.16**) and its epimer. Condensation with the phosphorane (from sodium triphenyl 4-carboxybutyl-phosphonate) gave 15-methyl-prostaglandin $F_{2\alpha}$ (**5.5**, R = H) and its C_{15}-epimer. These were esterified with diazomethane to permit separation by chromatography providing 15-methylprostaglandin $F_{2\alpha}$ methyl ester (**5.5**, R = CH$_3$).

Transformation of (**5.5**, $R = CH_3$) to 15-methylprostaglandin E_2 methyl ester (**5.17**) was carried out using methods already discussed, i.e. selective silylation and oxidation.

Bundy *et al.* also presented a novel method for the conversion of 15-methylprostaglandin E_2 methyl ester to the A-type ester (**5.10**). This comprised acetylation to (**5.18**) with acetic anhydride, followed by potassium acetate-induced elimination.

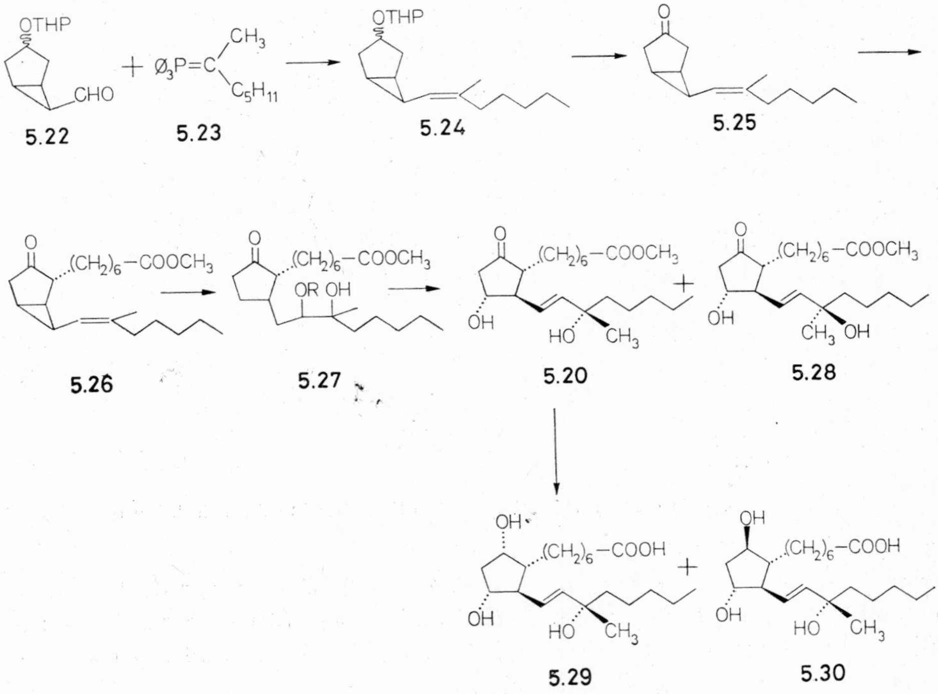

Fig. 5.2. Synthesis of 15-methylprostaglandins starting from bicyclohexane derivative

Transition to the PG_1 series was possible by selective hydrogenation of the double bond in the upper chain of 15-methylprostaglandin $F_{2\alpha}$ methyl ester at low temperature ($-15\,^{\circ}C$) over palladium catalyst. The product, 15-methylprostaglandin $F_{1\alpha}$ methyl ester (**5.19**), could be oxidized — as shown before — to the E_1 analogue (**5.20**), which gave the A_1 ester (**5.21**) in an elimination reaction.

The syntheses of 15-methylprostaglandins E_1 and $F_{1\alpha}$ have been realized by Bundy *et al.* using rearrangement of cyclopropyl carbinyl cations as the key step; this process had been worked out earlier for the synthesis of prostaglandin E_1 (Fig. 5.2; *cf.* Chapter 2). Accordingly, the aldehyde (**5.22**) was condensed with the phosphorane (**5.23**), followed by cleavage of the tetrahydropyranyl group of the product (**5.24**) and oxidation of the alcohol with chromium trioxide–pyridine complex to a ketone (**5.25**), which was alkylated with methyl ω-iodoheptanoate. Oxidation of the product (**5.26**) to a diol (**5.27**, R = H), conversion of the diol to the mesylate (**5.27**, R = Ms) and solvolysis of the latter gave 15-methylprostaglandin E_1 methyl ester

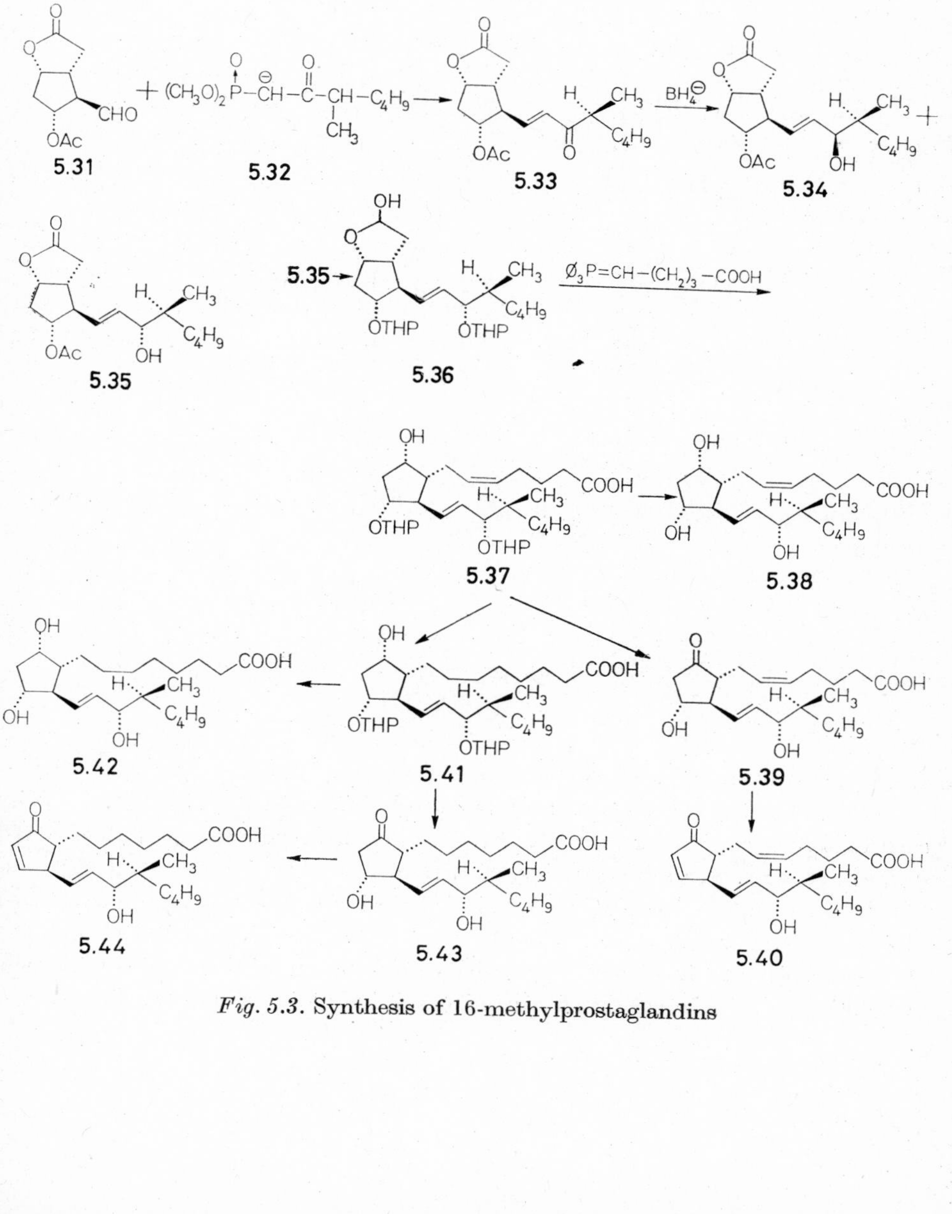

Fig. 5.3. Synthesis of 16-methylprostaglandins

(5.20) and its C_{15} epimer (5.28). The reduction and ester hydrolysis of (5.20) afforded the corresponding $F_{1\alpha}$ analogues (5.29) and (5.30).

The excellent clinical results attained with 15-methylprostaglandins stimulated the synthesis of other methyl analogues. Thus, processes for preparing (16R)- and (16S)-methylprostaglandins have been worked out by Hayashi *et al.* (Fig. 5.3) [17], exemplified here by that yielding the (16S)-derivative.

The sequence commenced with Corey's lactone-aldehyde intermediate (5.31); this was condensed with (3S)-methyl-2-oxoheptylphosphonate (5.32) to yield a ketone (5.33). This ketone was reduced with sodium borohydride to a mixture of alcohols from which the (15S)-component (5.35) was isolated by chromatography. Deacetylation, tetrahydropyranylation of the resulting diol and reduction with diisobutylaluminium hydride afforded the lactol (5.36); the lactol, on condensation with the phosphorane derived from triphenyl-4-carboxybutylphosphonium salt gave (5.37) and removal of the blocking groups yielded (16S)-methylprostaglandin $F_{2\alpha}$ (5.38).

The product of the Wittig condensation (5.37) was suitable for the preparation of other (16S)-methylprostaglandins, too. Oxidation with chromic acid and acid hydrolysis led to (16S)-methylprostaglandin E_2 (5.39), which yielded on acid-catalyzed dehydration the (16S)-methylprostaglandin A_2 (5.40).

Selective saturation of the double bond in the upper chain on palladium catalyst and cleavage of the ether groups of the product (5.41) afforded (16S)-methylprostaglandin $F_{1\alpha}$ (5.42). Insertion of a chromic oxidation step before ether cleavage gave *via* (16S)-methylprostaglandin E_1 (5.43) the corresponding A_1 analogue (5.44).

Strong prostaglandin-like activity was demonstrated in the case of 16-methylprostaglandins in animal tests. In the inhibition of gastric secretion in rats, the potency of (16R)-methylprostaglandin E_2 (5.31) was of two orders of magnitude higher than that of natural prostaglandin E_2. In contrast to natural prostaglandins, the biological activity of C_{15}-epimers is of the same order.

A similar scheme was used by Magerlein *et al.* for the synthesis of 16,16-dimethylprostaglandins (Fig. 5.4) [18]. Corey's lactone-aldehyde, in this case in the benzoylated form (5.45), was allowed to react with sodium 3,3-dimethyl 2-oxoheptylphosphonate (5.46) and the resulting enone (5.47) was reduced with zinc borohydride to give epimeric alcohols separable by chromatography. Formation of the *bis*-tetrahydropyranyl ether (5.49) from the (15S)-component (5.48), reduction with diisobutylaluminium hydride to the lactol (5.50), Wittig condensation with triphenyl-4-carboxybutylphospho-

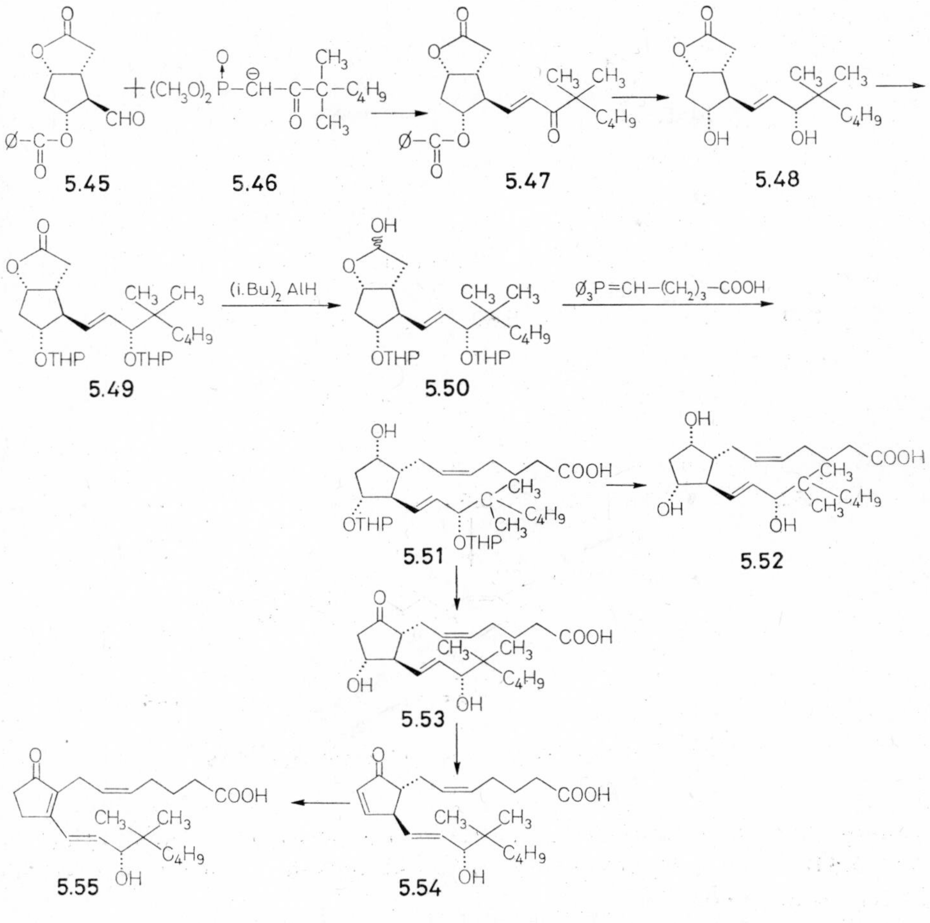

Fig. 5.4. Synthesis of 16,16-dimethylprostaglandins

rane to (5.51) and ether cleavage afforded 16,16-dimethylprostaglandin $F_{2\alpha}$ (5.52). Oxidation prior to the removal of the protecting group led to 16,16-dimethylprostaglandin E_2 (5.53), or after acid-catalyzed dehydration to the A_2-type derivative (5.54), which, in turn, could be easily isomerized by base to 16,16-dimethylprostaglandin B_2 (5.55).

16,16-Dimethylprostaglandins are much more resistant to metabolic deactivation than prostaglandin E_2 itself, and may therefore be useful as specific inhibitors of gastric secretion [19].

The metabolic deactivation mechanism of A-type prostaglandins, i.e. conversion *via* C-type intermediates to practically inactive B-type com-

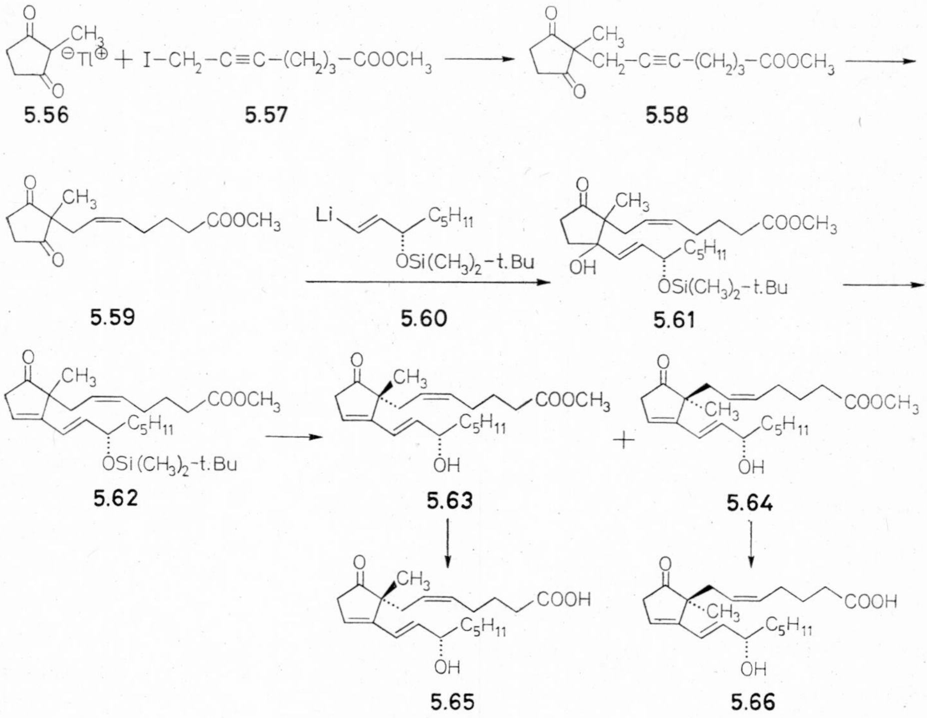

Fig. 5.5. Synthesis of 8-methylprostaglandin C$_2$

pounds, gave the idea for the preparation of 8-methylprostaglandin C$_2$ (Fig. 5.5, **5.65**), since a C$_8$-methyl group would prevent isomerization to the B-type compound.

The synthesis was realized by Corey and Sachter starting from 2-methyl-cyclopentane-1,3-dione (Fig. 5.5) [20]. Alkylation of the dione in the form of the thallium(I) salt (**5.56**) formed with thallium(I) ethoxide, using methyl 7-iodo-5-heptynoate (**5.57**) gave a product (**5.58**) that was transformed into a (Z)-olefin (**5.59**) by reduction of the triple bond over Lindlar catalyst. Grignard reaction with the vinyllithium compound (**5.60**) of this product yielded a mixture of stereoisomeric alcohols (**5.61**), which, at low temperature with thionyl chloride in pyridine, suffered dehydration to give the silyl ether (**5.62**); this was hydrolyzed to afford the esters (**5.63** and **5.64**) epimeric at C$_8$ and separable by thin-layer chromatography or high pressure liquid phase chromatography. Hydrolysis of the esters with lipase led to the acids (**5.65** and **5.66**).

Structural assignment of the products was based on differences in their biological activity and cannot therefore be regarded as final; one of them exhibited 10–30 times higher activity than the other, and it was assumed that the configuration of the more active compound (**5.66**) at C_8 corresponded to that of natural prostaglandins.

The physiological effects of 8-methyl- and natural prostaglandins are similar. Though the activity of compound (**5.63**) on smooth muscle contraction was lower by one order of magnitude than that of prostaglandin E_2, comparable inhibition of gastric secretion was observed with both esters (**5.63** and **5.64**).

5.67 5.68 5.69

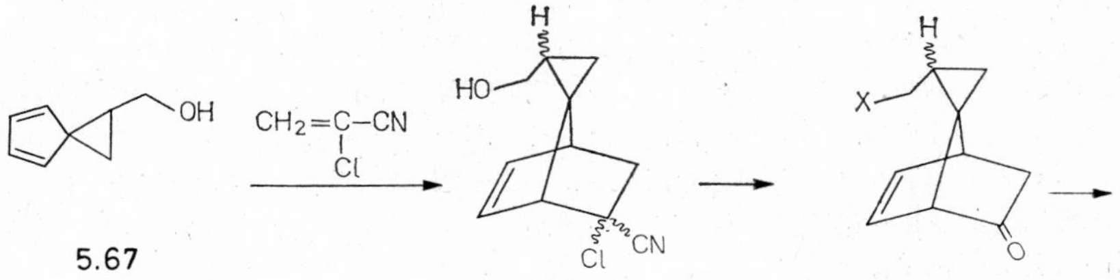

Preventing *in vivo* deactivation was also the idea that provided Corey *et al.* with the impetus to synthesize 12-methylprostaglandin A_2 (**5.76**, $R_1 =$ = H, $R_2 =$ OH) [21]. Sodium cyclopentadienide was made to react with

5.70 5.71 5.72

5.73 5.74

5.75 5.76

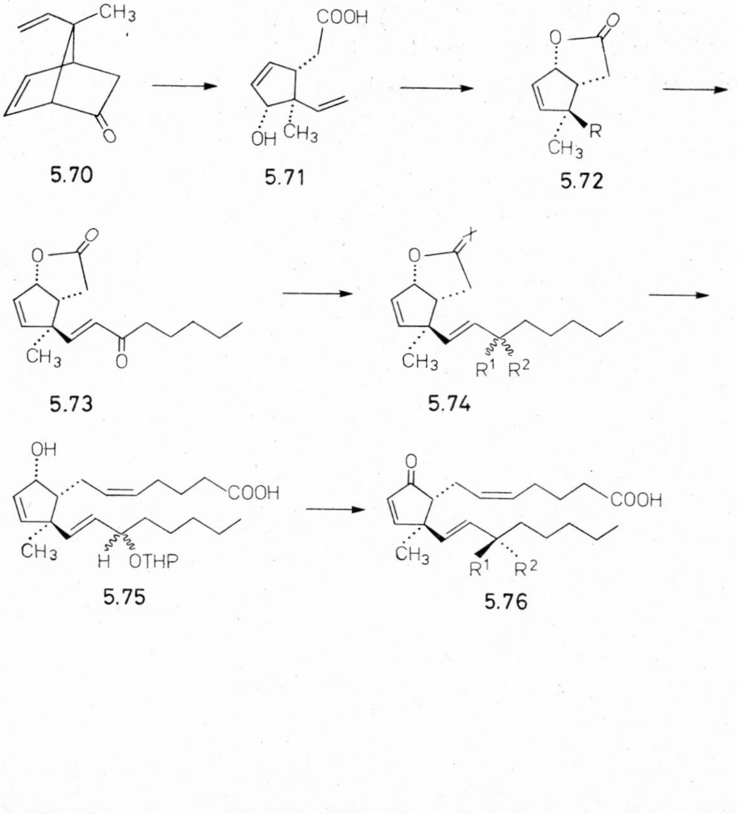

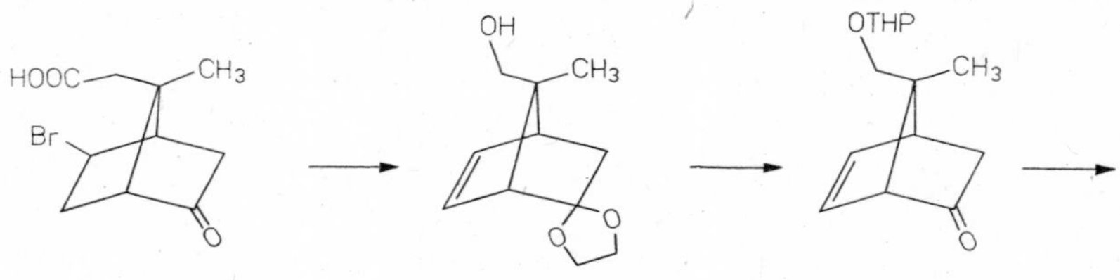

5.77　　　　　　　　5.78　　　　　　　　5.79

epichlorohydrine. A *spiro*-diene (**5.67**) was thus obtained that underwent Diels–Alder addition with 2-chloroacrylonitrile. Hydrolysis of the adduct (**5.68**) with ethanolic potassium hydroxide gave a ketone (**5.69**, R = OH). The corresponding mesylate (**5.69**, R = Ms) was exchanged with sodium iodide to give the iodo compound (**5.69**, R = I). This was reduced with tributyltin hydride. Baeyer–Villiger oxidation (H_2O_2–NaOH) of the product (**5.70**) to the hydroxy acid (**5.71**), lactonization with boron trifluoride-etherate and oxidation of the vinyl group of the lactone (**5.72**, R = $-CH=CH_2$) with sodium metaperiodate–osmium tetroxide to the aldehyde (**5.72**, R = = CHO), condensation with the sodium dimethyl 2-oxoheptylphosphonate and reduction of the product (**5.73**) with sodium borohydride gave a mixture of epimeric alcohols (**5.74**, X = O, R^1 = H, R^2 = OH and R^1 = OH, R^2 = $\neq$ H). After having protected the free hydroxyls by tetrahydropyranylation, the lactones were reduced to the lactols (**5.74**, X = OH, R^1 = H, R^2 = = OTHP and R^1 = OTHP, R^2 = H) with diisobutylaluminium hydride and coupled subsequently with triphenyl-5-carboxybutylphosphorane. Collins oxidation of the product followed by cleavage of the protecting tetrahydropyranyl ether groupings and separation of the products by thin-layer

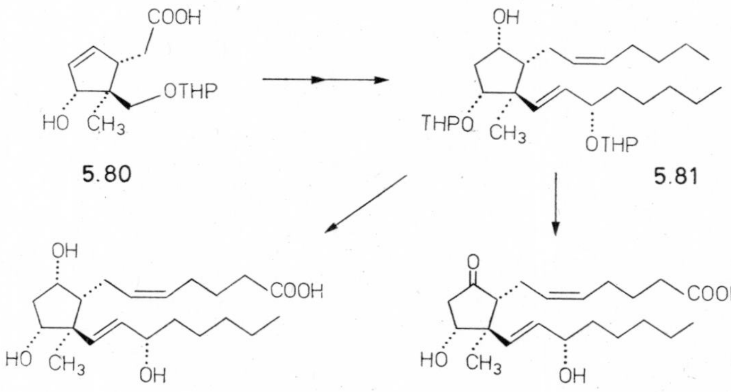

5.80　　　　　　　　　　　　　5.81

5.82　　　　　　　　　　　　5.83

chromatography furnished 12-methylprostaglandin A_2 (**5.76**, $R^1 = H$, $R^2 = $ = OH) and its C_{15}-epimer.

In animal tests, both compounds failed to have any effect on blood pressure and gastric secretion.

Recently Grieco *et al.* [22] also synthesized 12-methylprostaglandins $F_{2\alpha}$ (**5.82**) and E_2 (**5.83**) starting from the norbornene (**5.77**). This was first ketalized with ethylene glycol, the carboxyl reduced with lithium aluminium hydride to an alcohol, dehydrobrominated to (**5.78**) and deketalized. After protecting the free hydroxyl as the tetrahydropyranyl ether (**5.79**), Baeyer–Villiger oxidation (H_2O_2—NaOH) transformed the norbornene to the hydroxy acid (**5.80**) — an intermediate that could be transformed to the 12-methylprostaglandins (**5.82** and **5.83**) following the scheme of Corey's prostaglandin synthesis (*cf*. Chapter 2).

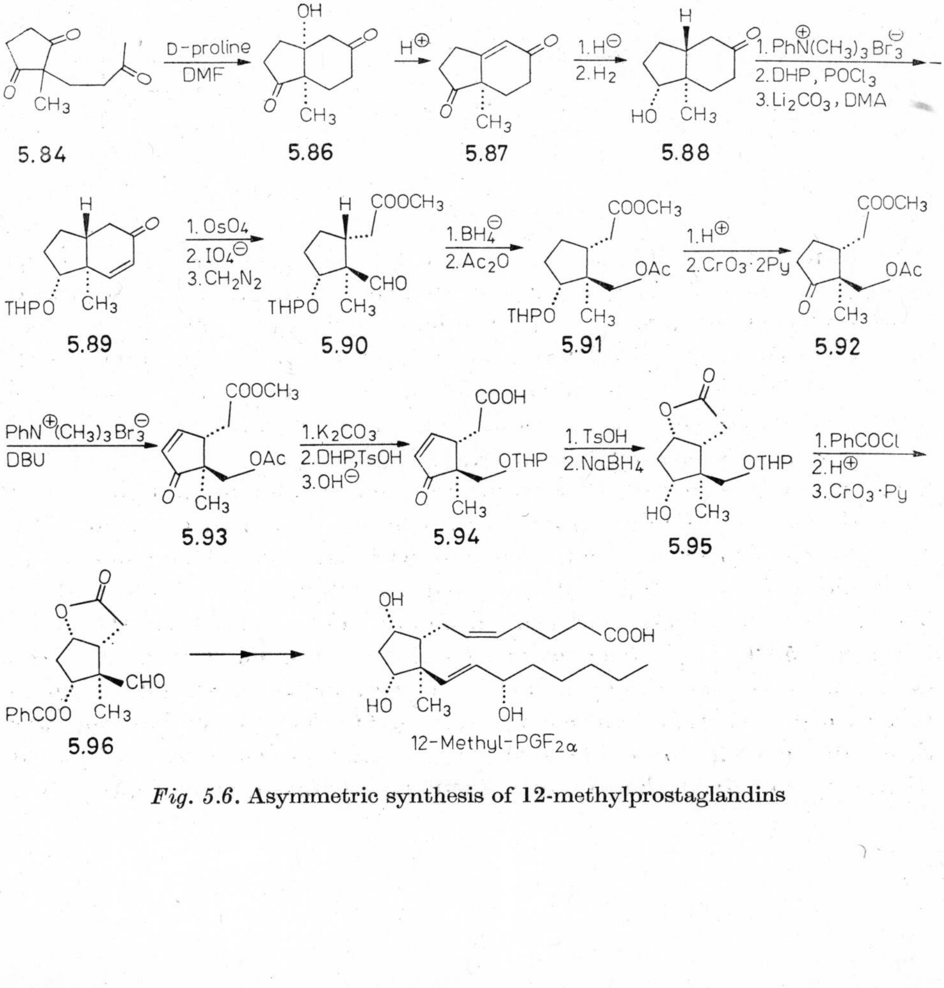

Fig. 5.6. Asymmetric synthesis of 12-methylprostaglandins

Grieco and his co-workers [61] also solved the asymmetric synthesis of the lactone aldehyde (**5.96**, Fig. 5.6), an intermediate which served to prepare optically active 12-methylprostaglandins without resolution. The key step of their procedure was the catalytic asymmetric cyclization of the achiral 1,3-cyclopentanedione (**5.84**) readily accessible from 2-methyl-1,3-cyclopentanedione with methyl vinyl ketone.

The catalytic asymmetric cyclization of 2-methyl-2-(3-oxobutyl)-1,3-cyclopentanedione (**5.84**) had been previously investigated in detail by Hajós and Parrish [62] in connection with the total synthesis of steroids. The carbonyl groups in (**5.84**) are enantiotopic, and one of them may react preferentially under chiral conditions to provide an optically active product. In fact, cyclization in the presence of (*S*)-(−)-proline afforded an optically active bicyclic ketol (**5.86**). The following mechanism was proposed to explain stereoselectivity in this reaction.

In the first step (*S*)-(−)-proline is added to the carbonyl group of the cyclopentadienone. The depicted arrangement of the Zwitter ion formed is the preferred one (**5.85**), because the bulky pyrrolidine moiety is remote from the methyl group. In (**5.85**) ring closure takes place from underneath the plane of the ring, i.e. from the side opposite to the methyl group.

Grieco *et al*. dehydrated the optically active ketol (**5.86**), prepared from the cyclopentanedione (**5.84**) with (*R*)-(+)-proline, with acid to the enone (**5.87**); this was then reduced with lithium *t*-butoxyaluminium hydride and the carbon-carbon double bond saturated by catalytic hydrogenation. The cyclohexanone (**5.88**) was α-brominated with trimethylphenylammonium tribromide, the free hydroxyl protected by dihydropyrane, followed by hydrogen bromide elimination using lithium carbonate, to obtain the cyclohexenone (**5.89**). Conversion of the latter with osmium tetroxide to the diol, cleavage of the diol by periodate to the aldehyde-acid and esterification with diazomethane yielded the ester (**5.90**). The aldehyde group was then reduced with sodium borohydride to an alcohol, which was acetylated with acetic anhydride. The product (**5.91**) was oxidized, after deprotection with Collins reagent to the ketone (**5.92**). Repeated α-bromination with trimethylphenylammonium tribromide followed by hydrogen bromide elimination with the aid of 1,5-diazabicyclo[5,4,0]undec-5-ene afforded the enone (**5.93**). The acyl group was then exchanged for tetrahydropyranyl followed by lactonization with p-toluenesulfonic acid and reduction of the carbonyl group with sodium borohydride. The hydroxylactone (**5.95**) was benzoylated and oxidized after removal of the blocking group with chromium(VI) oxide–pyridine to give the lactone-aldehyde (**5.96**).

5.2 OXAPROSTAGLANDINS

5.2.1 3-Oxaprostaglandins

The synthesis of 3-oxaprostaglandins was accomplished by Bundy and his group [7, 10]; it was based on steps already applied in the preparation of

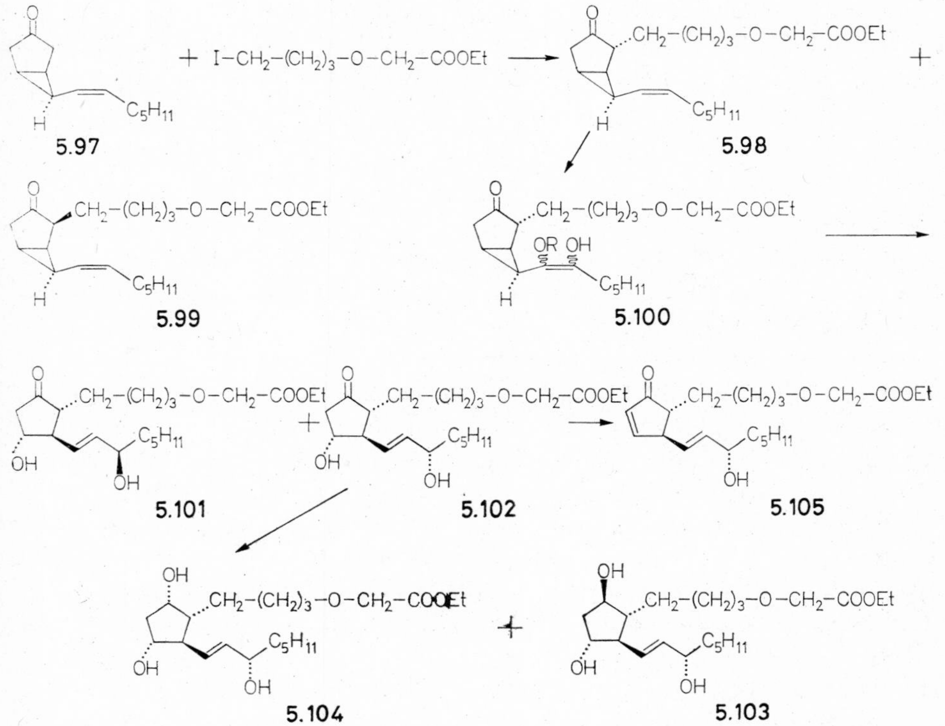

Fig. 5.7. Synthesis of 3-oxaprostaglandins

15-methylprostaglandin $F_{1\alpha}$ (Fig. 5.7; *cf.* Fig. 5.2 and Chapter 2). This comprised alkylation of the cyclopentanone (5.97), separation of the isomers produced (5.98 and 5.99) and oxidation of one of them (5.98) to a diol (5.100, R = H). Solvolysis of the corresponding mesylate (5.100, R = Ms) gave 3-oxaprostaglandin E_1 methyl ester and its C_{15} epimer (5.101). Borohydride reduction of the former (5.102) yielded both the $F_{1\alpha}$ (5.104) and $F_{1\beta}$ (5.103) type esters, whereas dehydration furnished 3-oxaprostaglandin A_1 ethyl ester (5.105).

5.2.2 *7-Oxaprostaglandins*

Procedures for the preparation of 7-oxaprostaglandins have been devised by Fried *et al.* [23]. This was applicable to all types of prostaglandins and will be exemplified here by the synthesis of 7-oxaprostaglandins E_1 and $F_{1\alpha}$ (Fig. 5.8, 5.115 and 5.119).

The known *cis*-1,2-epoxycyclopentane-3,5-diol (5.106) was used as starting material; it was alkylated in the form of the silyl ether (5.107) with diethyl-1-octynylalane (5.121). Ring opening of the epoxide was regio-

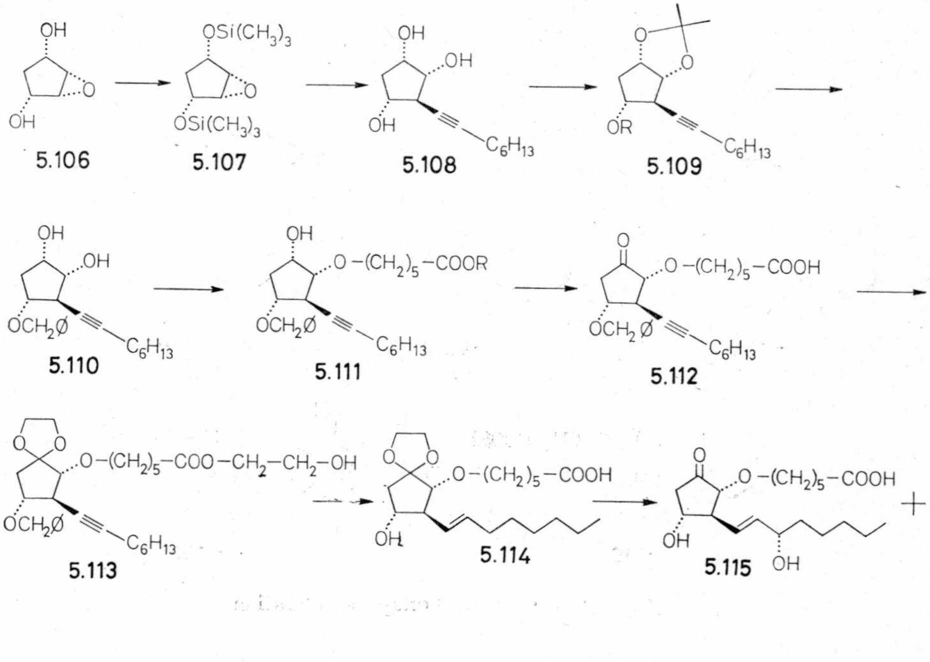

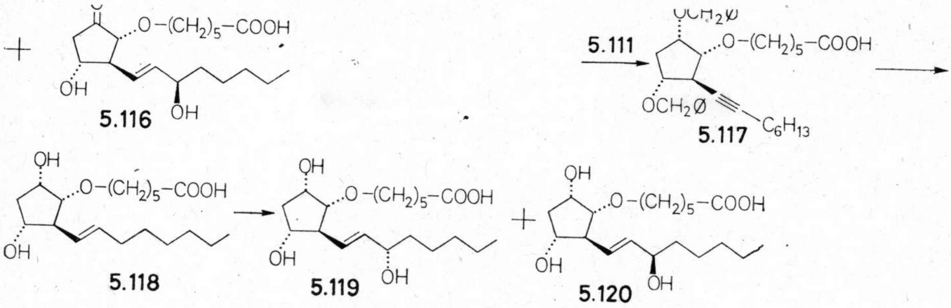

Fig. 5.8. Synthesis of 7-oxaprostaglandins

specific and proceeded fast even at room temperature. The alane component could be prepared from triethylaluminium–triethyl amine complex and 1-octyne.

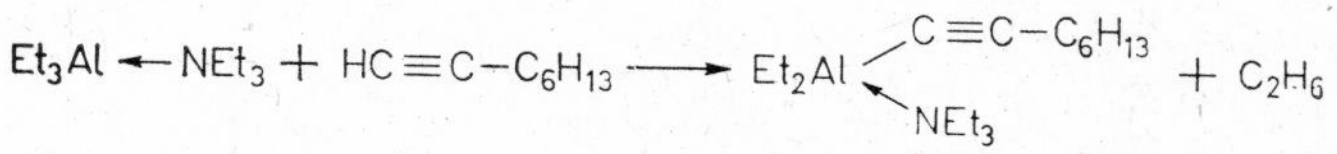

5.121

Two hydroxyls of the triol obtained (5.108) were blocked by forming the acetonide (5.109, R = H), the third was benzylated and the product (5.109, R = CH$_2$Ph) hydrolyzed with trifluoroacetic acid to the diol (5.110), followed by alkylation with t-butyl 6-iodohexanoate in dimethyl sulfoxide containing dimsyl sodium. This gave the required ether (5.111, R = t-butyl) in 65% yield, together with 20% of the alternative isomer.

After acidic ester hydrolysis, the hydroxy acid (5.111, R = H) was oxidized, the carbonyl of the product (5.112) masked as ketal when the carboxyl group became also esterified by ethylene glycol (5.113).

After ester hydrolysis, the triple bond of the side chain was reduced with lithium in methylamine to a double bond, and the olefin (5.114) oxidized in the allylic position with selenium(IV) oxide. This was the only non-stereo-specific step of the sequence giving equal amounts of (15S)- and (15R)-alcohols. After elimination of the blocking groups, racemic 7-oxaprosta-glandin E$_1$ (5.115) and the C$_{15}$-epimer (5.116) were obtained.

The bis-benzyloxy compound (Fig. 5.8, 5.117) prepared from the inter-mediate (5.111) could be converted to racemic 7-oxaprostaglandin F$_{1\alpha}$ (5.119) and its C$_{15}$-epimer (5.120) by reducing it with lithium in methyl-amine to the olefin (5.118), and subsequent oxidation with selenium(IV) oxide.

7-Oxaprostaglandins are strong antagonists of prostaglandins in smooth muscle tests [24–31].

7-Oxa-13-prostynoic acid (**5.122**), though of simpler structure, is an even more potent prostaglandin antagonist than the aforementioned compounds.

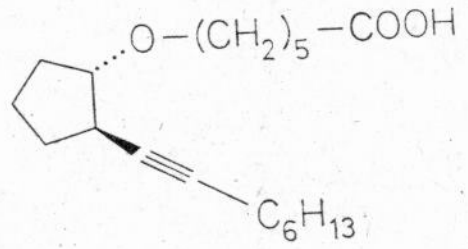

5.122

This compound also came from the laboratory of Fried; its detailed pharmacological examination was performed by Kuehl *et al.* [31]. 7-Oxa-13-prostynoic acid competitively antagonizes in low concentration the effect of prostaglandins E_1 and E_2 on cyclic adenosine monophosphate release.

5.2.3 *9-Oxaprostaglandins*

A general procedure suitable for the synthesis of 9-oxaprostaglandin analogues was elaborated by Vlattas and Dellavecchia [32] and will be discussed here in connection with the preparation of 9-deoxy-9-oxaprostaglandin E_1 (Fig. 5.9, **5.136**). The synthesis started from 7-cyanoheptalde-

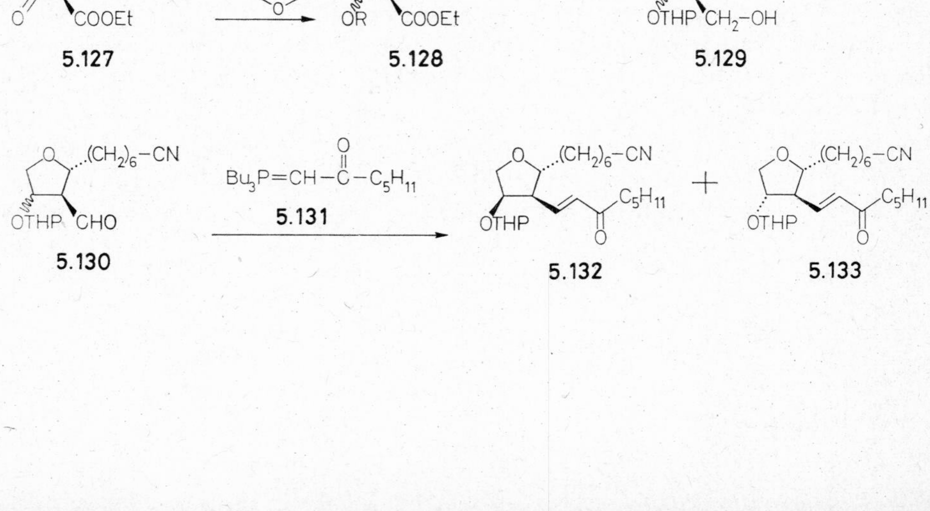

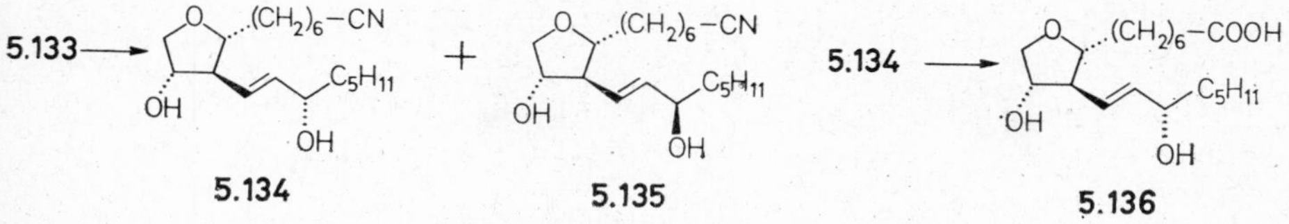

$Fig.$ $5.9.$ Synthesis of 9-oxaprostaglandins

hyde (**5.123**), which was condensed with the sodium phosphonate (**5.124**) to obtain a β-substituted acrylic acid (**5.125**); this product was made to react with the sodium salt of ethyl glycolate (**5.126**). The reaction was initiated by the nucleophilic addition of the glycolate ester anion to the β-carbon of the acrylic ester moiety, followed by a nucleophilic attack of the inter- mediate anion (**5.24**) on the carbon atom of the ester group.

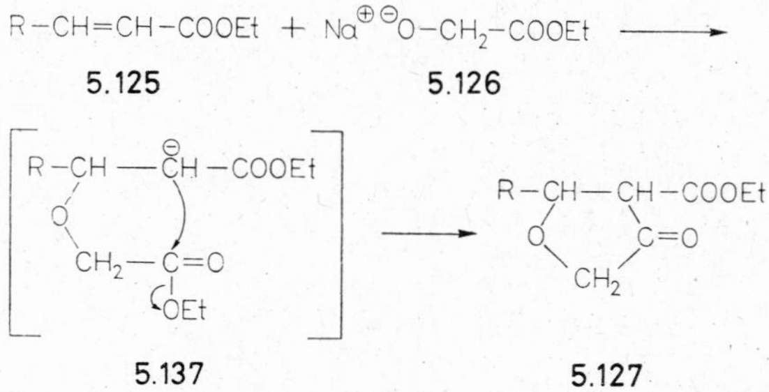

Reduction of keto-ester (**5.127**) with sodium borohydride gave rise to a pair of epimeric alcohols (**5.128**, R = H). These were tetrahydropyranylated without separation and the ethers (**5.128**), R = THP) first reduced with lithium aluminium hydride to the alcohols (**5.129**) and then reoxidized with Collins reagent to the aldehydes (**5.130**). After coupling with tributyl- -2-oxoheptylphosphorane (**5.131**), the resulting epimers (**5.132** and **5.133**) were separated by thin-layer chromatography and the 2,4-*cis*-compound (**5.133**) was reduced by sodium borohydride. This, after acid hydrolysis, again resulted in a mixture of epimeric alcohols (**5.134** and **5.135**) requiring chromatographic separation. On alkaline hydrolysis, the component with structure (**5.134**) afforded racemic 9-deoxy-9-oxaprostaglandin E_1 (**5.136**).

No pharmacological data have as yet been published on 9-oxaprosta- glandins.

5.2.4 *10-Oxaprostaglandins*

10-Oxa-11-deoxprostaglandin E_1 (Fig. 5.10, **5.151**, R = H) is a substance of relatively low toxicity having strong prostaglandin-like physiological effects. It influences gastric secretion and blood pressure, and may find use in labour stimulation.

The synthesis of 10-oxa-11-deoxyprostaglandin E_1 has been achieved by Japanese researchers (Fig. 5.10) [33, 34]. First, dimethyl 2-bromoazelate **(5.138)** was allowed to react with the anion generated from di-*t*-butyl malonate **(5.139)** with sodium hydride; the product **(5.140)** was then treated with paraformaldehyde and sodium methoxide. The latter process involved hydroxymethylation of the malonic ester moiety immediately followed by intramolecular transesterification; the isolated product was therefore the lactone **(5.141)**.

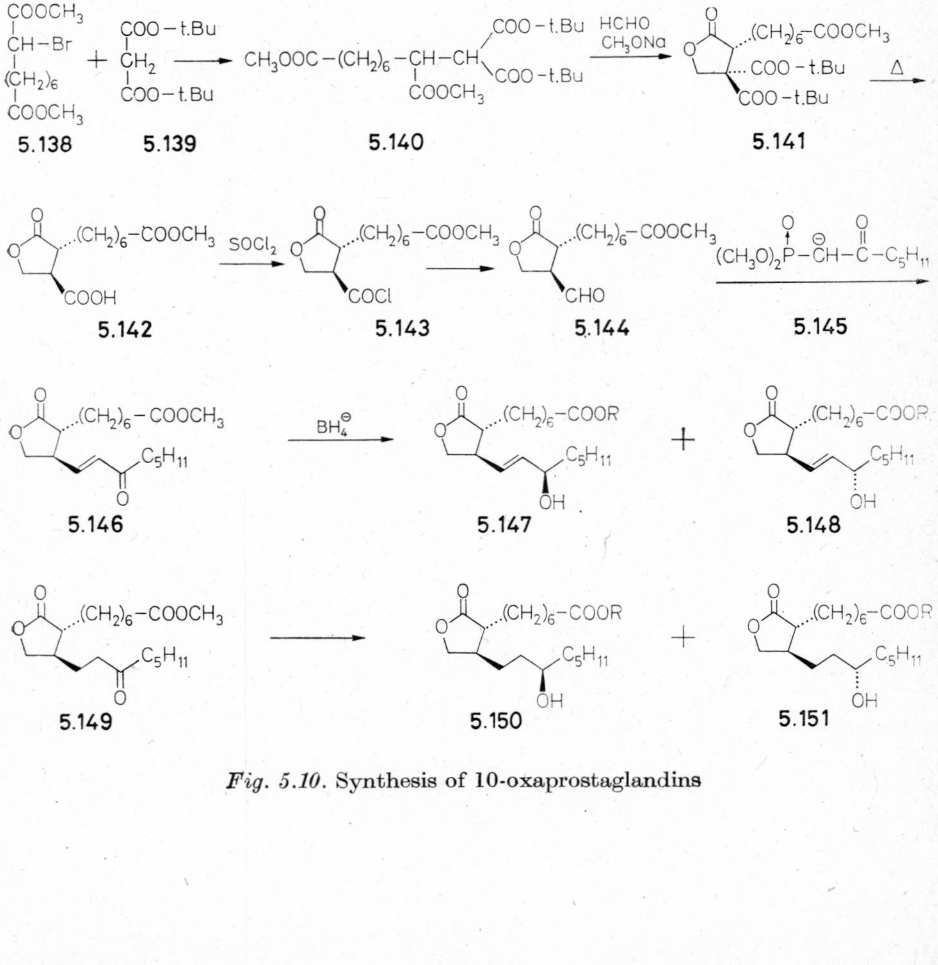

Fig. 5.10. Synthesis of 10-oxaprostaglandins

The t-butyl ester groups of the lactone were eliminated by pyrolysis at 150–170 °C; this process also effected decarboxylation. The monoacid (5.142) was converted with thionyl chloride to the acid chloride (5.143), which was reduced to an aldehyde (5.144). Condensation with sodium dimethyl 2-oxoheptylphosphonate (5.145) and reduction of the enone produced (5.146) with sodium borohydride gave an approximately 1 : 1 mixture of racemic 11-oxa-11-deoxyprostaglandin E_1 methyl ester (5.148, R = CH$_3$) and the C$_{15}$-epimers (5.147, R = CH$_3$). After separation by thin-layer chromatography alkaline hydrolysis furnished the corresponding acids (5.148, R = H) and (5.147, R = H).

The same Japanese also prepared the 13,14-dihydro derivatives of the aforementioned compounds by hydrogenation of the enone (5.146) and subsequent borohydride reduction of the ketone (5.149). The epimeric alcohols (5.150 and 5.151, R = CH$_3$) were separated by thin-layer chromatography and hydrolyzed to give racemic 10-oxa-11-deoxy-13,14-dihydro-prostaglandin E_1 (5.151) and the 15-epi analogue (5.150, R = H).

Later the lactone aldehyde intermediate (5.144) of the above synthesis was synthesized by Hauser and Huffman in a different way (Fig. 5.11) [35].

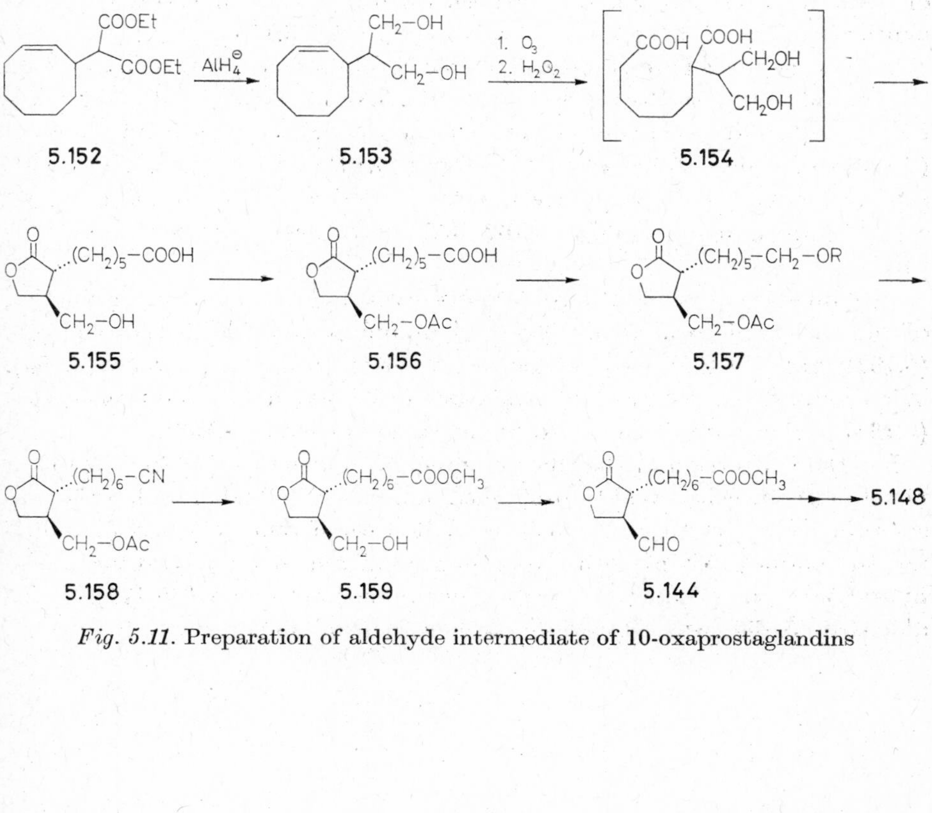

Fig. 5.11. Preparation of aldehyde intermediate of 10-oxaprostaglandins

They started from the cyclooctenylmalonic ester (**5.152**) that was reduced with lithium aluminium hydride to the 1,3-propanediol (**5.153**), ozonolyzed and oxidized with hydrogen peroxide to a dicarboxylic acid (**5.154**), which cyclized instantaneously to a γ-lactone (**5.155**).

The upper chain of this lactone was by one carbon shorter than the C_{1-7} chain of prostaglandins. The necessary lengthening of the chain was accomplished in a five-step sequence. First the hydroxyl group of the lactone acid was acetylated (**5.156**); the reduction of the carboxyl group with diborane to an alcohol followed. The alcohol (**5.157**, R = H) was converted to the tosylate (**5.157**, R = Ts), and then with sodium cyanide to the nitrile (**5.158**). Alkaline hydrolysis to carboxylic acid and oxidation of the corresponding ester (**5.159**) with chromium trioxide–pyridine complex gave the aldehyde (**5.144**), whose conversion to racemic 10-oxa-11-deoxyprostaglandin E_1 (**5.148**) had been solved earlier.

5.2.5 *11-Oxaprostaglandins*

A general procedure for the preparation of 11-oxaprostaglandins was elaborated by Vlattas and Lee [36]. This will now be demonstrated for the synthesis of the E_2-type representative (Fig. 5.12, **5.173**).

The method was based on the glycolate addition reaction, already utilized in the synthesis of the 9-oxa analogues (Fig. 5.9). Here, methyl 4,4-diethoxycrotonate (**5.160**) was made to react with the sodium salt of methyl glycolate (**5.126**) to produce an oxo-tetrahydrofuran (**5.161**), which was reduced with sodium borohydride to an epimeric pair of alcohols. After chromatographic separation, the major epimer (**5.162**, 65%) was carried further in the synthesis.

The subsequent steps comprised tetrahydropyranylation and reduction of the carboxylic acid with diisobutylaluminium hydride to the aldehyde (**5.163**); the aldehyde was condensed with the thiaphosphorane (**5.164**). Wittig reaction gave rise to a mixture of (*Z*)- and (*E*)-vinyl thioethers (**5.165**), which were decomposed to the same aldehyde (**5.166**).

For the conversion of the thioenol ethers to aldehydes (**5.165** → **5.166**) a novel method, using weakly basic medium, has been elaborated. This consists of treating the thioether in acetonitrile with mercury(II) acetate, reducing the adduct (**5.176**) with aluminium amalgam in tetrahydrofuran and hydrolyzing the product, an acetoxyphenylmercapto acetal (**5.177**), to the aldehyde (**5.166**) with potassium carbonate in methanol.

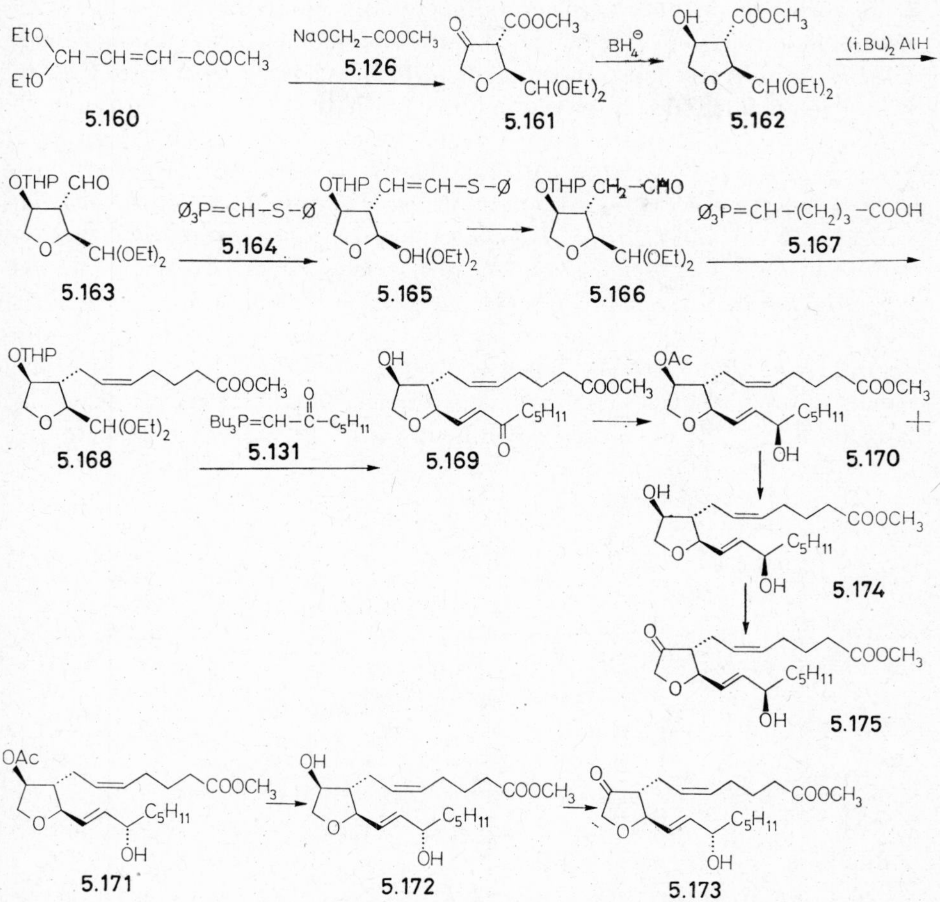

Fig. 5.12. Synthesis of 11-oxaprostaglandins according to Vlattas and Lee [36]

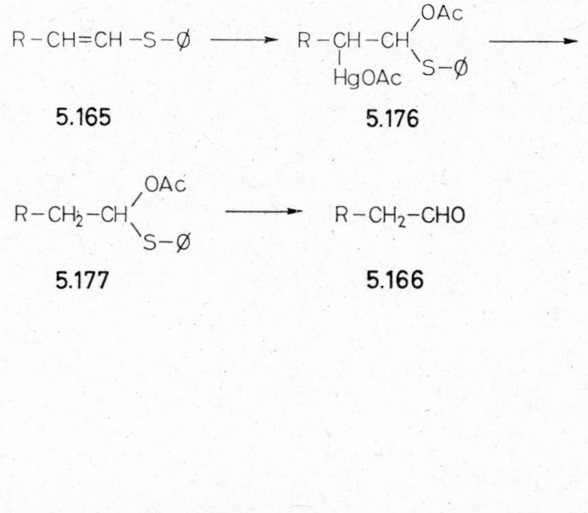

The aldehyde (**5.166**) was then subjected to Wittig condensation with triphenyl-4-carboxybutylidenephosphorane (**5.148**) and the product converted with diazomethane to the ester (**5.168**). After acetal hydrolysis the newly formed aldehyde group was coupled with tributyl-2-oxoheptylidene-phosphorane (**5.131**) to give the enone (**5.169**); this was reduced in the form of its acetate with zinc borohydride to a pair of epimeric alcohols (**5.170** and **5.171**) separable by thin-layer chromatography. The alcohol of structure (**5.171**) was transformed to the tetrahydropyranyl ether, deacetylated and the mono-alcohol (**5.172**) was oxidized using Corey's method (*N*-chlorosuccinimide, triethylamine; *cf*. Chapter 2) to obtain a ketone giving rise, on acidic hydrolysis, to racemic 11-deoxy-11-oxaprostaglandin E$_2$ (**5.173**).

Identical operations starting from the other alcohol (**5.170**) gave racemic 15-*epi*-11-deoxy-11-oxaprostaglandin E$_2$ (**5.175**).

The key step in the synthesis of 11-oxaprostaglandin E$_1$, worked out by Fried *et al*. [37] (Fig. 5.13) was, like in the preparation of 9-oxaprostaglan-

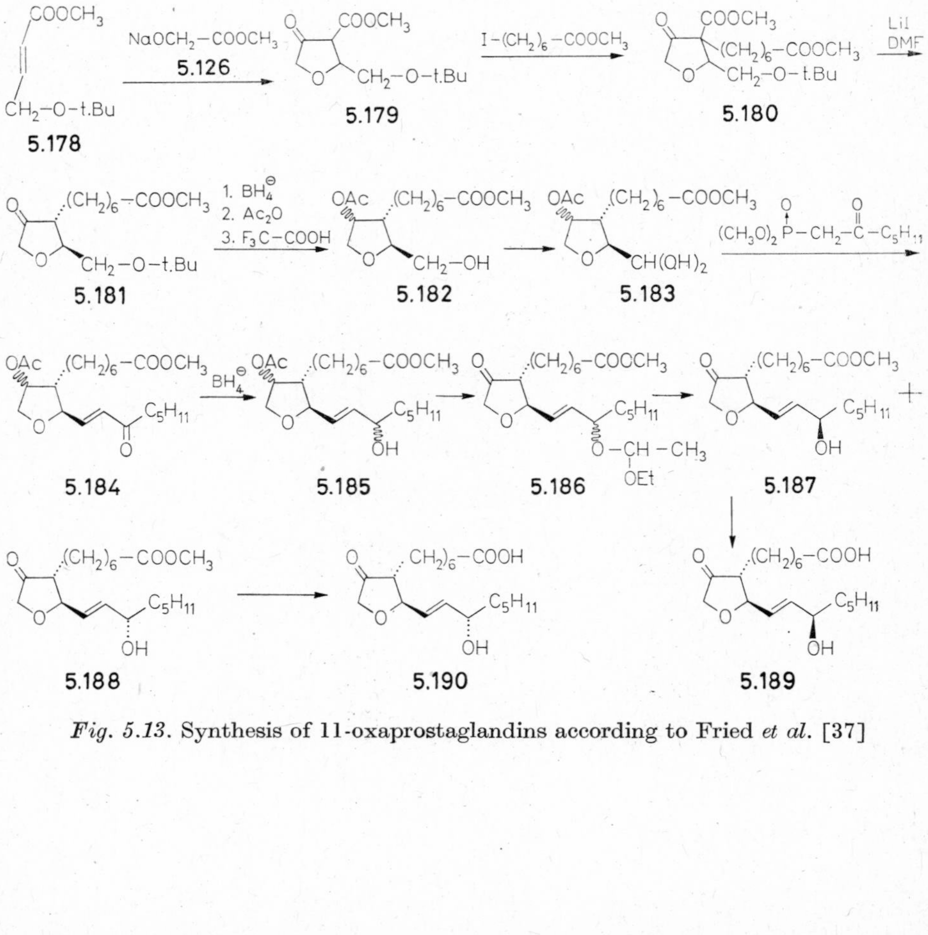

Fig. 5.13. Synthesis of 11-oxaprostaglandins according to Fried *et al*. [37]

dins, the addition of methyl glycolate sodium salt to an α,β-unsaturated ester (**5.178**) followed by Dieckmann condensation. The sodium salt of the product, a tetrahydrofuranone (**5.179**), was alkylated with methyl 7-iodoheptanoate. Decomposition of the resulting diester (**5.180**) with lithium iodide in dimethylformamide to the keto-ester (**5.181**), reduction with sodium borohydride, acetylation of the mixture of epimeric alcohols, and cleavage of the t-butyl ether blocking group afforded a primary alcohol (**5.182**); this was oxidized to an aldehyde (**5.183**) with Moffatt's reagent (dicyclohexyl-carbodiimide–dimethyl sufoxide–dichloroacetic acid). Condensation of (**5.183**) with sodium dimethy l2-oxoheptylphosphonate provided the lower chain in the form of an enone (**5.184**); the enone was reduced with sodium borohydride to alcohols epimeric at C_{15} (**5.185**). After forming the acetal with ethyl vinyl ether, the ester was deacetylated with methanolic sodium methoxide and oxidized at C_9 with Collins reagent to the ketone (**5.186**). After removing the protecting groups and separation of the products (**5.187** and **5.188**) by chromatography, hydrolysis of the ester moiety with alkali furnished racemic 11-deoxy-11-oxaprostaglandin E_1 (**5.190**) and the racemate of its C_{15} epimer (**5.189**).

Both analogues possess weak prostaglandin-like smooth muscle contracting activity.

The preparation of an intermediate which may be suitable for the synthesis of optically active 11-oxaprostaglandin E_2 (**5.173**) was reported by Canadian workers starting from 1,4-anhydro-D-glucitol (Fig. 5.14, **5.191**) [38]. The 5,6-acetonide of the glucitol (**5.192**, R = H) was mono-mesylated (**5.192**, R = Ms), and the mesylate converted to an epoxide (**5.193**) using methanolic sodium methoxide. Nucleophilic epoxide ring opening with the sodium salt of diethyl malonate gave the isomeric esters (**5.194** and **5.195**). After chromatographic separation, (**5.194**) was hydrolyzed with alkali, decarboxylated, reesterified and the ester (**5.196**) subjected to glycol cleavage with sodium metaperiodate to give the aldehyde (**5.197**). Condensation with sodium diethyl 2-oxoheptylphosphonate (**5.145**) led to a potential intermediate (**5.173**) of 11-deoxy-11-oxaprostaglandin E_2. The concluding steps have yet to be reported.

Lourens and Koekemoer succeeded in converting both D-glucose and D-xylose to 11-deoxy-11-oxaprostaglandin $F_{2\alpha}$ (**5.203**) [39, 40]. Here the route departing from glucose will be briefly discussed.

D-Glucose can be conveniently transformed by known methods to the 3-keto derivative (**5.199**). Reaction with the potassium salt of triethyl phosphonoacetate followed by saturation of the double bond by catalytic hydrogenation gave an ester (**5.200**). First, the 5,6-isopropylidene group

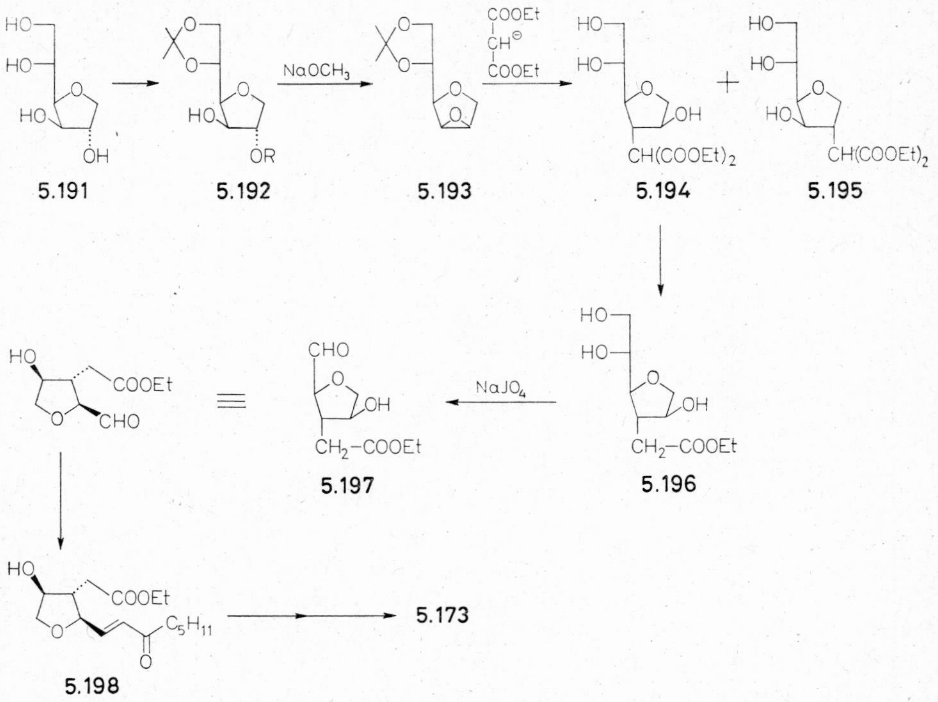

Fig. 5.14. Synthesis of 11-oxaprostaglandins according to Hanessian *et al.* [38]

was exchanged to acetyl groups and then, by treatment with acetic acid, lactonization was effected involving the loss of the 1,2-isopropylidene group. The single remaining hydroxyl of the lactone (**5.201**, R = OH) was acylated with *p*-nitrobenzoyl chloride; the ester (**5.201**), R = *p*-NO$_2$C$_6$H$_4$CO$_2$) when treated with hydrogen bromide and thereafter with thiophenol gave rise to a phenylthio glycoside (**5.201**, R = C$_6$H$_5$S). Elimination of the phenylthio moiety with nickel in alcohol and deacetylation gave a diol (**5.202**, R =

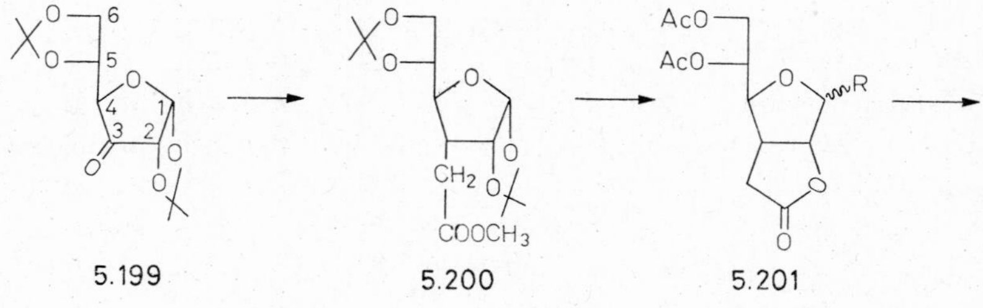

5.202   5.203

$= CHOH-CH_2OH$), which was oxidized to the aldehyde (**5.202**, R =
$= CHO$). Introduction of the lower chain with dimethyl 2-oxoheptylphos-
phonate, reduction of the lactone to lactol and reaction with triphenyl-5-
carboxybutylphosphorane afforded 11-deoxy-11-oxaprostaglandin $F_{2\alpha}$ (**5.203**).

5.2.6 *9,11-bis-Oxaprostaglandins*

Recently Harrison and Fletcher reported the synthesis of such prostaglandin analogues in which both hydroxymethyl functions incorporated into
the cyclopentane ring were replaced by oxygen atoms. The general scheme
will be exemplified by the preparation of 9,11-bis-deoxy-9,11-bis-oxaprosta-
glandin E_1 (Fig. 5.15, **5.214**) [41].

The synthesis departed from the (*E*)-olefin (**5.204**), which was *cis*-hy-
droxylated with barium chlorate–osmium(IV) oxide in aqueous tetrahydrofuran to the *threo*-diol (**5.205**). The five-membered ring (**5.206**) was formed
at this point by acetalization of the diol with paraformaldehyde in benzene
in the presence of perchloric acid. The carboxyl that had been esterified
with benzyl alcohol was liberated by hydrogenolysis to obtain (**5.207**), and
this was converted to a mixed anhydride (**5.208**) with ethyl chloroformate
and triethylamine in order to permit selective reduction to the alcohol
(**5.209**) with sodium borohydride. Moffat oxidation to the aldehyde (**5.210**)
and condensation with sodio dimethyl 2-oxoheptylphosphonate (**5.145**) gave
the enone (**5.211**). Zinc borohydride reduction led to the epimeric alcohols
(**5.212** and **5.213**), which were separated by chromatography and hydrolyzed
with alkali to racemic 9,11-bisdeoxy-9,11-bisoxaprostaglandin E_1 (**5.214**)
and the racemic C_{15}-epimer (**5.215**).

The smooth muscle contracting effect of bis-oxaprostaglandins is by two
orders of magnitude lower compared with natural prostaglandin E_2.

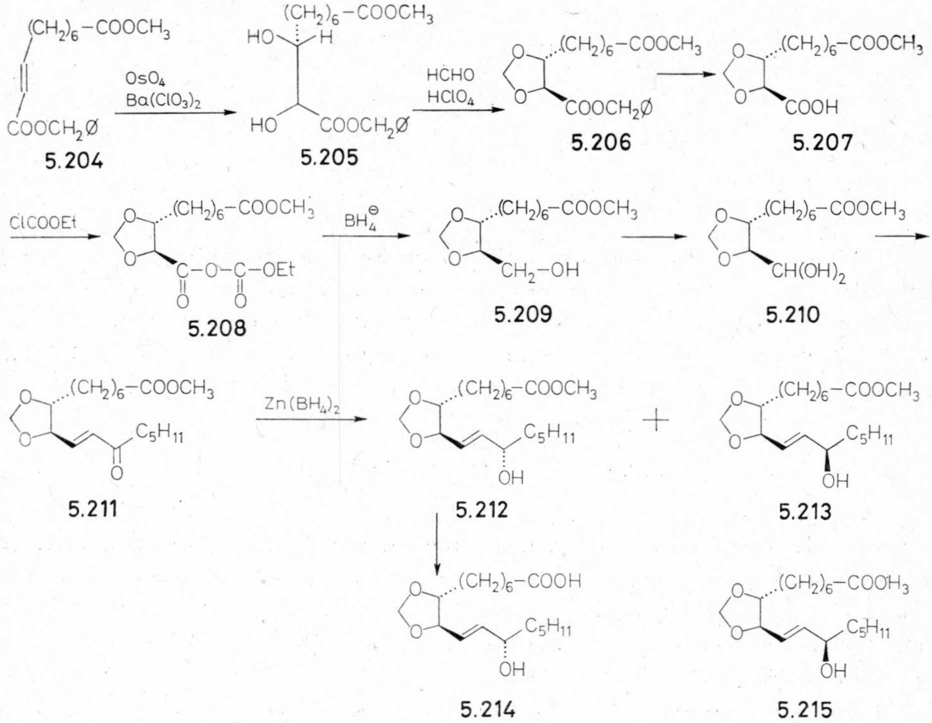

Fig. 5.15. Synthesis of 9,11-bis-oxaprostaglandins

5.3 THIAPROSTAGLANDINS

The valuable prostaglandin agonist and antagonist effects of the 7-oxa analogues stimulated research on thiaprostaglandins. There had also been ample precedence for interesting and pharmaceutically valuable changes in biological activity connected with the replacement of oxygen by sulfur (e.g., steroids, biotin).

5.3.1 7-Thiaprostaglandins

A stereocontrolled synthesis of 7-thiaprostaglandin F_1 has been elaborated by Fried *et al.* (Fig. 5.16) [42]. The key step of the sequence was the stereospecific ring opening of a symmetrical epoxycyclopentane derivative (**5.216**) with the anion of methyl 6-mercaptohexanoate (**5.217**) giving the thioether (**5.218**) in good yield and free of stereoisomers.

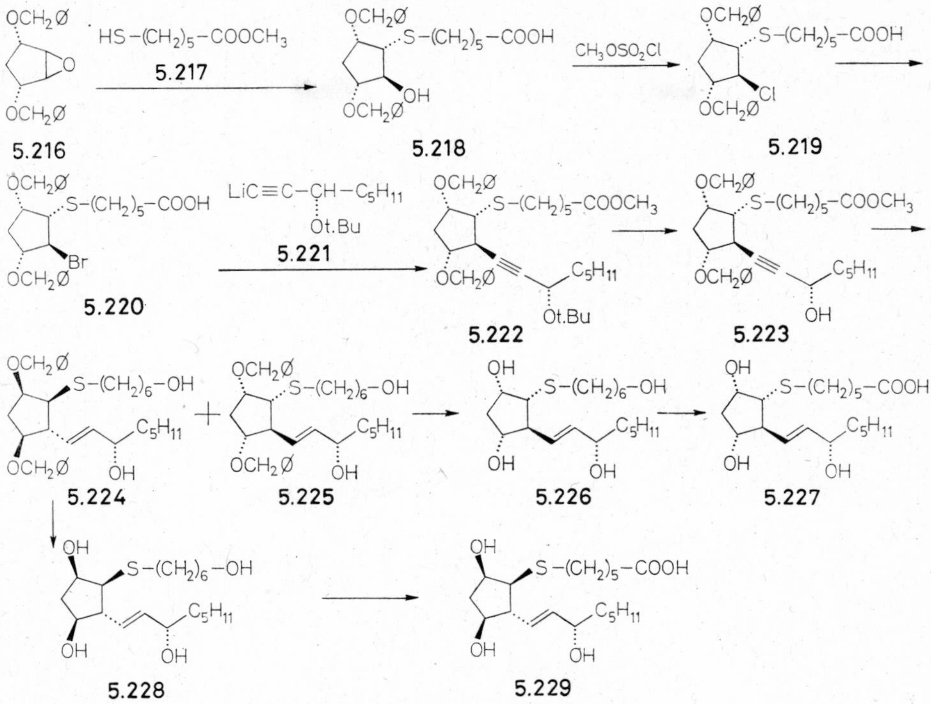

Fig. 5.16. Synthesis of 7-thiaprostaglandins

Treatment of the product with mesyl chloride in pyridine effected the exchange of hydroxyl to chlorine with retention of configuration to give (**5.219**). This process can be rationalized by assuming the primary formation of an episulfonium cation that was opened in the second step by the chloride anion in a regio- and stereospecific manner.

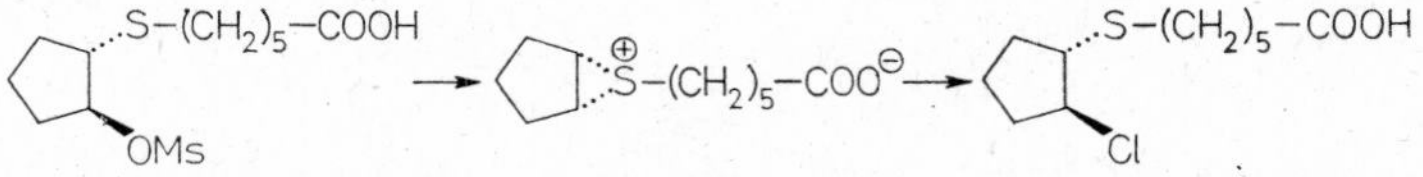

The existence of the episulfonium intermediate (type **5.231**) was verified in a model experiment involving the optically active compound (**5.230**) that underwent racemization in the course of hydroxyl–chlorine exchange carried out with mesyl chloride in pyridine.

In the next step chlorine was substituted by the more reactive bromine (**5.220**) and the bromoacid was made to react as the sodium salt with (3S)-

-*t*-butoxyoctynyllithium (**5.221**) to give a pair of diastereomers. These were converted without separation to the methyl esters (**5.222**, only one stereo-isomer shown) and treated with trifluoroacetic acid to accomplish ether cleavage. The hydroxy-esters (**5.223** and its stereoisomer) were reduced with lithium aluminium hydride to the allylic alcohols (**5.224** and **5.225**). Separation was carried out at this stage and the required diastereomer (**5.225**) was debenzylated with lithium in liquid ammonia.

The crucial step of the synthesis, namely selective reoxidation of primary hydroxyl of the tetrahydroxy compound (**5.226**), could be carried out satis-factorily using platinum(IV) oxide in aqueous acetone containing potas-sium bicarbonate and furnished optically active 7-thiaprostaglandin $F_{1\alpha}$ (**5.227**).

Identical transformations converted the other diol (**5.224**) to 15-*epi*-7-thia-*ent*-prostaglandin $F_{1\alpha}$ (**5.229**).

Both 7-thia analogues are inhibitors of prostaglandin dehydrogenase. The compound of natural configuration (**5.227**) influences the synthesis of cyclic AMP in animal experiments.

5.3.2 *9-Thiaprostaglandins*

Two independent methods have been reported by Vlattas and Della-Vecchia for the synthesis of 9-deoxy-9-thiaprostaglandin E_1 (Figs 5.17 and 5.18) [43, 44]. One of them is essentially an adaptation of a scheme by Corey for the synthesis of natural prostaglandins [45].

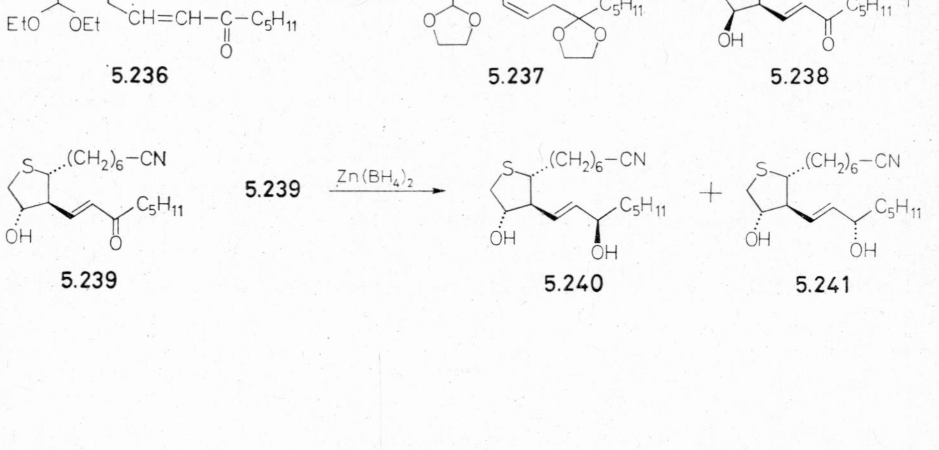

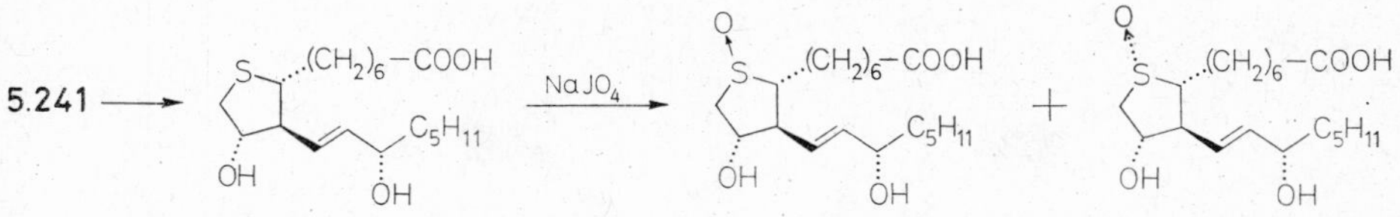

5.242 5.243 5.244

Fig. 5.17. Synthesis of 9-thiaprostaglandins I

The sulfur atom was introduced in both procedures at the outset, in the first version by triethylamine-catalyzed addition of the thiol (Fig. 5.17, **5.234**) to 9-cyanononenal (**5.233**). The product (**5.235**) was condensed with tributyl-2-oxoheptylidenephosphorane to produce an enone (**5.236**) converted with ethylene glycol to a bis-dioxolane (**5.237**). Ketalization was associated with an interesting migration of the double bond into β,γ-position. Treatment with *p*-toluenesulfonic acid in acetone effected cyclization to give the epimeric tetrahydrothiophens (**5.238** and **5.239**) separable by chromatography.

The aforementioned version of prostaglandin synthesis by Corey was based on a similar cyclization: reaction of an analogous bis-dioxolane (**5.245**) in the presence of acid or Lewis acid (e.g. tin(IV) chloride) led to two epimeric cyclopentane derivatives (**5.248** and **5.249**). This is a composite process which can be interpreted as a nucleophilic carbonyl addition involving the enol form (**5.247**) of the enone (**5.246**), the latter being produced in the introducing steps by dioxolane cleavage.

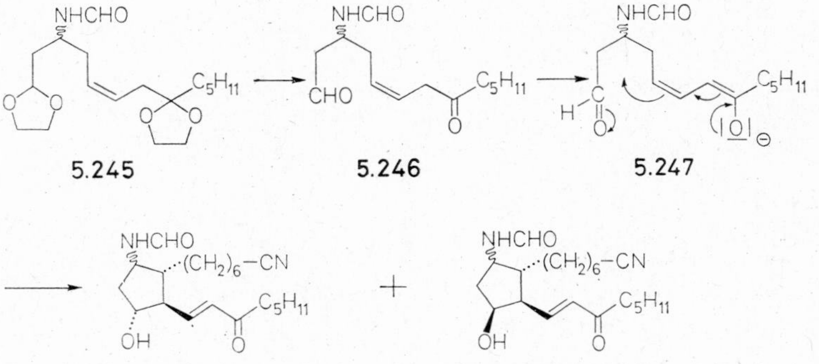

5.245 5.246 5.247

5.248 5.249

The sequence was continued by reducing the 11α-isomer (**5.239**) with zinc borohydride, separating the resulting diols (**5.240** and **5.241**) on thin-layer and hydrolyzing the required C_{15}-epimers (**5.241**) with potassium hydroxide to racemic 9-deoxy-9-thiaprostaglandin E_1 (**5.242**) which, in turn,

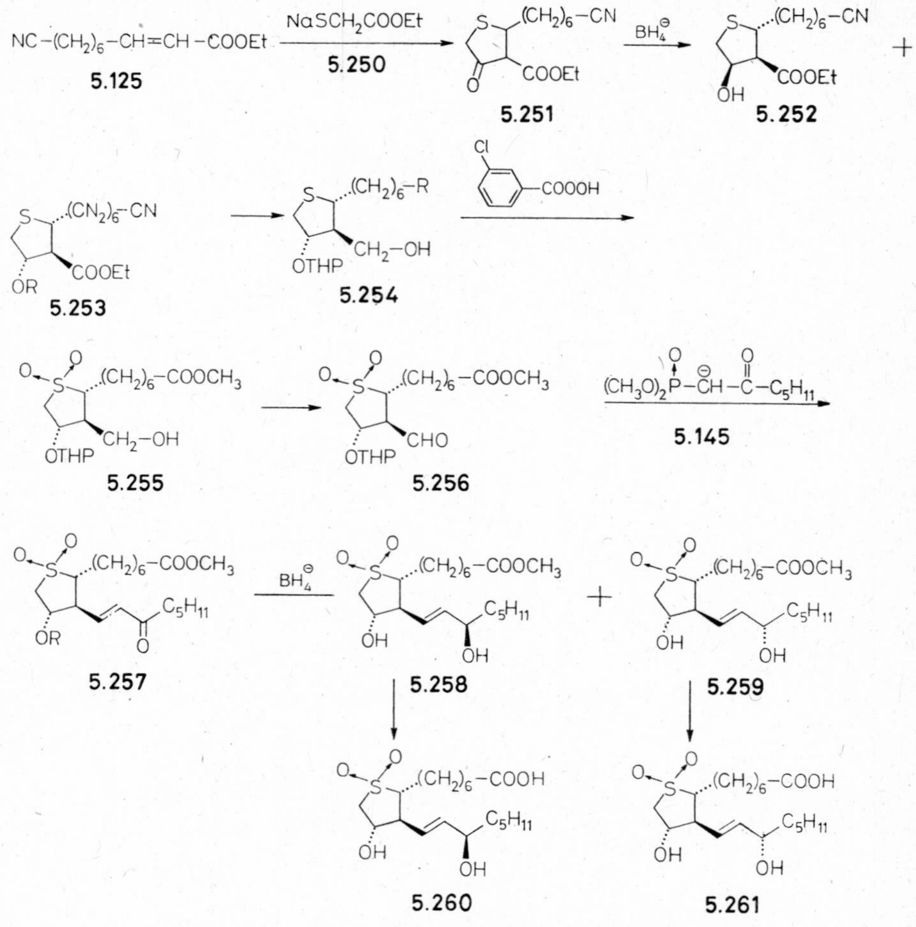

Fig. 5.18. Synthesis of 9-thiaprostaglandins II

afforded the corresponding sulfoxides (**5.243** and **5.244**) on oxidation with sodium periodate.

A rather similar sequence, carried out by the same authors starting with 9-cyanononenoic ester (**5.125**) instead of the corresponding aldehyde, produced the 9,9-dioxides of 9-thiaprostaglandins (Fig. 5.18). Addition of ethyl mercaptoacetate sodium salt (**5.250**) afforded in a multistep process the tetrahydrothiophenone (**5.251**). Reduction with sodium borohydride gave the epimeric alcohols (**5.252** and **5.253**, R = H). After separation by thin-layer chromatography, one of them (**5.253**, R = H) was reduced as the tetrahydropyranyl ether (**5.253**, R = THP) to the carbinol (**5.254**, R = CH), which was hydrolyzed with alkali to the acid (**5.254**, R $=$ CO$_2$H). Oxidation in the form of the ester (obtained with diazomethane (**5.254**, R $=$ CO$_2$Me) with m-chloroperbenzoic acid transformed the sulfide to the sulfone (**5.255**).

The concluding steps comprised Collins oxidation to the aldehyde (**5.256**). Introduction of the lower chain using dimethyl 2-oxoheptylidene phosphonate, borohydride reduction of the enone as the tetrahydropyranyl ether (**5.257**, R $=$ THP), ether cleavage, and chromatographic separation to give the alcohols (**5.258** and **5.259**). Hydrolysis of the alcohol (**5.259**) furnished racemic 9,9-dioxy-9-deoxy-9-thiaprostaglandin E$_1$ (**5.261**); hydrolysis of (**5.258**), in turn, gave the C$_{15}$-epimer (**5.260**).

The foregoing analogues have also been prepared in the optically active form. These optically active forms were synthesized by hydrolyzing the enone (**5.257**, R $=$ THP) with acid to the alcohol (**5.257**, R $=$ H); this was esterified with (R)-($-$)-α-methoxyphenylacetyl chloride and the diastereomeric esters (**5.257**, R $=$ Ph–CH(OMe)–CO–) were separated by chromatography. After hydrolysis one of the enantiomers was reduced with zinc borohydride. This gave diols epimeric at C$_{15}$ (**5.258** and **5.259**) which, after chromatographic separation and alkaline hydrolysis, afforded the optically active 9-thiaprostaglandin E$_1$ derivatives (**5.261** and **5.260**).

5.3.3 *11-Thiaprostaglandins*

Fried and his co-workers have also solved the synthesis of 11-deoxy-11-thiaprostaglandin E$_1$ (**5.263**) and F$_{1\alpha}$ (**5.264**) [46] by adapting their procedure elaborated earlier for 11-deoxy-11-oxyprostaglandins (Fig. 5.12). The key intermediate, a β-oxotetrahydrothiophene (**5.262**), was prepared by the addition of methyl thioglycolate sodium salt to the α,β-unsaturated ester (**5.178**).

5.4 FURTHER PROSTAGLANDIN ANALOGUES

Recently Ambrus *et al.* in the Pharmaceutical Research Institute (Budapest, Hungary) synthesized a series of prostaglandin analogues containing, in place of the cyclopentane moiety, a five-membered heteroaromatic ring (furan or thiazol) [47, 48]. Some of these compounds showed, in certain biological tests (e.g. effect on the muscles of the uterus), prostaglandin-like activity and inhibited prostaglandin metabolizing enzymes.

Here we discuss, as an example, the synthesis of the furan analogue of 9,11-dideoxyprostaglandin E_1 (Fig. 5.19, **5.274**). Sodium acetoacetate was

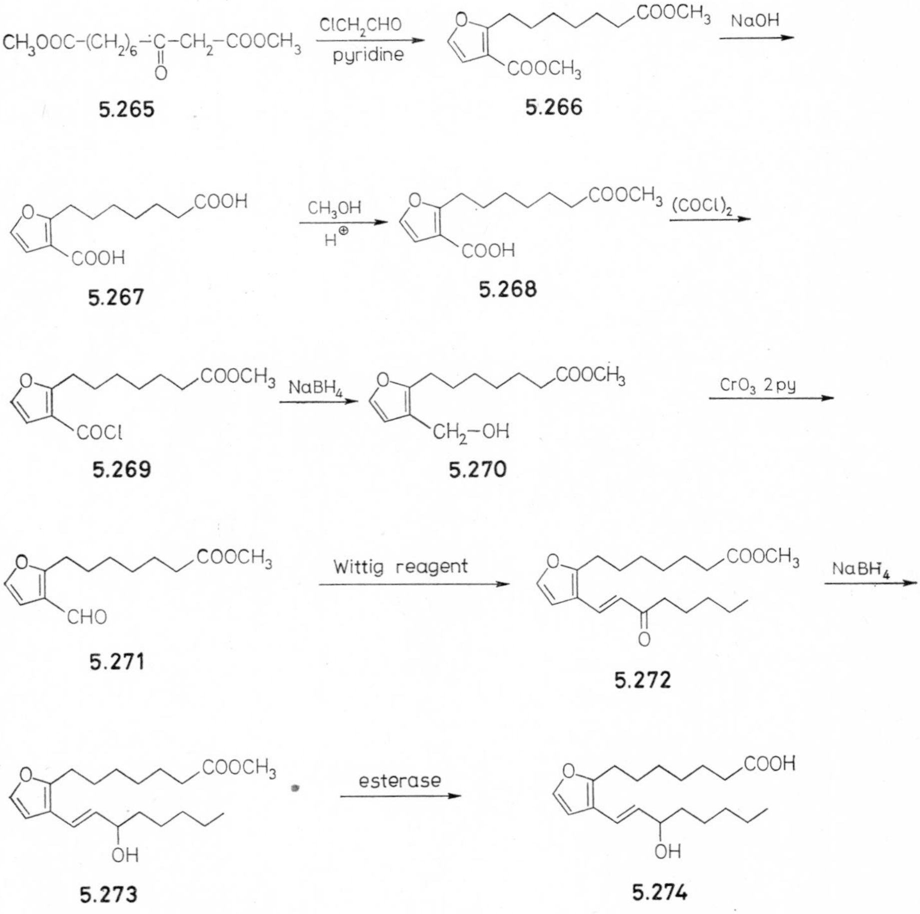

Fig. 5.19. Synthesis of the furan analogue of 9,11-dideoxyprostaglandin E_1

acylated with 7-methoxycarbonylheptanoyl chloride and the product degraded with sodium methoxide to the β-ketoester (**5.265**). Alkylation of the ester with chloroacetaldehyde gave directly the furandicarboxylic ester (**5.266**), which was saponified and selectively reesterified in the side chain to give the monoacid (**5.268**). The corresponding acid chloride (**5.269**), made with oxalyl chloride, was reduced with sodium borohydride to the alcohol (**5.270**) and the latter oxidized with chromium trioxide–pyridine complex to the aldehyde (**5.271**). Condensation with sodium dimethyl 2-oxo-heptylphosphonate, borohydride reduction of the enone obtained (**5.272**) and hydrolysis of the alcohol (**5.273**) with lipase furnished the furan ana-logue (**5.274**) as the racemate.

In addition to those discussed in this chapter, the synthesis of many other congeners has been reported, e.g. that of homoprostaglandins [49], the cyclohexane analogues [50], halogenated prostaglandins [51–54], etc. Among these, from the pharmacological point of view, two groups deserve special attention.

In the group of homoprostaglandins, when administered orally, bis-homoprostaglandin $F_{2\alpha}$ (**5.275**) is twenty times more active in labour induc-tion than the parent compound [55, 56].

5.275   5.276

Prostaglandins containing an alkoxycarbonyl group at C_8 [57, 58] are also of interest. Some of them, e.g. (**5.276**), show a marked spasmolytic effect.

From the recently synthesized group of azaprostaglandins the synthesis of 11-deoxy-8-azaprostaglandin E_1 (**5.282**) and 9,11-azoprostaglandin $F_{2\alpha}$ (**5.288**) will be described here.

Methyl L-(+)-pyroglutamate (**5.277**) served as starting material for the 8-aza compound. Alkylation of (**5.277**) with 7-bromoheptanoic acid to the diester (**5.278**), $R = CH_3$) introduced the upper chain. After partial hydro-lysis, a mixed anhydride was formed from the monoacid (**5.278**, $R = H$) with ethyl chloroformate–triethylamine and this was reduced to the alcohol (**5.279**) with sodium borohydride, then reoxidized with Collins reagent to

15*

the aldehyde (**5.280**). Condensation with sodium dimethyl 2-oxoheptylphos-phonate, reduction of the enone (**5.281**) with sodium borohydride, separation of the C_{15}-epimers by thin-layer chromatography and hydrolysis furnished 11-deoxy-8-azaprostaglandin E_1 (**5.282**) [59].

For the synthesis of 9,11-bisdeoxy-9,11-azoprostaglandin $F_{2\alpha}$ (**5.288**), prostaglandin A_2 methyl ester acetate (**5.283**), readily accessible from *Plexaura homomalla*, was utilized [60]. Oxidation of the acetate in basic medium with hydrogen peroxide gave a mixture of the α- and β-10,11-epoxides (**5.284**, $\alpha/\beta = 1.25 : 1$), which could be reduced to the 11α- and 11β-hydroxy compounds (**5.285** and its 11α-epimer). Reduction of the oxo-

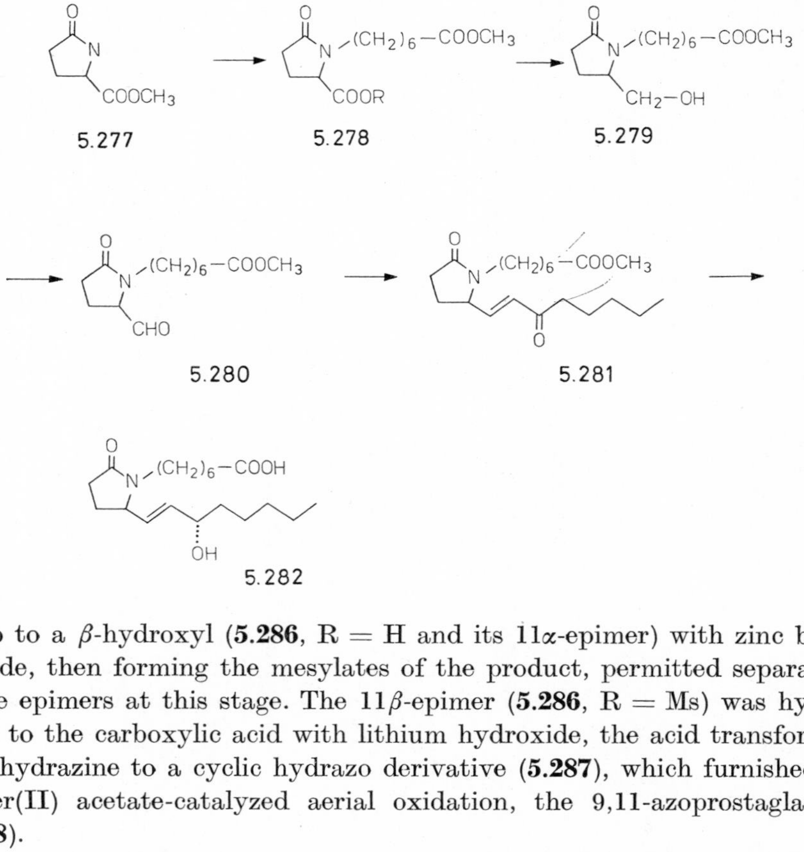

5.277   5.278   5.279

5.280   5.281

5.282

group to a β-hydroxyl (**5.286**, R = H and its 11α-epimer) with zinc borohydride, then forming the mesylates of the product, permitted separation of the epimers at this stage. The 11β-epimer (**5.286**, R = Ms) was hydrolyzed to the carboxylic acid with lithium hydroxide, the acid transformed with hydrazine to a cyclic hydrazo derivative (**5.287**), which furnished on copper(II) acetate-catalyzed aerial oxidation, the 9,11-azoprostaglandin (**5.288**).

The 9,11-azo compound can be considered as an isoelectronic aza analogue of prostaglandin endoperoxides (PGH_2 and PGG_2) (*cf.* Chapter 6). In contrast to endoperoxides, azoprostaglandins are relatively stable and can be stored at 0°C in aqueous solution. Their biological activity is of longer duration and, for example the smooth muscle contraction stimulating effect is about seven times higher than that of prostaglandin G_2.

5.283

5.284

5.285

5.286

5.287

5.288

REFERENCES

1. HAMBERG, M., SAMUELSSON, B., *J. Am. Chem. Soc.*, *91*, 2177 (1969).
2. HAMBERG, M., SAMUELSSON, B., *J. Biol. Chem.*, *246*, 6713 (1971).
3. HAMBERG, M., SAMUELSSON, B., *J. Biol. Chem.*, *247*, 3495 (1972).
4. ANGGÅRD, E., SAMUELSSON, B., *Ark. Kemi*, *25*, 293 (1966).
5. SHIO, H., RAMWELL, P. W., ANDERSEN, N. H., COREY, E. J., *Experientia*, *26*, 335 (1970).
6. NAKANO, J., ANGGÅRD, E., SAMUELSSON, B., *Pharmacologist*, *11*, 238 (1969).
7. BUNDY, G., LINCOLN, F., NELSON, N., PIKE, J., SCHNEIDER, W., *Ann. N. Y. Acad. Sci.*, *180*, 76 (1971).
8. RAWIS, R. L., *Chem. Eng. News*, June, 19, 1974.
9. KARIM, S. M. M., SHARMA, S. D., *J. Obstet. Gynaec. Brit. Commonw.*, *79*, 737 (1972).
10. BUNDY, G. L., YANKEE, E. W., WEEKS, J. R., MILLER, W. L., "The Synthesis and Biological Activity of a Series of 15-Methyl-prostaglandins." International Conference on Prostaglandins. Vienna, 1972. *Advances in the Biosciences*, *9*, 125 (1973).
11. BUNDY, G. L., *U. S. Patent* 3.728.382, 1973.
12. CHIDESTER, C. G., DUCHAMP, D. J., *Abstracts of the American Crystallographic Association, Winter Meeting*, 1974, Vol. 2, Series 2, 34.
13. YANKEE, E. W., BUNDY, G. L., *J. Am. Chem. Soc.*, *94*, 3651 (1972).
14. BAGLI, J. F., BOGRI, T., SEHGAL, S. N., *Tetrahedron Lett.*, *1973*, 3329.
15. IGUCHI, S., TANOUCHI, F., KIMURA, K., HAYASHI, M., *Prostaglandins*, *4*, 535 (1973)
16. YANKEE, E. W., AXEN, U., BUNDY, G. L., *J. Am. Chem. Soc.*, *96*, 5865 (1974).
17. HAYASHI, M., MIYAKE, H., TANOUCHI, T., IGUCHI, S., IGUCHI, Y., TANOUCHI, F., *J. Org. Chem.*, *38*, 1250 (1973).

18. MAGERLEIN, B. J., DuCHARME, D. W., MAGEE, W. E., MILLER, W. L., ROBERT, A., WEEKS, I. R., *Prostaglandins*, *4*, 143 (1973).
19. ROBERT, A., MAGERLEIN, B. J., "15-Methyl PGE$_2$ and 16,16-Dimethyl PGE$_2$: Potent Inhibitors of Gastric Secretion." International Conference on Prostaglandins. Vienna, 1972. *Advances in the Biosciences*, *9*, 247. Pergamon Press, Oxford, 1973.
20. COREY, E. J., SACHTER, H. S., *J. Am. Chem. Soc.*, *95*, 8483 (1973).
21. COREY, E. J., SHINER, Ch. S., VOLANTE, R. P., CYR, C. R., *Tetrahedron Lett. 1975*, 1161.
22. GRIECO, P. A., POGONOWSKI, Ch. S., NISHIZAWA, M., WANG, C.-L. J., *Tetrahedron Lett. 1975*, 2541.
23. FRIED, J., HEIM, S., ETHEREDGE, S. J., SUNDER-PLASSMAN, P., SANTHANAKKRISHNAN, T. S., HIMIZU, J., LIN, C. H., *Chem. Commun.*, *1968*, 634.
24. FRIED, J., LIN, C. H., MEHRA, M. M., KAO, W. L., DAHREN, P., *Ann. N. Y. Acad. Sci.*, *180*, 38 (1971).
25. FRIED, J., HEIM, S., SUNDER-PLASSMAN, P., ETHEREDGE, S. J., SANTHONAKRISHNAN, T. S., HIMIZU, J., "Synthesis of 15-Desoxy-7-oxa-Prostaglandin F$_{1\alpha}$ and Related Substances." *Prostaglandin Symposium of the Worcester Foundation for Exp. Biol.* (Eds. RAMWELL, P. W., SHAW, J. E., Interscience, New York, 1968, p. 351.
26. FRIED, J., LIN, C. H., FORD, S. M., *Tetrahedron Lett.*, *1969*, 1379.
27. FRIED, J., SANTHANAKRISHNAN, T. S., HIMIZU, J., LIN, C. H., FORD, S. M., RUBIN, B., GRIGAS, E. O., *Nature*, *233*, 208 (1969).
28. KANTOR, H. S., TAO, P., KIEFER, H. C., *Proc. Nat. Acad. Sci. U.S.*, *71*, 1317 (1974).
29. RATNER, A., WILSON, M. C., PEAKE, G. T., *Prostaglandins*, *3*, 413 (1973).
30. BARTMANN, W., *Angew. Chem.*, *87*, 143 (1975).
31. KUEHL, F. A., CIRILLO, V. J., HAM, E. A., HUMES, J. L., "The Regulatory Role of the Prostaglandins on the Cyclic 3',5'-AMP System." International Conference on Prostaglandins. Vienna, 1972. *Advances in the Biosciences*, *9*, 155. Pergamon Press, Oxford, 1973.
32. VLATTAS, I., DELLAVECCHIA, L., *Tetrahedron Lett.*, *1974*, 4455.
33. JUNICHI, H., SHOICHI, H., AKIHIKO, I., KAORU, Y., MASANORI, S., Japanese Patent 7308774 (to Tanabe Seiyaku Co. Ltd. Osaka).
34. JUNICHI, H., SHOICHI, H., AKIHIKO, I., KAORU, Y., MASANORI, S., Ger. Appl. 2229225, 1972; *Chem. Abstr.*, *78*, 147776b (1973).
35. HAUSER, F. M., HUFFMAN, R. C., *Tetrahedron Lett.*, *1974*, 905.
36. VLATTAS, I., LEE, A. C., *Tetrahedron Lett.*, *1974*, 4451.
37. HARRISON, I. T., FLETCHER, V. H., FRIED, J. H., *Tetrahedron Lett.*, *1974*, 2733.
38. HANESSIAN, S., DEXTRAZE, P., FOUGEROUSSE, A., GUINDON, Y., *Tetrahedron Lett.*, *1974*, 3983.
39. LOURENS, G. J., KOEKEMOER, J. M., *Tetrahedron Lett.*, *1975*, 3719.
40. LOURENS, G. J., KOEKEMOER, J. M., *Tetrahedron Lett.*, *1975*, 3715.
41. HARRISON, I. T., FLETCHER, V. R., *Tetrahedron Lett.*, *1974*, 2729.
42. FRIED, J., MEHRA, M. M., CHAN, Y. Y., *J. Am. Chem. Soc.*, *96*, 6759 (1974).
43. VLATTAS, I., DELLAVECCHIA, L., *Tetrahedron Lett.*, *1974*, 4459.
44. VLATTAS, I., DELLAVECCHIA, L., *Tetrahedron Lett.*, *1974*, 4267.
45. COREY, E. J., VLATTAS, I., ANDERSEN, N. H., HARDIG, K., *J. Am. Chem. Soc.*, *90*, 3248 (1968).
46. HARRISON, I. T., TAYLOR, R. J. K., FRIED, J. H., *Tetrahedron Lett.*, *1975*, 1165.
47. AMBRUS, G., BARTA, I., CSEH, Gy., TOLNAI, P., MÉHESFALVI, Z., "Procedure for the Preparation of 9-Oxaprostanoic Acid Derivatives." *Hung. Appl.*, GO 1292 (1974); AMBRUS, G., BARTA, I., *Prostaglandins*, *10*, 661 (1975)
48. AMBRUS, G., BARTA, I., MÉHESFALVI, Z., HORVÁTH, G., "Procedure for the Preparation of Novel Thiazol Derivatives." *Hung. Appl.*, 169072 (1974).
49. HARRISON, I. T., GRAYSHAN, R., WILLIAMS, T., SEMENOVSKI, A., FRIED, J. H., *Tetrahedron Lett.*, *1972*, 5151.
50. CROSSLEY, N. S., *Tetrahedron Lett.*, *1971*, 3327.
51. GANDOLFI, C., DORIA, G., GAIO, P., *Il Farmako*, *27*, 1125 (1972).
52. YANKEE, E. W., "Synthesis and Biological Activity of New Prostanoids." Lecture held at the International Conference on Prostaglandins, Florence, May 1975.

53. FRIED, J., "Chemical and Biological Studies on 13-dehydroprostaglandins." Lecture held at the International Conference on Prostaglandins, Florence, May 1975.
54. GANDOLFI, C., PELLEGATA, R., DRADI, E., PELLA, E., "α-Halo-α,β-unsaturated Ketones: A Synthetic Approach to 13-Dehydroprostaglandins." Lecture held at the International Conference on Prostaglandins, Florence, May 1975.
55. LABHSETWAR, A. P., *Nature*, *238*, 400 (1972).
56. CRABBÉ, P., "Prostaglandins, Production and Prospects." *Chemistry in Britain*, *11*, 132 (1975).
57. Hoechst Co., Unpublished results.
58. BARTMANN, W., *Angew. Chem.*, *87*, 143 (1975).
59. BOLLIGER, G., MUCHOWSKI, J. M., *Tetrahedron Lett.*, *1975*, 2931.
60. COREY, E. J., NICOLAOU, K. C., MACHIDA, J., MALMSTEN, C. L., SAMUELSSON, B., *Proc. Nat. Acad. Sci. USA*, *72*, 3355 (1975).
61. GRIECO, P. A., FUKAMIYA, N., MIYASHITA, M., *Chem. Commun.*, *1976*, 573.
62. HAJÓS, Z. G., PARRISH, D. R., *J. Org. Chem.*, *39*, 1615 (1974).

6. ISOLATION OF PROSTAGLANDINS FROM NATURAL SOURCES

As pointed out in the introduction, prostaglandins are ubiquitous in mammalian tissues; recently they have been detected even in plant cells (e.g. in onions). The concentration of prostaglandins in tissues and body fluids is extremely low, generally of the order of 10^{-7}–10^{-9} g/g tissue. The isolation of sensitive substances present in such low concentrations is an exacting task requiring special techniques.

Although several methods had earlier been reported for the isolation of prostaglandins from various tissues, none of them was economic until it was discovered that the gorgonian sea whip, *Plexaura homomalla*, a species of coral native in the Caribbean, contained substantial amounts of a stereo-isomer of prostaglandin A_2. No prostaglandin-like activity was shown by this compound, but its isolation by extraction was relatively simple, and it could be transformed to natural prostaglandins.

In the organism prostaglandins are formed from the essential fatty acids by an enzyme system known as prostaglandin synthetase. Several proce-dures are known for the preparation of the appropriate precursors. The enzyme system has been isolated from various organs and the *in vitro* trans-formation of fatty acids to prostaglandins using this system has been solved,

6.1 BIOSYNTHESIS OF PROSTAGLANDINS

The first studies on the biosynthesis of prostaglandins were conducted independently by two research groups. In 1964, Bergström and his co-work-ers of the Karolinska Institute [1] and van Dorp *et al.* [2] of the research laboratories of Unilever reported the transformation of dihomo-γ-linoleic acid (Fig. 6.1, **6.3**) to prostaglandin E_1, of arachidonic acid (**6.4**) to prosta-glandin E_2 and of 5,8,11,14,17-eicosapentaenoic acid (**6.5**) to prostaglandin

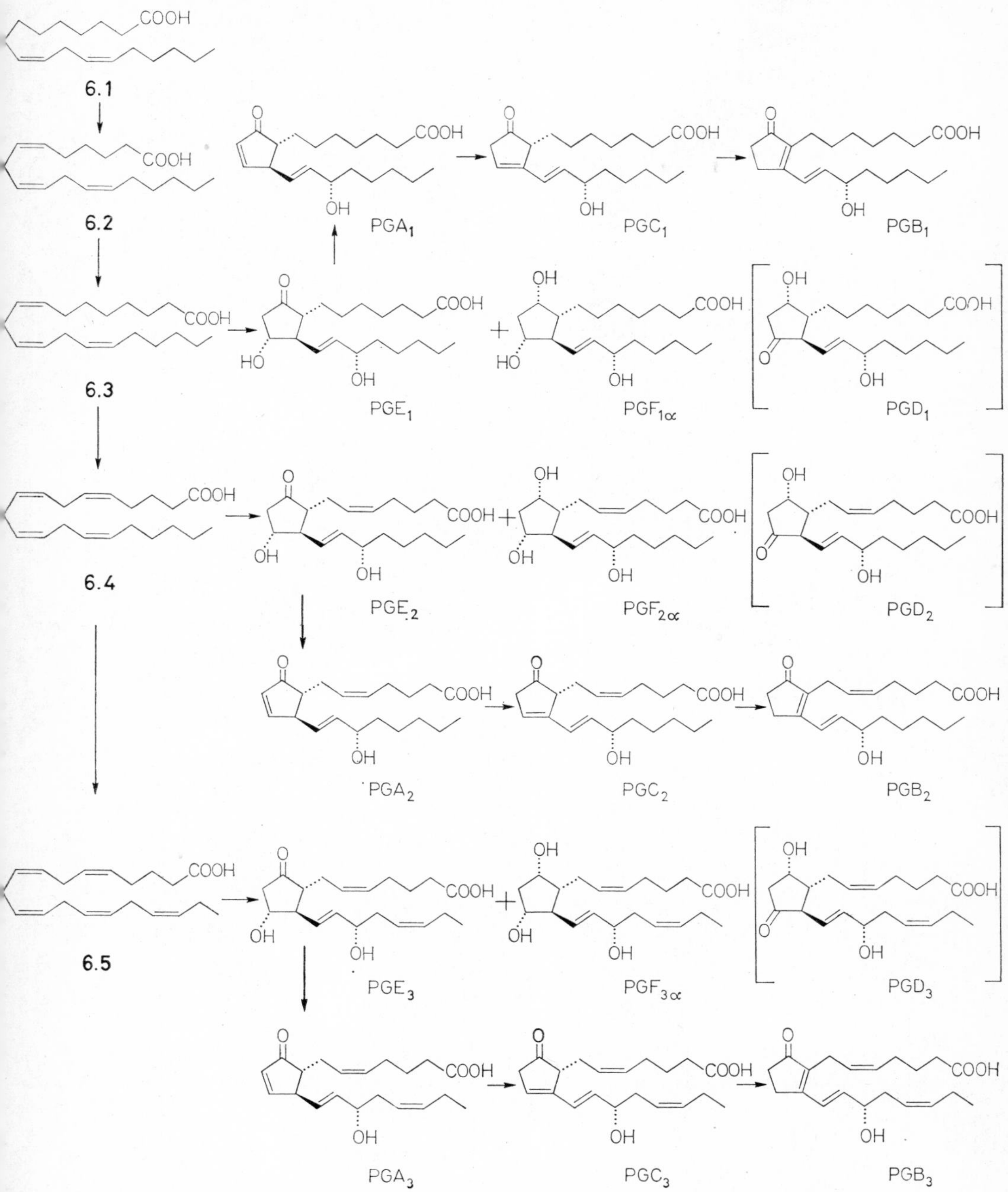

Fig. 6.1. Overall bioconversion reaction showing formations of prostaglandins from their fatty acid precursors

E_3 by the homogenates of ram seminal vesicles. Later Wallach described the transformation of arachidonic acid to prostaglandin E_2 using an acetone powder of bovine seminal vesicles [3]. The first example of the biological synthesis of an F-type prostaglandin was described by Kupiecki in 1965; he prepared prostaglandin $F_{1\alpha}$ from dihomo-γ-linoleic acid using the enzyme systems prepared from bovine seminal vesicles [4]. These pioneering experiments initiated the rapid progress in this field. In 1967 Samuelsson and associates [5] as well as Nugteren *et al.* [6] succeeded in elucidating the detailed mechanism of bioconversion.

In biological systems the immediate precursors of prostaglandins are formed from linoleic acid (Fig. 6.1, **6.1**). This is first dehydrogenated to γ-linolenic acid (**6.2**) and subsequently to dihomo-γ-linolenic acid (8,11,14-eicosatrienoic acid, **6.3**). In the presence of some co-factors, under the action of the prostaglandin synthetase enzyme system, the latter is transformed to a mixture of prostaglandin E_1 and $F_{1\alpha}$. The product ratio is influenced by co-factors and reaction conditions. As a minor product, prostaglandin D_1 also appears.

The biosynthetic sequence branches off at the stage of dihomo-γ-linolenic acid which is further dehydrogenated to arachidonic acid (5,8,11,14-eicosatetraenoic acid, **6.4**) and ends up with prostaglandin E_2 and $F_{2\alpha}$. The bioconversion of 5,8,11,14,17-eicosapentaenoic acid (**6.5**) gives rise to prostaglandin E_3 and $F_{3\alpha}$.

Primary prostaglandins formed in the way described above decompose in part by dehydration to A-type prostaglandins and then *via* C-type intermediates to prostaglandin B.

Prostaglandin synthetase is obtained from animal organs, most often from cattle vesicular gland [1–4, 7–10]. After slaughtering the animal, the organs are immediately freed from fat and connective tissues, then homogenized in a buffer solution. Remnants of disintegrated tissues and the microsomal fraction are separated by successive centrifuging and high speed ultracentrifuging.

Prostaglandin synthetase is not strictly substrate specific and is able to transform not only the above mentioned C_{20} fatty acids, but also certain C_{19} and C_{21} analogues to nor- and homo-prostaglandins, respectively [11–15].

Both the position and the geometry of the double bonds in the C_{20} fatty acids are of importance in bioconversion, being most efficient with all-(Z)-dihomo-γ-linolenic acid (**6.3**) and all-(Z)-arachidonic acid (**6.4**).

Bioconversion depends on the presence of certain co-factors, among them thiols, antioxidants and haem-type compounds, and it is an aerobic process [16–18]. Molecular oxygen is necessary for fatty acid oxidation. Antioxi-

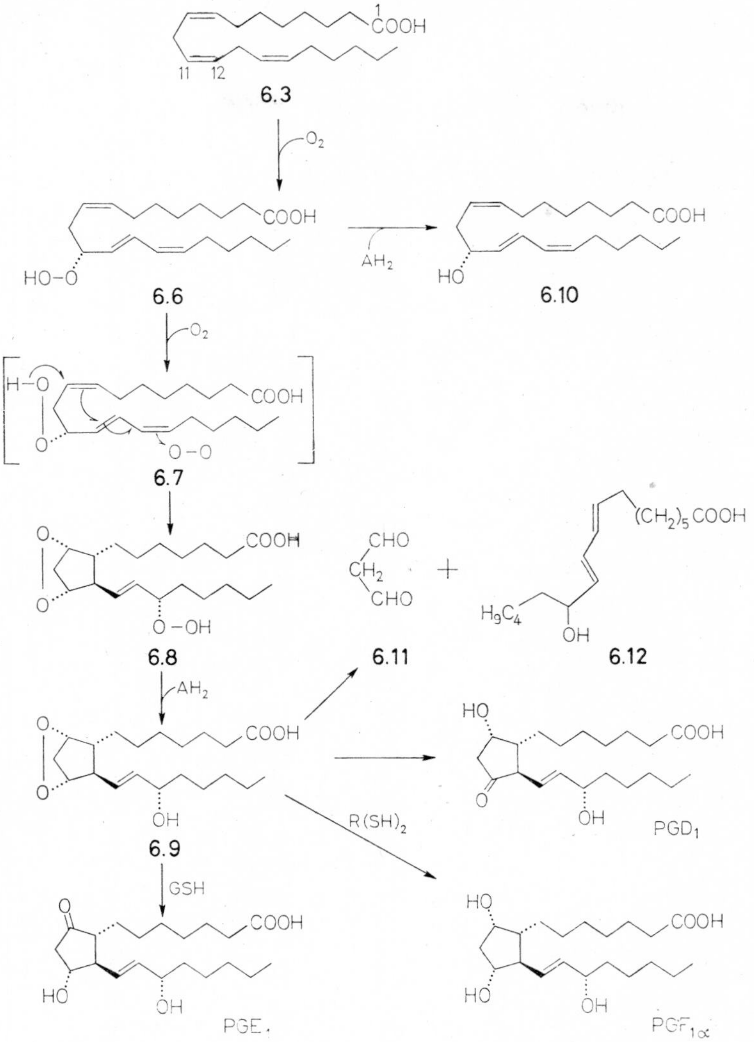

Fig. 6.2. Mechanism of biosynthesis of prostaglandins E_1 and $F_{1\alpha}$

dants and haem-type co-factors mediate oxygen uptake; the role of thiols (which will be discussed in detail later), is in the reduction of intermediates of the biosynthesis.

Biosynthesis in $^{18}O_2$ atmosphere demonstrated that each of the three oxygen atoms associated with C_9, C_{11} and C_{15} originated from molecular oxygen. Concerning the mechanism of oxidation it is of special interest that two moles of oxygen were used during the formation of one mole prostaglandin, and that both oxygen atoms linked to the cyclopentene ring originated from the same oxygen molecule. It was found that on incubation with a mixture of $^{16}O_2$ and $^{18}O_2$, oxygen atoms associated with the same molecule were either both $^{16}O_2$ or both $^{18}O_2$ isotopes [19–22].

The detailed mechanism of biosynthesis is illustrated by the example of prostaglandin E_1 and $F_{1\alpha}$ (Fig. 6.2). The reaction sequence is started by the lipoxygenase (fatty acid dioxygenase) component of the enzyme, which attacks the C_{11}-C_{12} double bond of dihomo-γ-linolenic acid (6.3). In the first stage oxygen is added and the double bond migrates to the position C_{12}-C_{13}.

Abstraction of the hydrogen atom from the C_{13} methylene group is stereospecific. It was established that the prostaglandin obtained from (13R)-^{3}H--3-^{14}C-8,11,14-eicosatrienoic acid contained tritium, whereas that derived from the (13S)-epimer was devoid of tritium.

The addition of another molecule of oxygen onto 11-hydroperoxyeicosatrienic acid (6.6) triggers a synchronous reaction involving the closure of the cyclopentane ring, transposition of the C_{12}-C_{13} double bond, formation of both a C_9-C_{11} endoperoxide bridge and a hydroperoxy group at C_{15} (6.6 → 6.8).

Of the two peroxy groups of (6.8), it is the C_{15} hydroperoxy group which is first reduced by a co-factor present in the system to the hydroxy-endoperoxide (6.9), the further reduction of which is controlled in *in vitro* experiments by additives. Glutathion induces a rearrangement of the endoperoxide moiety to a β-hydroxyketone, i.e. to prostaglandin E_1, whereas in the presence of dithiols (e.g. dithiothreitol) reduction becomes predominant and the product is mainly prostaglandin $F_{1\alpha}$. Prostaglandin D_1 was invariably formed as a minor product; its proportion could be increased when serotonin (5-hydroxytryptamine) was added to the system [23].

Glutathion-controlled rearrangement of the hydroxy-endoperoxide (6.9) to prostaglandin E_1 was investigated by Lands *et al.* [15, 24] who proposed the following mechanism (6.13 → 6.15):

6.13   6.14   6.15

It is conceivable that the process leading to prostaglandin $F_{1\alpha}$ proceeds in the way described above only under *in vitro* conditions, since *in vivo* there is not sufficient dithiol available and the reducing agent was efficient only in the presence of complexing agents (e.g. copper salts).

Recently Samuelsson and his group succeeded in isolating the two key intermediates of the bioconversion: the endoperoxides of type (6.8) and (6.9) [25–27, 41]. They incubated arachidonic acid (6.4) with a homogenate of sheep vesicular gland for a brief period and then isolated the endoperoxides by chromatographing the ethereal extract of the mixture. The pure endoperoxides (6.16 and 6.17) are relatively stable in aprotic solvents but decompose rapidly in alcohol or water. The trivial names prostaglandin G and prostaglandin H were recommended for the endoperoxide (6.16) and the hydroxy-endoperoxide (6.17), respectively.

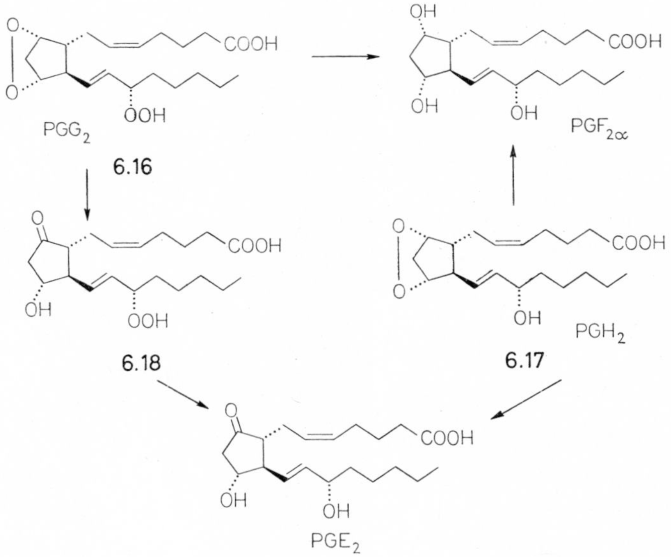

Both of the newly discovered prostaglandins can easily be converted to prostaglandin E_2 and $F_{2\alpha}$. Treatment of prostaglandin G_2 with a reducing agent (e.g. tin(II) chloride) gave excellent yields (90%) of prostaglandin $F_{2\alpha}$. In a buffer of pH 7.4 the endoperoxide (6.16) afforded 15-hydroperoxy-prostaglandin E_2 (6.18) which yielded, on reduction with tin(II) chloride, prostaglandin E_2. Similarly with tin(II) chloride, prostaglandin H_2 gave prostaglandin $F_{2\alpha}$, whereas in a buffer solution it gave prostaglandin E_2.

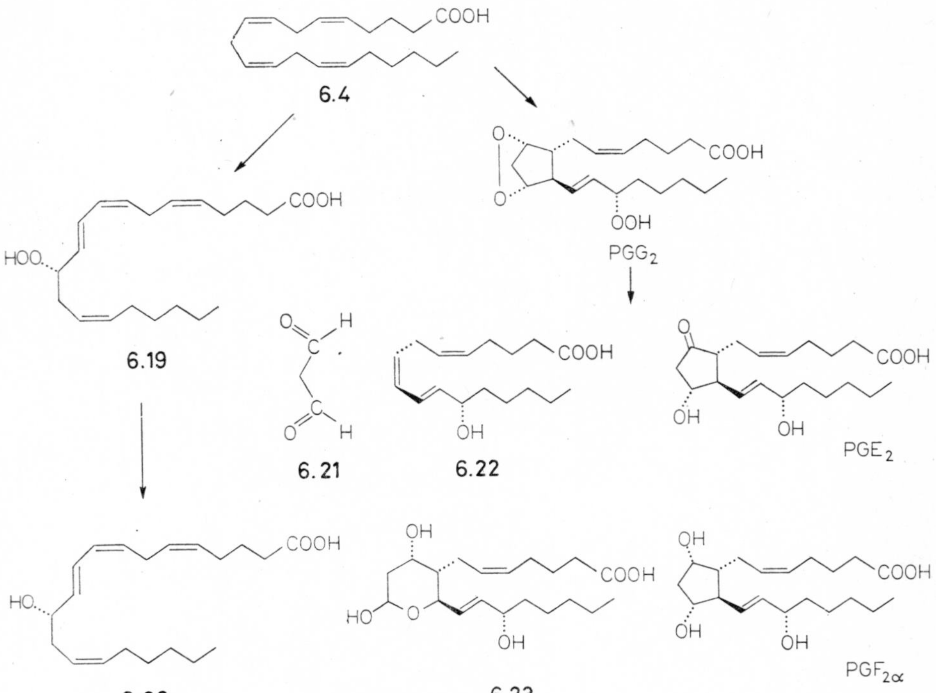

Fig. 6.3. Formation of the peroxy compound

Isolation of prostaglandin G_2 provided the first direct evidence that a hydroxyl at C_{15} was introduced by means of a dioxygenase type reaction. This prompted Samuelsson *et al.* to recommend that the enzyme system accomplishing the bioconversion of arachidonic acid should be termed fatty acid cyclooxygenase. According to these authors, the formation of the peroxy compound from arachidonic acid (**6.19**, Fig. 6.3) under the action of the lipoxygenase enzyme system, followed by reduction of the latter to the hydroxy acid (**6.20**), is not linked directly with prostaglandin biosynthesis.

Both peroxy-type prostaglandins (G_2 and H_2) exhibited very strong prostaglandin-like activity. Smooth muscle stimulation by prostaglandin G_2 and H_2 was 5–200 and 100–450 times higher, respectively, than by prostaglandin E_2.

Recently the transformation of arachidonic acid in human plasma was investigated and the metabolites were isolated. The main intermediates of the bioconversion were found to be: (12*R*)-hydroxy-5,8,10,14-eicosatetraenoic acid (**6.20**, HETE), (12S)-hydroxy-5,8,10-heptadecatrienoic acid (**6.22**, HHT), and 8-[(1-hydroxy-3-oxopropyl)-12S]-dihydroxy-5,10-heptadeca-dienoic acid in the hemiketal form (**6.23**, PHD). As is apparent from the biosynthesis and metabolism of prostaglandins discussed before (Fig. 6.2 and Chapter 5), none of these compounds originate from the metabolism of prostaglandin E$_2$ nor of F$_{2\alpha}$. HETE was thus the product of a side reaction whereas HHT and PHD were derived directly from the endoperoxides. In this experiment the amount of prostaglandin G$_2$ calculated from the measured amount of HHT and PHD was by two orders of magnitude higher than that of prostaglandin E$_2$ and F$_{2\alpha}$ actually identified. Consequently, in this system prostaglandin-like activity could be ascribed to the endoper-oxides which gave almost exclusively non-prostaglandin metabolites and only a small amount of prostaglandin.

Later Samuelsson *et al.* also isolated thromboxane A$_2$ (**6.24**), the inter-mediate of the PGG$_2$ → PHD (**6.23**; thromboxane B$_2$) transformation [42].

6.24

6.23

A new transformation of the endoperoxide (PGG$_2$) has been described recently by Vane *et al.* [43—45]. An enzyme found in arterial walls converts PGG$_2$ into prostaglandin φX (PGX ≡ PGI$_2$), which inhibits the aggrega-tion of platelets. Most probably the chemical structure of prostaglandin X is 9-deoxy-6,9α-epoxy-Δ^5-PGF$_1$ (the trivial name prostacyclin was pro-posed for the compound) [46].

These results led Samuelsson and his co-workers to propose a new inter-pretation of the biological mechanism of prostaglandin action. According to this, the physiological effects of prostaglandins should be mainly attributed to the endoperoxides, the prostaglandins proper being only minor metabo-lites thereof. This hypothesis naturally needs further corroboration.

The practical application of bioconversion is severely handicapped.

First of all, it is characteristic of enzymatic reactions that maximal conversions are associated with minimal concentrations. Therefore, no efforts were made to achieve high conversion yields, but large amounts of enzyme preparation and precursor were used. For instance the standard method for bioconversion used by the Upjohn group involved the incubation of 37 g precursor fatty acids with 75 kg of homogenized sheep vesicular gland to obtain a few grams of prostaglandin. Poor conversion made isolation of the product even more difficult than usual. High costs of the isolation and purification of enzymes presented further problems. Taking all these factors into account, the production of prostaglandins by biosynthesis seems at present to be uneconomical.

6.2 ISOLATION OF PROSTAGLANDINS FROM THE CORAL GORGONIAN (*PLEXAURA HOMOMALLA*)

In 1969 a study by Weinheimer and Spraggins concerning the constituents of lower animals inhabiting the Caribbean sea revealed that certain varieties of *Plexaura homomalla* (Esper), a coral native in this area, contained prostaglandins [28–31]. This coral is an exceptionally abundant source of $(15R)$-prostaglandin A_2 methyl ether (**6.24**, Fig. 6.4) of which it contains 1–2% on a dry weight basis. Later it turned out that (**6.25**) was characteristic of the particular variety called *Plexaura homomalla* (R) collected on the shores of Florida, whereas a variety indigenous to the Grand Cayman island *(Plexaura homomalla (S))* contained prostaglandins of the configuration pertinent to mammalian prostaglandins, i.e. $15S$ [32–35]. In fact, the coral cortex immediately frozen with liquid nitrogen after harvesting contained predominantly the primary prostaglandin E_2 and its methyl ester, whereas samples that had been stored after collection under water or methanol yielded mainly prostaglandin A_2 and its methyl ester. The latter prostaglandin (A_2) and its methyl ester can therefore be considered here as artefacts.

No explanation of the high prostaglandin content of this coral species has as yet been proposed. One of the hypotheses suggests that prostaglandins are not formed in the coral itself but in symbiotic algae. Alternatively the algae, which are known to contain considerable amounts of unsaturated C_{20} fatty acids, only synthesize the precursors, and these are then utilized by the host coral. An investigation of this problem by Corey and Washburn demonstrated that prostaglandins were biosynthesized in the coral itself under the action of the prostaglandin synthetase enzyme system [39, 40].

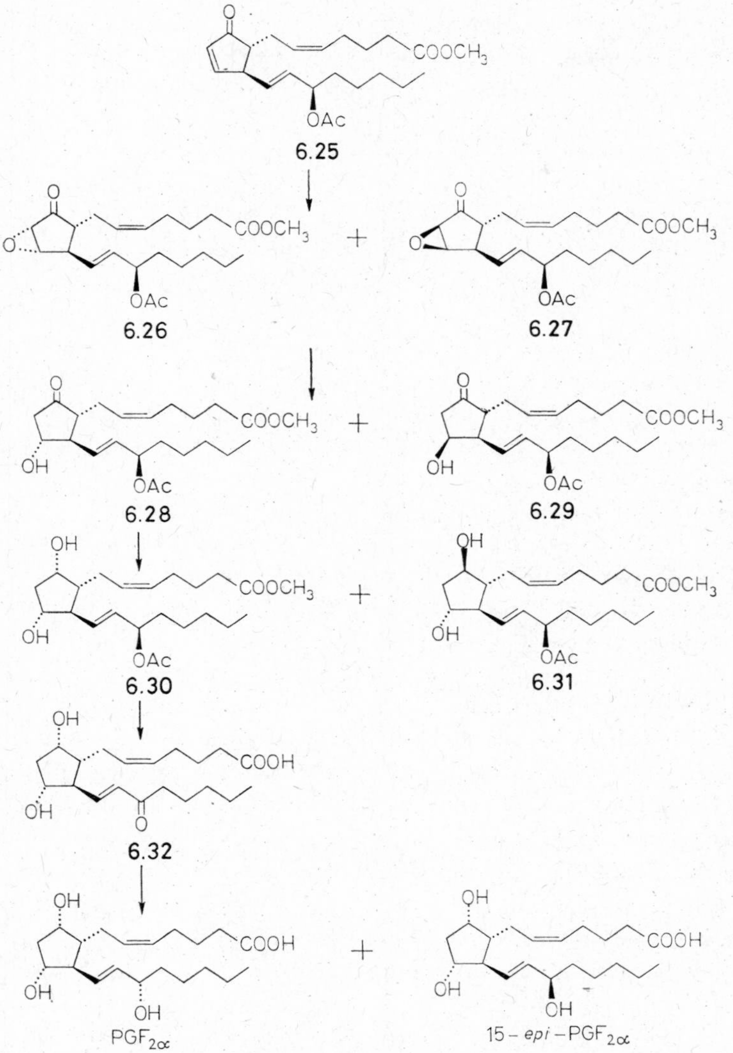

Fig. 6.4. The conversion of prostaglandin A$_2$ acetate into PGF$_{2\alpha}$

The high prostaglandin content of *Plexaura homomallá* has aroused considerable interest concerning the conversion of prostaglandins isolable from this source into primary prostaglandins. Earlier Bundy *et al.* [36] carried out the conversion of (15R)-prostaglandin methyl ester acetate (**6.25**) to prostaglandin $F_{2\alpha}$ and to E_2 (Fig. 6.4). This required an inversion of configuration at C_{15} and the introduction of a hydroxyl at the β-carbon of the enone system. For this purpose the ester (6.25) was first epoxidized with alkaline hydrogen peroxide to give a pair of stereoisomeric epoxides (6.26 and 6.27), mainly the α-isomer; 75%, 6.26). The mixture was reduced with chromium(II) acetate in acetic acid, and the mixture of epimeric alcohols (6.28 and 6.29) was separated by chromatography. The trimethylsilyl ether of the 11α-epimer (prepared with trimethylsilyl chloride), was reduced with sodium borohydride, and the major 9α-epimer (86%, 6.30) of the resulting mixture of alcohols (6.30 and 6.31) was separated by chromatography. Base-catalyzed hydrolysis of the hydroxy acid and selective oxidation with 2,3-dichloro-5,6-dicyano-1,4-benzoquinone to 15-oxo-prostaglandin $F_{2\alpha}$ (6.32) was followed by reduction with zinc borohydride to afford a mixture of prostaglandin $F_{2\alpha}$ and its C_{15}-epimer, which could be separated by chromatography.

A modification of the above sequence was applied to the transformation of 15-*epi*-prostaglandin A_2 (6.33), a minor component of the coral (0.2% of the dry weight), to prostaglandin E_2 methyl ester (6.38). Introduction of the hydroxyl was also solved in this case by successive epoxidation and reduction; the inversion of configuration was effected by solvolysis of the corresponding mesylate.

Accordingly, first the methyl ester was prepared, then its mesylate (6.34); the latter was solvolyzed with aqueous acetone. Prostaglandin A_2 methyl ester (6.35) obtained in this way in moderate yield was subjected to oxidation with alkaline hydrogen peroxide to give a mixture of epoxides (6.36 and 6.37, $\alpha/\beta = 1 : 3$); this mixture was reduced with chromium(II) acetate. Chromatography afforded mainly prostaglandin E_2 methyl ester (6.38), its C_{11}-epimer (6.39), together with a small amount of prostaglandin A_2 methyl ester.

Later, a process giving better yields was found by Corey and Ensley for the transformation of prostaglandin A_2 into prostaglandin E_2 (cf. Section 1.3).

The epoxidation and reduction procedure can also be used for the conversion of (15S)-prostaglandin A_2 methyl ester acetate (6.40), a constituent (about 1.4%) of the (S)-variety of *Plexaura homomalla*, into prostaglandin E_2. The transformation was started with the enzymic hydrolysis of the acetate ester (6.40) to prostaglandin A_2 methyl ester (6.35), using an esterase isolated from coral [35, 37]. Fast base-catalyzed elimination of the elements of acetic acid gives a 15-deoxydehydroprostaglandin derivative (6.41); this precluded the direct hydrolysis of the sensitive substrate.

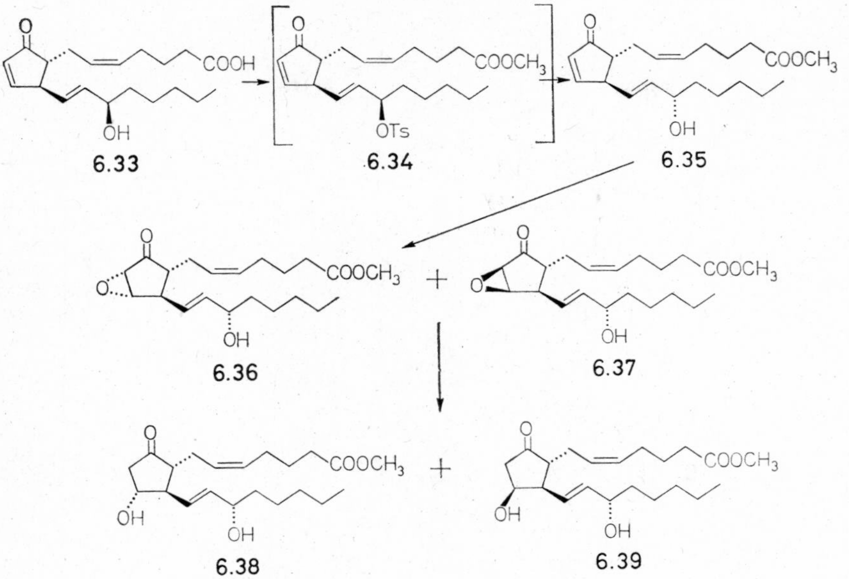

Recently an interesting method for the selective removal of the C_{15} acetyl group has been reported [25]. This comprised the addition of methane-thiol to the enone moiety of prostaglandin A_2 methyl ester (**6.40**), followed by the hydrolysis of the acetoxy group in the product (**6.42**, a mixture of C_{11}-epimers), with sodium carbonate; treatment of the resulting alcohol (**6.42**) obtained with methyl iodide in the presence of base gave excellent yields of prostaglandin A_2 methyl ester (**6.35**).

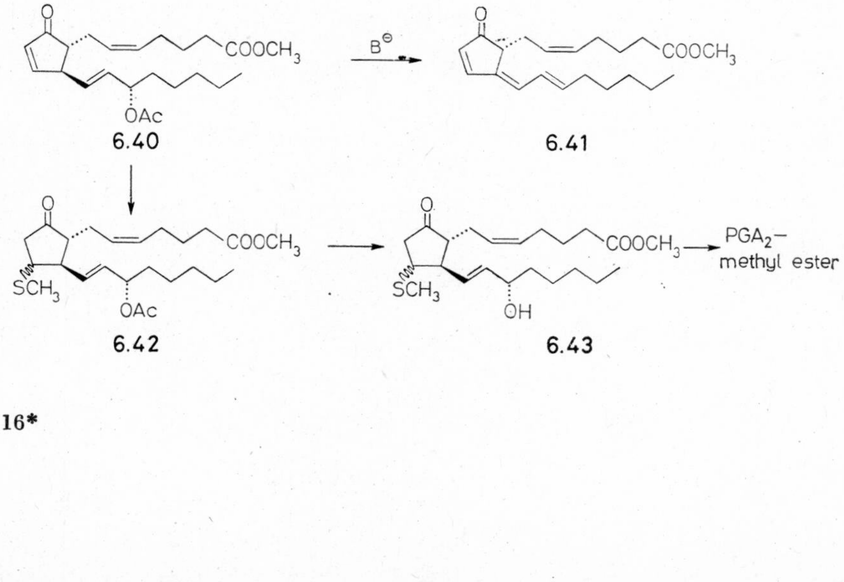

In addition to the known representatives, the (S)-variety of *Plexaura homomalla* yielded a new prostaglandin, *viz.* (5E)-prostaglandin A$_2$ (**6.44**). The epoxidation method was useful for the transformation of (**6.44**) to (5E)-prostaglandin E$_2$ (**6.45**), and by subsequent reduction with sodium borohydride a mixture of (5E)-prostaglandin F$_{2\alpha}$ (**6.46**) and (5E)-prostaglandin F$_{2\beta}$ (**6.47**) was obtained. (5E)-Prostaglandin E$_2$ (**6.45**) had been prepared earlier by van Dorp [11] by way of the bioconversion of (5E)-arachidonic acid. Photoisomerization of prostaglandin E$_2$ (*cf.* Section 1.3) also gave (**6.45**).

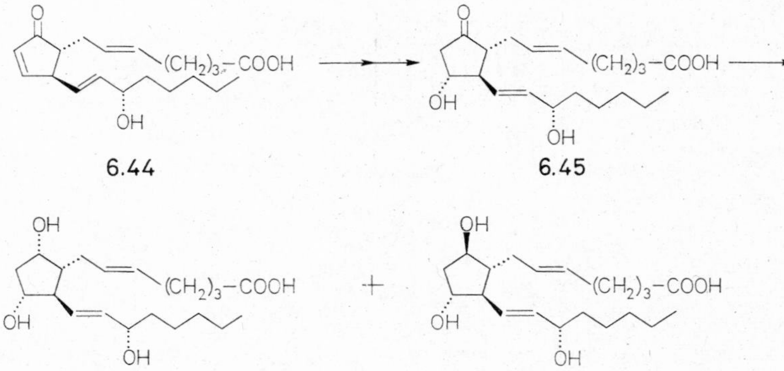

It may be possible that corals will provide starting material for the preparation of prostaglandin A$_2$ and various artificial prostaglandins. The action of prostaglandin A$_2$ is more selective than that of the primary prostaglandins. Its influence on smooth muscle contraction is relatively unimportant, but its hypotensive effect is of considerable value. The clinical application of prostaglandin A$_2$ is restricted because of fast metabolism.

The use of coral prostaglandins for the preparation of derivatives has already been illustrated in Chapter 5, by the conversion of (15R)-prostaglandin A$_2$ acetate to 15-oxoprostaglandin F$_{2\alpha}$. From this latter, by the Grignard reaction, 15-methylprostaglandin F$_{2\alpha}$ marketed as a pharmaceutical was obtained. The (15S)-analogue could, in turn, be reduced with sodium cyanoborohydride to 11-deoxyprostaglandin F$_2$, giving rise after oxidation to 11-deoxyprostaglandin E$_2$ with exhibits valuable pharmacological properties [38].

REFERENCES

1. BERGSTRÖM, S., DANIELSSON, H., SAMUELSSON, B., *Biochim. Biophys. Acta, 90,* 207 (1964).
2. VAN DORP, D. A., BEERTHUIS, R. K., NUGTEREN, D. H., VONKEMAN, H., *Biochim. Biophys. Acta, 90,* 204 (1964); *Nature, 203,* 839 (1964).
3. WALLACH, D. P., *Life Sci., 4,* 361 (1965).
4. KUPIECKI, F. P., *Life Sci., 4,* 1811 (1965).
5. SAMUELSSON, B., GRANSTRÖM, E., HAMBERG, M., "On the mechanism of the biosynthesis of prostaglandins." *The Prostaglandins. Proc. II. Nobel Symp.* (Eds BERGSTRÖM, S., SAMUELSSON, B.). Almqvist and Wicksell, Stockholm, 1967.
6. NUGTEREN, D. H., BEERTHUIS, R. K., VAN DORP, D. A., "Biosynthesis of Prostaglandins." *The Prostaglandins. Proc. II. Nobel Symp.* (Eds BERGSTRÖM, S., SAMUELSSON, B.). Almqvist and Wicksell, Stockholm, 1967.
7. ANGGÅRD, E., *Ann. N. Y. Acad. Sci., 180,* 200 (1971).
8. YOSHIMOTO, A., ITO, H., TOMITA, K., *J. Biochem. (Tokyo), 68,* 487 (1970).
9. TAKEGUCHI, C., KOHNO, E., SIH, C. J., *Biochemistry, 10,* 2372 (1971).
10. KUNZE, H., VOGT, W., *Ann. N. Y. Acad. Sci., 180,* 123 (1971).
11. VAN DORP, D. A., *Ann. N. Y. Acad. Sci., 180,* 182 (1971).
12. HAMBERG, M., SAMUELSSON, B., *J. Biol. Chem., 242,* 5329 (1967).
13. STRUIJK, C. B., BEERTHUIS, R. K., PABON, H. J. J., VAN DORP, D. A., *Rec. Trav. Chim., 85,* 1233 (1966).
14. BEERTHUIS, R. K., NUGTEREN, D. H., PABON, H. J. J., STEENHOEK, A., VAN DORP, D. A., *Rec. Trav. Chim., 90,* 943 (1971).
15. LANDS, E. M., LE TELLIER, P. R., ROME, L. H., VANDERHOEK, J. Y., "Inhibition of Prostaglandin Biosynthesis". International Conference on Prostaglandins. Vienna, 1972. *Advances in the Biosciences. 9,* 15 (1973), Pergamon Press, Oxford.
16. VONKEMAN, H., NUGTEREN, D. H., VAN DORP, D. A., *Biochim. Biophys. Acta, 187,* 581 (1969).
17. SIH, C. J., AMBRUS, G., FOSS, P., LAI, C. J., *J. Am. Chem. Soc., 91,* 3686 (1969).
18. SIH, C. J., TAKEGUCHI, C., FOSS, P., *J. Am. Chem. Soc., 92,* 6670 (1970).
19. RYHAGE, R., SAMUELSSON, B., *Biochem. Biophys. Res. Commun., 19,* 279 (1965).
20. SAMUELSSON, B., *J. Am. Chem. Soc., 87,* 3011 (1965).
21. NUGTEREN, D. H., VAN DORP, D. A., *Biochim. Biophys. Acta, 98,* 654 (1965).
22. KLENBERG, D., SAMUELSSON, B., *Acta Chim. Scand., 19,* 534 (1965).
23. FOSS, P. S., SIH, C. J., TAKEGUCHI, C., SCHNOES, H., *Biochemistry, 11,* 2271 (1972).
24. LANDS, W., LEE, R., SMITH, W., *Ann. N. Y. Acad. Sci., 180,* 108 (1971).
25. HAMBERG, M., SAMUELSSON, B., *Proc. Nat. Acad. Sci. USA, 70,* 899 (1973).
26. HAMBERG, M., SVENSSON, J., WAKABAYASHI, T., SAMUELSSON, B., *Proc. Nat. Acad. Sci. USA, 71,* 345 (1974).
27. HAMBERG, M., SVENSSON, J., SAMUELSSON, B., *Proc. Nat. Acad. Sci. USA, 71,* 3824 (1974).
28. WEINHEIMER, A. J., SPRAGGINS, R. L., *Tetrahedron Lett., 1969,* 5185.
29. SPRAGGINS, R. L., *Tetrahedron Lett., 1972,* 4343.
30. "Research lags on drugs from marine sources." *Chem. Eng. News,* p. 25, Sept. 11, 1972.
31. RAWIS, R. L., "Prostaglandins: Chemical foundation is laid." *Chem. Eng. News,* p. 18, June 24, 1974.
32. SCHNEIDER, W. P., HAMILTON, R. D., RHULAND, L. E., *J. Am. Chem. Soc., 94,* 2122 (1972).
33. BUNDY, G. L., SCHNEIDER, W. P., LINCOLN, F. H., PIKE, J. E., *J. Am. Chem. Soc., 94,* 2123 (1972).
34. BUNDY, G. L., DANIELS, E. G., LINCOLN, F. H., PIKE, J. E., *J. Am. Chem. Soc., 94,* 2124 (1972).
35. PRICE, A., ALVAREZ, F. S., YOUNG, J., *Prostaglandins, 3,* 531 (1973).
36. BUNDY, G., LINCOLN, F., NELSON, N., PIKE, J., SCHNEIDER, W., *Ann. N. Y. Acad. Sci., 180,* 76 (1971).
37. SCHNEIDER, W. P., BUNDY, G. L., LINCOLN, F. H., *Chem. Commun. 1973,* 254.
38. GRUDZINSKAS, CH. V., WEISS, M. J., *Tetrahedron Lett., 1973,* 141.

39. COREY, E. J., WASHBURN, W. N., CHEN, J. C., *J. Am. Chem. Soc.*, *95*, 2054 (1973).
40. COREY, E. J., ENSLEY, H. E., HAMBERG, M., SAMUELSSON, B., *Chem. Commun.*, *1975*, 277.
41. HAMBERG, M., SVENSSON, J., SAMUELSSON, B., "Novel transformations of endo-peroxides." Lecture held at the International Conference on Prostaglandins. Florence, May 1975.
42. SAMUELSSON, B., HAMBERG, M., MALMSTEN, C., SVENSSON, J., "The Role of Pros-taglandin Endoperoxides and Thromboxanes in Platelet Aggregation." *Advances in Prostaglandin and Thromboxane Research*, Vol. 2, 737 (Eds SAMUELSSON, B., PAOLETTI, R.). Raven Press, New York, 1976.
43. MONCADA, S., GRYGLEWSKI, R., BUNTING, S., VANE, J. R., *Nature*, *263*, 663 (1976).
44. GRYGLEWSKI, R., BUNTING, S., MONCADA, S., FLOWER, R. J., VANE, J. R., *Prosta-glandins*, *12*, 685 (1976).
45. MONCADA, S., GRYGLEWSKI, R., BUNTING, S., VANE, J. R., *Prostaglandins*, *12*, 715 (1976).
46. JOHNSON, R. A., MORTON, D. R., KINNER, J. H., GORMAN, J. C., McGUIRE, J. C., SUN, F. F., *Prostaglandins*, *12*, 915 (1976).

7. THE ANALYTICAL CHEMISTRY
OF PROSTAGLANDINS

Appropriate analytical methods are indispensable for prostaglandin research whether it be the pharmacological, clinical or synthetic aspect. Concentration of prostaglandins in tissues and body fluids being extremely low, in the order of a few μg/ml, the assay of such minute quantities of unstable material is an exacting task.

A great number of methods have been elaborated for the analytical determination of prostaglandins. Most of them consist of three phases: extraction, purification and determination of the active principle. Here we discuss only the third one with emphasis on chromatographic methods — since the latter are of most interest to synthetic organic chemists [1–6].

7.1 BIOLOGICAL METHODS

Prostaglandins exert characteristic effects on certain organs. Certain tissues (e.g. rabbit intestines, slices of rat stomach) are exceptionally sensitive to prostaglandins. The response induced in a given animal organ prepared under standardized conditions can be correlated with the prostaglandin concentration. Such methods are extremely sensitive and may be used for the determination of prostaglandins in the μg/ml range [7–14].

7.2 ENZYMATIC ASSAY

Metabolism of prostaglandins is initiated by the enzyme 15-hydroxy-prostaglandin dehydrogenase (*cf.* Chapter 5). The enzyme (which can be isolated from lung or kidney tissue), oxidizes the C_{15}-hydroxyl to a carbonyl group and its action requires nicotinamide adenine dinucleotide (NAD) as a cofactor:

$$PG + NAD^+ \xrightarrow{\text{15-OH-PGD}} \text{15-oxo-PG} + NADH + H^+$$

Both 15-oxoprostaglandin and the reduced coenzyme can be determined photometrically [1, 15, 16].

7.3 RADIOIMMUNOASSAY

Radioimmunoassay is at present the most sensitive method for the determination of prostaglandins. It is suitable for the detection of as little amounts as 10^{-3} mole and may be modified to be specific for individual prostaglandins [17–23]. The basic principle of the assay is that if a prostaglandin–serum protein complex is injected into an animal, it induces the formation of specific antibodies in the serum, i.e. the animal becomes immunized. On incubation with prostaglandin, the serum containing this antibody produces an antigen–antibody reaction as a consequence of which a precipitate is formed. Determination is carried out by incubating the sample containing the prostaglandin together with some radioactive, usually tritium-labelled prostaglandin, with the serum containing the antibody. The precipitate formed during the antigen–antibody reaction and its radioactivity are measured by which the prostaglandin content of the sample can be calculated.

Highest sensitivity is obtained for that particular prostaglandin with which the animal has been immunized.

7.4 CHROMATOGRAPHY

7.4.1 *Thin-layer Chromatography*

One of the most generally applicable methods for both qualitative and quantitative determination of prostaglandins is thin-layer chromatography. The literature covering this subject in extensive; almost every publication on prostaglandins contains references concerning this topic.

Problems arising in separation fall into two categories: (*a*) separation of synthetic prostaglandin intermediates (e.g. prostaglandins $F_{1\alpha}$ and $F_{1\beta}$), and (*b*) separation of natural prostaglandins. We restrict our discussion to the latter.

While E- and F-type prostaglandins can be easily separated from those of the A and B series, distinction between the latter two requires special techniques.

R_f-values in three of the most often used solvent systems are compiled in Table 7.1 [1].

Table 7.1
TLC Solvent Systems for Group Separation of Prostaglandins

Prostaglandins	R_f values		
	(a)	(b)	(c)
PGF	0.36	0.16	0.12
PGE	0.60	0.31	0.25
PGA-PGB	0.87	0.55	0.57

(a) Benzene–dioxane–acetic acid (20 : 20 : 1)
(b) Chloroform–methanol–acetic acid (18 : 1 : 1)
(c) Chloroform–tetrahydrofuran–acetic acid (10 : 2 : 1)

In weakly acidic solvent mixtures on neutral or acidic adsorbents it is possible to separate prostaglandins E_1 and F_1, as well as diastereomers of the A series (Table 7.2).

Table 7.2
TLC Separation Using a Weakly Acidic System
(Ethyl acetate–formic acid 400 : 5)

Prostaglandins	R_f values	
	(a)	(b)
$PGF_{1\beta}$	0.09	0.12
$PGF_{1\alpha}$	0.16	0.23
PGE_1	0.24	0.37
11-epi-PGE_1	0.29	0.49
15-epi-PGE_1	0.36	0.58
11,15-epi-PGE_1	0.34	0.59
PGA_1	0.5	0.79
PGB_1	0.5	0.79
15-epi-PGA_1	0.51	0.83

(a) Merck silica plates, Brinkman (neutral)
(b) Mallinckrodt Chrom AR plate 4GF (acidic)

Some time ago a method was developed for the separation of compounds containing a different number of double bonds using chromatography on silica gel impregnated with silver nitrate [24]. Separation is based on the formation of π-complexes between double bonds and silver ions. Since every prostaglandin contains double bonds, the number of which differs between those characterized with different subscript numbers (e.g. $PGF_{1\alpha}$ and $PGF_{2\alpha}$), the method is useful for distinguishing prostaglandins of different unsaturation.

Green and Samuelsson [25] impregnated the silicagel with 3–20% silver nitrate solution and activated the plates for 30 minutes at 110–115°C. Ascending chromatography in benzene–dioxane–acetic acid (20 : 20 : 1) gave good results in the separation of primary prostaglandins, but failed with the separation of prostaglandin A_2 and B_2 [4].

Later Spraggins investigated in detail the chromatographic separation of prostaglandins on plates impregnated with salts of metals in the iron group. Precoated Brinkman plates were impregnated with a 10% solution of iron(III) chloride in ethanol and the substrate was eluted with ethyl acetate–hexane–acetic acid (40 : 59 : 1) ($R_f = 0.16$ and 0.23). The method is suitable for the analysis of *Plexaura homomalla* extracts [26].

Researchers with the Upjohn Co. extended this method for the separation of C-type prostaglandins. Prostaglandins A_1, B_1, E_1 and C_1 could be separated on iron(III) chloride-impregnated plates by elution with ethyl acetate–acetic acid–hexane (30 : 1 : 19).

7.4.2 *Gas Chromatography*

As natural prostaglandins are decomposed at the high temperatures necessary for gas chromatographic separation prior to analysis, they have to be converted to volatile derivatives — usually by acetylation or silylation of the methyl esters prepared with diazomethane (*cf.* Chapter 1). For silylation, N-(trimethylsilyl)imidazole, N, O-bis-(trimethylsilyl)acetamide and N,O-bis-(trimethylsilyl)-trifluoroacetamide can be used [4, 27–37].

In E-type prostaglandins the β-hydroxyketone moiety is so labile that even the trimethylsilyl ethers are partially decomposed in the gas chromatograph. To avoid this, E-type prostaglandins are analyzed in the form of their oximes [33] or, as recommended later by Middleditch and Desiderio, as the O-methyloximes [38, 39]. The latter are mixtures of *syn-* and *anti-*oximes, which can be distinguished by gas chromatography.

Sensitivity to gas chromatography is mainly limited by sensitivity of detection. Flame ionization detectors are capable of indicating down to 10^{-11} moles; the recently introduced combined gas chromatography and mass spectrometry has extended this limit to 10^{-12} moles.

The most advanced method for the analysis of prostaglandins is gas chromatography coupled with mass spectrometry; detection and identification of the separated products are both performed by a mass spectrometer [32, 38, 40–43]. With recent models the process is computer-controlled.

In the above method, error is introduced by irreversible adsorption and decomposition of some of the material on the column. To eliminate this problem, Samuelsson and others worked out a method based on isotope dilution. This consists of adding deuterium labelled prostaglandin to the sample and the ratio of deuterated and unlabelled prostaglandin is measured in a mass spectrometer coupled with a gas chromatograph. If the amount of labelled prostaglandin introduced is known, the prostaglandin content of the sample can be calculated precisely from this ratio. A computerized version of this method is capable of detecting as little as 0.1 nanogram of material [44, 45–49].

REFERENCES

1. SHAW, J. E., RAMWELL, P. W., "Separation, Identification, and Estimation of Prostaglandins." *Methods of Biochem. Anal.*, *17*, 325 (1969).
2. RAMWELL, P. W., SHAW, J. E., CLARKE, G. B., GROSTIC, M. F., KAISER, D. G., PIKE, J. E., "Prostaglandins." *Progress in the Chemistry of Fats and other Lipids.* (Ed. Holman), *9*, 231. Pergamon Press, Oxford, 1968.
3. RAMWELL, P. W., *Lipid Chromatographic Analysis* (Ed. MARINETTI), *2*, 313, M. Dekker, New York, 1969.
4. CRAIN, P. F., DESIDERIO, D. M., McCLOSKEY, J. A., "Mass Spectrometry of Prostaglandins." *Methods of Enzym.*, *35*, 359 (1975).
5. ANGGÅRD, E., *Ann. N. Y. Acad. Sci.*, *180*, 200 (1971).
6. FINÁLY, I., "The Analytical Chemistry of Prostaglandins" in *"The Prostaglandins,"* *Technical and Scientific Information Bulletin*, Chinoin Pharmaceutical and Chemical Works Ltd., Budapest, 1972.
7. ANGGÅRD, E., GREEN, K., SAMUELSSON, B., *J. Biol. Chem.*, *240*, 1932 (1965).
8. BERGSTRÖM, S., CARLSON, L. A., WEEKS, J. R., *Pharmacol. Rev.*, *20*, 1 (1968).
9. HICKLER, R. B., LAULER, D. P., SARAVIS, C. A., VAGNACCI, A. I., STEINER, G., THORN, G. W., *Can. Med. Ass. J.*, *90*, 280 (1964).
10. HORTON, E. W., MAIN, I. H. M., *Brit. J. Pharmacol.*, *24*, 470 (1965).
11. ADAMSON, U., ELIASSON, R., WIKLUNG, B., *Acta Physiol. Scand.*, *70*, 451 (1967).
12. KARIM, S. M. M., DEVLIN, J., HILLIER, K., *Eur. J. Pharmac.*, *4*, 416 (1968).
13. KUEHL, F. A., HUMES, J. L., *Proc. Nat. Acad. Sci. USA*, *69*, 480 (1972).
14. MILLER, O. V., MAGEE, W. E., "Specificity of Prostaglandin Binding Sites in Rat Forestomach Tissue and Their Possible Use as a Quantitative Assay." International Conference on Prostaglandins, Vienna, 1972. *Adv. in Biosci.*, *9*, 83 (1973). Pergamon Press, Oxford.
15. ANGGÅRD, E., SAMUELSSON, B., *Methoden der enzymatischen Analyse* (Ed. Bergmeyer), *3*, 1814. Akad. Verlag, Berlin, 1970.
16. VONKEMAN, H., NUGTEREN, D. H., VAN DORP, D. A., *Biochim. Biophys. Acta*, *187*, 581 (1969).
17. CALDWELL, B. V., BURSTEIN, S., BROCK, W. A., SPEROFF, L., *J. Clin. Endocrin.* *33*, 171 (1971).
18. GOODFRIEND, T. L., LEVINE, L., FASMAN, G. D., *Science*, *144*, 1344 (1964).
19. GERSHMAN, H., POWERS, G., LEVINE, L., VAN VUNAKIS, H., *Prostaglandins*, *1*, 407 (1972).
20. JAFFE, B. M., SMITH, J. W., NEWTON, W. T., PARKER, C., *Science*, *171*, 494 (1971).
21. KIRTON, E. T., CORNETTE, J. C., BARR, K. L., *Biochem. Biophys. Res. Commun.*, *47*, 903 (1972).

22. LEVINE, L., GUTIERREZ-CERNOSEK, R. M., VAN VUNAKIS, H., *J. Biol. Chem.*, *246*, 6782 (1971).
23. LEVINE, L., VAN VUNAKIS, H., *Biochem. Biophys. Res. Commun.*, *41*, 1171 (1970).
24. BARRETT, C. B., DALLAS, M. S. J., PADLEY, F. B., *Chem. and Ind. (London)*, *1962*, 1050.
25. GREEN, K., SAMUELSSON, B. J., *J. Lipid Res.*, *5*, 117 (1964).
26. SPRAGGINS, R. L., *J. Org. Chem.*, *38*, 3661 (1973).
27. WICKRAMASINGHE, J. A. F., SHAW, S. R., *Prostaglandins*, *4*, 903 (1973).
28. BERGSTRÖM, S., RYHAGE, R., SAMUELSSON, B., SJÖVALL, J., *J. Biol. Chem.*, *238*, 3555 (1963).
29. ALBRO, P. W., FISHBEIN, L., *J. Chromatogr.*, *44*, 443 (1969).
30. JONVENAZ, G. H., NUGTEREN, R. K., BEERTHUIS, R. K., VAN DORP, D. A., *Biochim. Biophys. Acta*, *202*, 231 (1970).
31. SZEDERKÉNYI, F., KOVÁCS, G., *Prostaglandins*, *8*, 285 (1974).
32. GREEN, K., *Chem. Phys. Lipids*, *3*, 254 (1969).
33. VANE, F., HORNING, M. G., *Anal. Letters*, *2*, 357 (1969).
34. PACE-ASCIAK, C., WOLFE, L. S., *J. Chromatogr.*, *56*, 129 (1971).
35. THOMPSON, C. J., LOS, M., HORTON, E. W., *Life Sci.*, *9* (1) 983 (1970).
36. GRANSTRÖM, E., LANDS, W. E. M., SAMUELSSON, B., *J. Biol. Chem.*, *243*, 4104 (1968).
37. MIDDLEDITCH, B. S., DESIDERIO, D. M., *Prostaglandins*, *2*, 115 (1972).
38. MIDDLEDITCH, B. S., DESIDERIO, D. M., *J. Org. Chem.*, *38*, 2204 (1973).
39. MIDDLEDITCH, B. S., DESIDERIO, D. M., *Prostaglandins*, *4*, 31 (1973).
40. GREEN, K., GRANSTRÖM, E., SAMUELSSON, B., "Quantitative Gas Chromatography — Mass Spectrometry of Prostaglandins." *Third Conference on Prostaglandins in Fertility Control* (Eds BERGSTRÖM, S., GREEN, K., SAMUELSSON, B.). Karolinska Institute, Stockholm, 1972.
41. WATSON, J. TH., SWEETMAN, B. J., *Org. Mass Spectrometry*, *9*, 39 (1974).
42. SWEETMAN, B. J., FRÖLICH, J. C., WATSON, J. TH., *Prostaglandins*, *3*, 75 (1973).
43. WATSON, J. TH., PELSTER, D. H., SWEETMAN, B. J., FRÖLICH, J. C., CATES, J. A., *Anal. Chem.*, *45*, 2071 (1973).
44. SAMUELSSON, B., HAMBERG, M., *Anal. Biochem.*, *38*, 301 (1970).
45. SAMUELSSON, B., GRANSTRÖM, E., GREEN, K., HAMBERG, M., *Ann. N. Y. Acad. Sci.*, *180*, 138 (1971).
46. AXEN, U., GREEN, K., HÖRLIN, D., SAMUELSSON, B., *Biochem. Biophys. Res. Commun.*, *45*, 519 (1971).
47. GREEN, K., "Quantitative Mass Spectrometric Analysis of Prostaglandins." *International Conference on Prostaglandins.* Vienna, 1972. *Advances in the Biosciences 9*, 91 (1973). Pergamon Press, Oxford.
48. AXEN, U., BACZYNSKYJ, L., DUCHAMP, D. J., KIRTON, K. T., ZIERSL, J. F., "Differentiation between Endogenous and Exogenous Prostaglandins in Biological Fluids." *Advances in the Biosciences*, *9*, 109 (1973).
49. THOMPSON, C. J., GOODE, C. N., "The Analysis of Prostaglandins Using a Computer for Plotting Ion Abundance Versus Time." *Advances in the Biosciences. 9*, 117 (1973).

ADDENDUM

After having completed our manuscript, many papers concerning the syntheses of prostanoids appeared which we had not been able to include in our book. Some of the most important ones are listed below.

Chapter 1

1. CHO, M. J., KRUEGER, W. C., OESTERLING, T. O., "Nucleophilic Addition of Bisulfite Ion to Prostaglandins E_2 and A_2." *J. Pharm. Sci.*, 66, 149 (1977).

2. RACKHAM, D. M., COWDREY, S. E., GUTTERIDGE, N. Y. A., OSBORNE, D. J., "N. M. R. Spectra of Prostaglandin Metabolites and Precursors and of Related Pyrazoline Adducts." *Org. Magn. Res.*, 9. 160 (1977).

3. NICOLAOU, K. C., "Synthesis of Macrolides." *Tetrahedron*, 33, 683 (1977).

Chapter 2

1. RANGANATHAN, S., RANGANATHAN, D., MEHROTRA, A. K., "Ketene Equivalents." *Synthesis*, 1977, 289.

2. TAKANO, S., KUBOCLERA, N., OGASAWARA, K., "A Stereoselective Route to the Prostaglandin Intermediate from Norbornadiene." *J. Org. Chem.*, 42, 786 (1977).

3. MUBARIK ALI, S., LEE, TH. V., ROBERTS, S. M., "The Use of Bicyclo[3.2.0] Heptanones as Versatile Synthons in Organic Chemistry." *Synthesis*, 1977, 155.

4. CRABBE, P., BARREIRO, E., CRUZ, A., DEPRES, J.-P., MEANA, M. C., GREENE, A. E., "New Syntheses of Prostaglandins." *Heterocycles*, 5, 725 (1976).

5. ANDERSEN, N. H., IMANOTO, S., "An Alternative Prostaglandin Analog Synthesis Strategy. An Initial α-Ylation Sequence for bis-Unsaturated Prostaglandins." *Synthetic commun.*, 6, 33 (1976).

6. KONDO, K., HIRO, E., TUNEMOTO, D., "Synthesis and Nucleophilic Ring-opening Reactions of Activated Bicyclo[3.1.0] Hexanes." *Tetrahedron Lett.*, 1976, 4489.

7. BOON-WAIAU-YEUNG, FLEMING, I. "Allylsilanes in Organic Synthesis: A Synthesis of Prostaglandins." *J. C. S. Chem. Commun.*, 1977, 79.

Chapter 3

1. COOPER, G. K., DOLBY, L. J., "The Chemistry of γ-Oxosulfones. II. 4-Hydroxycyclopentenones." *Tetrahedron Lett.*, 1976, 4675.

2. KIECZYKOWSKI, G. R., POGONOWSKI, C. S., RICHMAN, J. E., SCHLESSINGER, R. H., "Prostaglandins. An Efficient Synthesis of a 2-Alkyl-4-hydroxycyclopentenone." *J. Org. Chem.* **42**, 175 (1977).

3. PIANCATELLI, G., SCETTRI, A., "A Simple Conversion of 4-Substituted 5-Hydroxy-3-oxocyclopentenes into the 2-Substituted Analogs." *Synthesis*, *1977*, 116.

4. PIANCATELLI, G., SCETTRI, A., "A Useful Preparation of ($\pm$) t-Butyl-3-hydroxy-5-oxo-1-cyclopentene Heptanoate and its 3-Deoxy-derivative, Important Prostaglandin Intermediates." *Tetrahedron Lett.*, *1977*, 1131.

5. DE CLERQ, P., COEN, R., VAN HOOF, E., VANDEWALLE, M., "Prostaglandin Synthesis Involving Catalytic Hydrogenation of 2,3-Dialkyl-4-hydroxy-2-cyclopentenones." *Tetrahedron*, *32*, 2747 (1976).

6. VAN HAVER, D., SAMSON, M., VANDEWALLE, M., "¹H NMR Spectral Parameters and Configurational Assignment of the Isomeric 1,4-Diacetoxy-2-t-butyl-3-methylcyclopentanes." *Tetrahedron*, *33*, 255 (1977).

7. KOBAYASHI, M., KUROZUMI, S., TORU, T., ISHOMOTO, S., "Prostaglandin Chemistry. 9. An Alternative Synthesis of Prostaglandin Intermediates." *Chem. Lett.*, *1976*, 1341.

8. DOLEZAL, S., "The Synthesis of New Derivatives and Homologues of Prostanoic Acid." *Coll. Czech. Chem. Commun.*, *41*, 2755 (1976).

9. SAMSON, M., DE CLERCQ, P., VANDEWALLE, M., "Cyclopentanones. XVIII. The Lithium–liquid Ammonia Reduction of Some 2,3-Dialkyl-(4-hydroxy)-2-cyclopentenones. The Importance of the Protonation of Intermediate Enolate Anions on the Stereochemical Outcome." *Tetrahedron*, *33*, 249 (1977).

10. D'ANGELO, J., "Ketone Enolates. Regiospecific Preparation and Synthetic Uses." *Tetrahedron*, *32*, 2979 (1976).

11. STORK, G., KRAUS, G., "The Ene Reaction as a Route to 3-Hydroxycyclopentanone Derivatives. Application to the Prostaglandins." *J. Am. Chem. Soc.* *98*, 6747 (1976).

12. EVANS, D. A., CRANFORD, TH. C., THOMAS, R. C., WALKER, J. A., "Studies Directed toward the Synthesis of Prostaglandins. Useful Boron-mediated Olefin Syntheses." *J. Org. Chem.*, *41*, 3947 (1976).

13. BURTON, T. S., CATON, M. P. L., COFFEE, E. C. J., PARKER, T., STUTTLE, K. A. J., WATKINS, G. L., "Prostaglandins. Part 4. Synthesis of ($\pm$)-11-Deoxyprostaglandins from 2-(ω-Hydroxyheptyl)-cyclopent-2-enones." *J. Chem. Soc. Perkin I*, *1976*, 2550.

14. HALLETT, W. A., WISSNER, A., GRUDZINSKAS, C. V., WEISS, M. J., "Prostaglandins and Congeners. 12. The Synthesis of DL-*Erythro* and DL-*Threo*-15,16-dihydroxyprostaglandins." *Chem. Lett.*, *1977*, 51.

Chapter 4

1. STORK, G., TAKAHASHI, T., "Chiral Synthesis of Prostaglandins (PGE₁) from D-Glyceraldehyde." *J. Am. Chem. Soc.*, *99*, 1275 (1977).

2. TERASHIMA, S., YAMADA, SHUN-ICHI, "Novel Use of *meso*-Compounds for the Preparation of Optically Active Compounds. Synthesis of Optically Active Prostaglandin Intermediates from *cis*-2-Cyclopentene-1,4-diol." *Tetrahedron Lett.*, *1977*, 1001.

Chapter 5

1. LIN, C. H., "Synthesis of 11-Methyl-Prostaglandins." *Chem. and Ind.*, *1976*, 994.

2. GRIECO, P. A., WANG, C. J., OKUNIEWICZ, F. J., "Total Synthesis of 12-Hydroxymethylprostaglandin F$_{2\alpha}$ Methyl Ester." *Chem. Commun.*, *1976*, 939.

3. Tôru, T., Kurozumi, S., Tanaka, T., Miura, S., Kobayashi, M., Ishimoto, S., "Prostaglandin Chemistry, VI. Synthesis of 8-Methoxycarbonylprostaglandins." *Tetrahedron Lett.*, *1976*, 4087.

4. Wissner, A., "Prostaglandins and Congeners. 11. Synthesis of *dl*-13-Hydroxyprostanoic Acids." *J. Org. Chem.*, *42*, 356 (1977).

5. Tanaka, T., Kurozumi, S., Tôru, T., Kobayashi, M., Miura, S., Ishimoto, S., "Prostaglandin Chemistry VIII. Synthesis of Optically Active 7-Oxo-prostaglandins." *Tetrahedron*, *33*, 1105 (1977).

6. Bartmann, W., Beck, G., Kunstmann, R., Lerch, U., Teufel, H., "Synthese von 13-Hydroxy-9-oxo-14-(*E*)-prostensäure durch Allylumlagerung aus 8-Äthoxycarbonyl-11-desoxy-PGE$_1$." *Tetrahedron Lett.*, *1976*, 3879.

7. Shimomura, H., Sugie, A., Katsube, J., Yamamato, H., "Synthesis of 9,10-Vinyleno-PGF$_{2\alpha}$ and its Diastereoisomer, Analogs of the PG Endoperoxide (PGH$_2$)." *Tetrahedron Lett.*, *1976*, 4099.

8. Greene, A. E., Depres, J. P., Meana, M. C., Crabbé, P., "Total Synthesis of 11-Nor Prostaglandins." *Tetrahedron Lett.*, *1976*, 3755.

9. Bicking, J. B., Robb, Ch. M., Smith, R. L., Cragoe, E. J., "11,12-Secoprostaglandins, 1. Acylhydroxyalkanoic Acids and Related Compounds," *J. Med. Chem.*, *20*, 35 (1977).

10. Jones, J. H., Holtz, W. J., Bicking, J. B., Cragoe, E. J., "11,12-Secoprostaglandins, 2. N-Acyl-N-alkyl-7-aminoheptanoic Acids." *J. Med. Chem.*, *20*, 44 (1977).

11. Taylor, R. J. K., Harrison, I. T., Application of the Ketovinylation Reaction to Prostaglandin Synthesis. *Tetrahedron Lett.*, *1976*, 4793.

12. Portoghese, P. S., Larson, D. L., Abatjoglou, A. G., Dunham, E. W., Gerrard, J. M., White, J. G., "A Novel Prostaglandin Endoperoxide Mimic." *J. Med. Chem.*, *20*, 320 (1977).

13. Kurozumi, S., Tôru, T., Tanaka, T., Kobayashi, M., Miura, S., Ishimoto, S., "Prostaglandin Chemistry VII. A Synthesis of New 8-Phenylthio-11-deoxyprostaglandins." *Tetrahedron Lett.*, *1976*, 4091.

14. Plattner, J. J., Gager, A. H., "Synthesis of Optically Active 15-Thiaprostaglandins." *Tetrahedron Lett.*, *1977*, 1629.

15. Kühlein, K., Linkies, A., Reuschling, D., "Synthese von 10-Aza-dihydro-A-Prostaglandinen." *Tetrahedron Lett.*, *1976*, 4463.

16. Rozing, G. P., Dekoning, H., Huisman, H. O., "Synthesis of 9-Azaprostaglandin Analogs." *Heterocycles*, *5*, 325 (1976).

17. Reuschling, D., Mitzlaff, M., Kühlein, K., "Synthese von 10-Aza-prostaglandinen." *Tetrahedron Lett.*, *1976*, 4467.

18. Zoretic, P. A., Barcelos, F., "Synthesis of 10-Azaprostaglandin E$_1$." *Tetrahedron Lett.*, *1977*, 529.

19. Scribner, R. M., "Azaprostanoids I. Synthesis of (rac)-11-Desoxy-12-azaprostanoids." *Tetrahedron Lett.*, *1976*, 3853.

20. Reuschling, D., Kuhlein, K., Linkies, A., "Synthesis of Cyclobutaneprostaglandins." *Tetrahedron Lett.*, *1977*, 17.

21. Lin, C. H., Stein, S. J., "The Synthesis of 4,5-Acetylenic Prostaglandins." *Synth. Commun.*, *6*, 503 (1976).

22. Sugil, A., Shimomura, H., Katsube, J., Yamomoto, H., *Tetrahedron Lett.*, *1977*, 2759.

25. Hansson, G., Granström, E., "Metabolism of 15-Methyl-PbF$_{2\alpha}$ in the Cynomolgus Monkey and Human Female.", *Biochem. Med. J.*, In press.

24. GRIECO, P. A., POGONOWSKI, S. Ch,, BURKE, S. D., NISHIZAWA, M., MIYASHITA, M., MASAKI, Y., WANG, C.-L. J., MAJETICH, G., "Total Synthesis of Racemic 12-Me-thylprostaglandins.", *J. Am. Chem. Soc.*, *99*. 4111 (1977).

Chapter 6

1. SCHNEIDER, W. P., BUNDY, G. L., LINCOLN, F. H., DANIELS, E. G., PIKE, J. E., "Isolation and Chemical Conversion of Prostaglandins from *Plexaura homomalla*. Preparation of "Prostaglandin E_2, Prostaglandin $F_{2\alpha}$, and Their 5,6-*Trans* Isomers." *J. Am. Chem. Soc.*, *99*, 1222 (1977).

2. COREY, E. J., KECK, G. E., SZÉKELY, I., "Synthesis of Vane's Prostaglandin X, 6,9α-Oxido-9α, 15α-dihydroxyprosta-(Z)5,(E)13-Dienoic acid." *J. Am. Chem. Soc.*, *99*, 2006 (1977).

3. LIN, C. H., "Prostaglandin Metabolites. Synthesis of E and F Urinary Metabolites." *J. Org. Chem.*, *41*, 4045 (1976).

4. SALOMON, M. F., SALOMON, R. G., GLEIM, R. D., "A Synthesis of Mixed Dialkyl Peroxides *via* Reaction of an Alkyl Hydroperoxide with Alkyl Trifluoromethanesul-fonates." *J. Org. Chem.*, *41*, 3983 (1976).

5. OHKI, S., OGINO, N., YAMAMOTO, S., HAYAISHI, O., YAMAMOTO, H., MIYAKE, H., HAYASHI, M., "Inhibition of Prostaglandin Endoperoxide Synthetase by Thiol Analogues of Prostaglandin." *Proc. Natl. Acad. Sci. U. S. A.*, *74*, 144 (1977).

6. ISAKSON, D. C., RAZ, A., DENNY, S. E., PURE, E., NEEDLEMAN, PH., "A Novel Prostaglandin is the Major Product of Arachidonic Acid Metabolism in Rabbit Heart." *Proc. Natl. Acad. Sci. U. S. A.*, *74*, 101 (1977).

7. COREY, E. J., SHIBASAKI, M., KNOLLE, J., "Simple, Stereocontrolled Synthesis of Thromboxane B_2 from D-Glucose." *Tetrahedron Lett.*, *1977*, 1625.

8. CHANG, W. C., MUROTA, S., TSURUFUJI, S., "Thromboxane B_2 Transformed from Arachidonic Acid in Carrageenin-induced Granuloma." *Prostaglandins*, *13*, 17 (1977).

9. GRANSTROM, E., KINDAHL, H., SAMUELSSON, B., "A Method for Measuring the Unstable Thromboxane A_2. Radioimmunoassay of the Derived Mono-O-methyl-thromboxane B_2." *Prostaglandins*, *12*, 929 (1976).

10. TÖMÖSKÖZI, I., GALAMBOS, G., SIMONIDESZ, V., KOVÁCS, G., "A Simple Synthesis of PGI_2." *Tetrahedron Lett*, *1977*. 2627.

11. WHITTAKER, N., "A Synthesis of Prostacyclin Sodium Salt.", *Tetrahechon Lett.*, *1977*. 2805.

12. JOHNSON, R. A., LINCOLN, F. H., THOMPSON, J. L., NIDY, E. G,, MIZSAK, S. A., AXEN, U., "Synthesis and Stereochemistry of Prostacyclin and Synthesis of 6-Ke-toprostaglandin $F_{1\alpha}$." *J. Am. Chem. Soc.* *99*. 4182 (1977).

13. FOLKO, G., GRANSTRÖM, E., KINDAHL, H., "Albumin Stabilizes Thromboxane-A_2." *FEBS Letters*, Manuscript accepted for publication.

AUTHOR INDEX*

Abraham, N. A. *28*
Abrahamsson, S. 16, 24
Adamson, U. *247*
Agresta, G. *163*
Akihiko, I. *212*
Albonico, S. M. *74*
Albro, P. W. *250*
Allinger, N. L. *132*
Alvarez, F. S. 115, 134, 145, *240, 242*
Ambrus, G. 226, *234*
Andersen, N. H. *63, 195, 222*
Änggard, E. *58, 195, 234, 247, 248*
Andrews, G. C. *152*
Angyal, S. J. *132*
Arnold, Z. *103*
Ashe, A. J. 100
Auber, W. *28*
Axen, U. *13, 102, 107, 108, 110, 196, 251*

Baczynskyj, L. *251*
Bagli, J. F. *13*, 114, 125, 130, 136, *196*
Barr, K. L. *248*
Barr, S. J. 24
Barrett, C. B. *249*
Barta, I. 226
Bartmann, W. 132, *209, 227*
Beames, D. J. *123*, 156
Beck, G. *132*
Becker, K. B. *74*
Beerthuis, R. K. *232, 234, 250*
Bentley, P. H. *13*
Bergström, S. 13, *16, 28, 51, 52,* 232, *234, 247, 250*
Bernady, K. F. *139*, 158
Bickart, P. *152*
Bindra, J. S. *96*
Blair, J. *166*
Bogri, T. 114, 125, *130*, 136, *196*
Bolliger, G. *228*
Brewster, D. *90*

Brock, W. A. *248*
Broger, E. *140*
Brown, D. J. *128*
Brown, E. D. 98, 99
Brown, H. C. *138*
Browster, D. 26
Brunnelle, D. J. *152*
Brutcher, F. V. *24*
Bundy, G. L. *28, 29, 53, 58,* 195, 196, 198, 207, *240, 241, 242*
Bunting, S. *239*
Burstein, S. *248*
Büchi, G. 125

Cae, S. *138*
Cahn, R. S. 76
Caldwell, B. V. *248*
Camnoch, S. *52, 88*
Carlson, R. M. *63, 247*
Carson, F. W. *152*
Carrophers, W. *144*
Casey, M. *146*
Cates, J. A. *250*
Caton, M. P. L. 131
Cesarini, R. *163*
Chachaty, C. 24
Chadha, N. K. *171, 172*
Chan, Y. Y. *220, 240*
Chern, Chuen-Ing, *79*
Chidester, C. G. *196*
Cirillo, V. J. *209, 210*
Clarke, G. B. *13, 55, 247*
Clarkson, R. 98
Cockerill, A. F. *32*
Coffee, E. C. J. *131*
Colbert, J. C. *13*
Collins, P. *119, 127, 142*
Cooms, R. V. *152*
Cooper, G. F. 24, 34, *161*
Corbett, B. J. *47*

* Italic page numbers indicate a citation by reference number only.

17 R.D.C.

SUBJECT INDEX